The Theory of
Linear Economic Models

DAVID GALE

Associate Professor of Mathematics, Brown University and
Consultant to Mathematics Division of The RAND Corporation

McGRAW-HILL BOOK COMPANY

New York   *Toronto*   *London*   1960

THE THEORY OF LINEAR ECONOMIC MODELS

Preface

This book is written at a time of revived activity in the field of applied mathematics. "Revived" is perhaps the wrong word to use in this connection, for the characteristic feature of the new applied mathematics is not an intensification of work on old problems but rather an attempt to extend the application of mathematical reasoning to entirely new kinds of situations. Information theory, cybernetics, game theory, theory of automata are but a few of the new disciplines. Naturally, much of the work in these subjects is of a tentative and experimental nature. On the other hand, there have been certain developments which after a decade's experience seem to be of permanent usefulness. One such is probably information theory. Another is linear programming and the related linear models. Being convinced that this latter subject is "here to stay," I felt it was appropriate to try preparing a suitable text. This book is the result.

Before asking the reader to plunge into the subject of linear models I shall, in accordance with a sensible custom, attempt in the few pages which follow to give some idea of what this subject is. An ideal preface is one which tells the reader in a few words exactly what the rest of the book contains and thus saves him the trouble of reading it. I regret that the writing of such a preface in the present case is beyond my powers of exposition. The best I can do is to describe in a general way the sort of problems we shall be concerned with, the approach we shall take to these problems, and the manner in which the relevant material will be organized.

The Subject Matter.   The term "economic model" is admittedly a vague one, but for our purposes we may think of such a model as an abstraction and simplification of some typical economic situation.   As an example, the first model we shall take up is that of linear programming, which in its abstract formulation is a certain kind of mathematical maximum or minimum problem.   The importance of this model derives from the fact that many actual economic situations lead to precisely this problem after the appropriate simplifying assumptions have been made.   Later we take up the two-person game model. This is again formulated in a purely abstract manner, but the significance of the model for us comes from the fact that it is designed to reflect the essential features of certain games of strategy, and thus indirectly certain aspects of economic competition.   Other models to be treated concern patterns of exchange between countries or industries, alternative schemes of production, certain economic equilibrium situations, and so on.   In each case the models will be introduced by first describing the economic situation, next stating what simplifications are to be made, and then giving the purely abstract formulation.

Having arrived at this abstractly formulated model, what do we intend doing with it?   By way of answer let us first state clearly some of the things we *do not* intend doing.   A very important question in relation to any model is that of applicability.   Does the model really give a reasonable approximation to the situation which gave rise to it?   Is it to be relied on in making decisions and predictions?   To what extent have predictions based on the model been borne out experimentally?   Such questions belong to pure economics and will not be touched on here.   Indeed, the models we have chosen to discuss vary widely as regards applicability.   At one extreme we have linear programming, which is already being used quite extensively in industrial planning.   At the other we have topics like game theory and some of the equilibrium models, which are in no sense ready for practical application in their present stage of development.

But if applicability is not the criterion for selection how then have we decided which topics to discuss?   The answer is this: We have tried to select those models which best illustrate the manner in which mathematical reasoning can be used to obtain information about idealized economic situations. In some instances we have had to make rather drastic simplifications. The resulting lack of realism is unfortunate but is to be expected in early attempts at understanding complex situations.

Having formulated our models, the rest of the task consists in analyzing them, that is, of deducing in a rigorous fashion the consequences of the assumptions which have been made. The procedure is quite analogous to deducing theorems from the axioms of, say, plane geometry. As in the case of geometry, some of the results we shall obtain could hardly have been guessed in advance. It is this fact which encourages one to believe that mathematical analysis may help to bring about new and significant advances in the understanding of economic phenomena.

We have restricted our presentation to the study of *linear* models, that is, roughly speaking, models in which the mathematical relations have the form of equations or inequalities of degree one. This restriction is due simply to limitations of space and time. An equal number of pages could have been devoted to nonlinear models. This would, however, have involved developing a great deal of additional mathematical machinery, and for this reason we chose to remain within the linear framework. A further justification for this decision was the fact that most of the nonlinear results make use of the linear theory. Much of this book may thus be regarded as foundation material for work on more advanced levels.

It might be thought from what has been said so far that we have gathered together a miscellaneous collection of problems whose only common features are an economic flavor and the occurrence of linear relations. Fortunately, this is not the case, for although there is considerable variety in the models to be studied, the mathematics involved will exhibit a noteworthy degree of unity. Most of our analysis will use the mathematical material developed in Chap. 2 on Real Linear Algebra or, in more everyday language, the theory of linear equations and inequalities in real numbers. The feature of this theory which plays the unifying role in most of the applications is the fundamental notion of *duality*. We shall not even attempt to define this term here but remark that it is the recurrent theme which ties together the various parts of the book into what may legitimately be called a theory.

The Approach. We have already remarked that this book is intended as a text. We hesitate to use the words "advanced text," for this suggests that preliminary familiarity with the subject matter is assumed, which is not the case. The book is advanced in the sense that it attempts to bring the reader to the frontiers of the subject, enabling him to understand and possibly contribute to current research in the field. In other words, we are trying primarily to fill the needs of the would-be specialist, be he mathematician, economist, business student, or engineer. But while our main objective is the training of experts, we have tried to arrange matters so that the book will also be useful to readers who wish to go into the subject less intensively. The less technical parts of the book, in particular Chapter 1 on linear programming and most of Chapter 6 on game theory, are designed to be usable in courses on these subjects on the level of an advanced undergraduate course in economics or engineering.

Concerning the use of the book as a basic text for a course, it should be explained that the book is itself based on a set of notes from a course given to a group of graduate students in pure and applied mathematics, and the treatment should be suitable for students at this level. We suspect the average graduate student in economics would have some difficulty in going through the book on his own, for we emphasize that this is a text not in economics but in applied mathematics. Nevertheless, the theorems we prove are about economics, are used by economists, and in many cases were first discovered by economists.

Concerning the use of this book by economists, a further word of caution is in order. It has been brought to my attention by Professor Dorfman that certain words and expressions mean quite different things to economists on the one hand and mathematicians on the other. It was both startling and illuminating to me to realize that the very first words of my title "The *Theory* of" belong to this category. By way of illustration, a mathematician or natural scientist on reading one of the important *theory of* books of economics, say Hicks or Keynes, might well remark "very interesting, but where is the theory?" The remark would imply no disparagement of these works but would simply point up a confusion of language, for the natural scientist expects a theory to consist of a large body of results derived from a small set of assumptions. What he has read consists instead of a careful formulation and detailed justification of a particular set of assumptions, with rather less formal deduction of implications than he would find in a theoretical treatise in the natural sciences. Analogously, an economist reading the present volume will undoubtedly feel that it has been misnamed in that most of the "theory" has been left out, and he will correctly point out that the book is teeming with economic assumptions for which little or no justification is given. We reply that the word "theory" is to be understood here as it is used in the natural rather than the behavioral sciences and is therefore not directly concerned with the justification of assumptions. We stress this point in order not to mislead the reader concerning our intentions.

It is our hope that our presentation of results will be useful to the economics student with exceptional aptitude for the mathematical approach. It should also be useful in the hands of a teacher of mathematical economics who can modify the exposition to suit the needs of his students, skimming over portions which present purely technical difficulties, elaborating on other parts in which our treatment has not been sufficiently detailed. As such this book might usefully supplement one of the texts in economics which covers the same material, such as "Linear Programming and Economic Analysis" by Dorfman, Samuelson, and Solow or "Mathematical Economics" by R. G. D. Allen.

Finally, we hope the book will be used as a reference for workers in the field of linear models who will find here a mathematically unified treatment of many important results which were previously available only in scattered sources in the economic and mathematical literature.

We come next to the question of mathematical prerequisites. It is customary to remark at this point that the only requirement for an understanding of what is to follow is a knowledge of elementary calculus. In the present case even this requirement may be waived, for calculus is never used. Our principal tool is matrix algebra, but no previous knowledge is required here either, as all necessary facts are developed in the text.   What is required is the ability to follow a moderately involved mathematical argument, an ability which generally comes only with a fair amount of experience and is often characterized by the illusive phrase "mathematical maturity."   Some of the proofs we shall present are quite difficult.   Even the proof of the "theorem of the separating hyperplane," which is the key mathematical result of the book, is not entirely straightforward.   There is no way around this difficulty, for most of the results we wish to present are not mathematical trivialities, and one cannot make things easy without omitting proofs altogether, which would defeat our main purpose.   We shall, of course, use all the available devices to help the reader's understanding such as geometric pictures, plausibility arguments, and numerical examples.

We may summarize what has been said in the foregoing paragraphs by remarking that a course based on this book would occupy a position somewhat analogous to a course in mathematical statistics.   Such courses are generally given in a mathematics department but are available to students in other fields with the necessary mathematical qualifications.

The Organization.   How to Use the Book.   We envision four possible courses which could be based on this book.

1. A full-year course covering the entire nine chapters.   It would not be necessary to take them up in order, as will be seen from the diagram on page ix.

2. A one-semester course on linear programming.   This would cover the first five chapters of the book.

3. A one-semester course in linear programming and game theory. This would consist of Chaps. 1, 2, 3, 6, and 7, omitting Sec. 2 of Chap. 7.

4. A one-semester course in linear economic models.   This would cover Chaps. 1, 2, 3, 8, and 9.

The schematic diagram on page ix shows how the various chapters depend on each other.

As the figure shows, Chap. 2 on Real Linear Algebra is necessary for all later chapters.   However, the second half of the chapter, from Sec. 5 on, is used only occasionally in subsequent chapters.   The instructor may wish, therefore, to take up only the first four sections of this chapter, which are sufficient for all the applications in Chaps. 3, 4, 6, and 8.

From a logical point of view it would have been most natural to begin with Chap. 2, in which the mathematical machinery is developed. This procedure would have the disadvantage, however, of requiring the reader to absorb a considerable amount of abstract material without knowing what it was to be used for. For this reason it seemed preferable to start with the applications, in this case linear programming, and state the main theoretical results without proof in order to motivate further study in the algebraic foundations. Chapter 1 is therefore devoted to describing the linear programming problem first by means of a set of illustrative examples, then by a formal definition. The discussion of the next section leads up to the state-

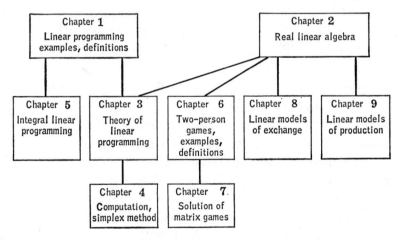

ment (but not the proof) of the fundamental duality theorem, which is then illustrated in specific cases. Assuming the duality theorem we then prove the important "equilibrium theorem" and give applications. The chapter, like all the others, ends in a short set of bibliographical references and a somewhat longer set of exercises of varying degrees of difficulty.

The first sections of Chap. 2 are devoted to introducing vectors and matrices and developing the classical theory of linear equations in a rapid but complete and self-contained manner. The mathematical heart of the chapter, and, in fact, of the book, is in Secs. 3

and 4, in which we develop the not so classical theory of real linear equations and linear inequalities. The latter half of the chapter is devoted to a more detailed and somewhat geometric analysis of the solutions of inequalities.

The reader who is acquainted with linear algebra may be struck by the fact that certain popular topics in this subject are conspicuous by their absence, among them the theory of determinants and of characteristic roots or eigen-values. The reason for this omission is simply that we know of no cases in which these particular algebraic objects are useful in drawing conclusions about economic models, and therefore there is no reason why the reader should spend time trying to master these somewhat intricate topics.[1]

In Chap. 3 we return to linear programming problems, which are now defined in complete generality. Using the algebraic apparatus developed in Chap. 2 it is possible to give a complete treatment of the duality and equilibrium theorems as well as the important result on basic solutions. The last part of the chapter is concerned with a most important economic application of linear programming theory, namely, the solution of the problem of optimal resource allocation by the method of price equilibrium under free competition.

Chapter 4 is devoted primarily to an exposition of the simplex method of Dantzig and its application not only to linear programming but also to such general problems as solving systems of inequalities and finding nonnegative solutions of linear equations. Our approach has been to show that the simplex method may be looked upon as an extension of the ordinary "high-school method of elimination" for solving sets of simultaneous linear equations. In vector language the

---

[1] In view of the rather frequent occurrence in the economic literature of results involving determinants and eigen-values, this statement perhaps calls for some amplification. An example will perhaps illustrate the point. It is a true theorem that a Leontief model is capable of producing a positive bill of goods if and only if the principal minors of the production matrix are all positive. This fact, however, gives us no new economic insight into the properties of Leontief models because there is no economic interpretation to be attached to these principal minors. Contrast this result with the theorem that if a Leontief model can produce one positive bill of goods it can produce any positive bill of goods. The latter statement is a useful and interesting result about the model itself, since both the hypothesis and the conclusion have an obvious economic meaning.

elimination of a variable becomes the replacement of a vector in a basis, and it is this "replacement operation" which becomes the basic computational unit in our presentation. The final section of the chapter presents the generalized simplex method of Dantzig, Orden, and Wolfe for resolving the problem of degeneracy.

Chapter 5 is devoted to the very important class of linear programs, including transportation problems, which always have integral solutions if the initial data are integral. As indicated by our schematic diagram, the material of this chapter is essentially independent of the previous theory. We begin by presenting the network-flow theory of Ford and Fulkerson which, together with the method of Kuhn for the optimal-assignment problem, provides us with a complete and elegant theory for a wide class of integral problems. The relationship of this theory to the classical notion of price equilibrium is given in Sec. 6. The Hitchcock transportation problem is treated in detail as well as various other applications. Again in this chapter it is the duality concept which does the work.

In Chap. 6 we introduce two-person zero-sum games by a sequence of examples which lead first to the statement and then the proof of von Neumann's minimax theorem. The proof is that of Gale, Kuhn, and Tucker using the symmetrization of a game of von Neumann.

The "equivalence" of linear programming and matrix games is the first topic of Chap. 7, and it is shown that the minimax theorem can be derived as a special case of the fundamental duality theorem of linear programming. A short section is devoted to solving games by the simplex method. Several sections are then devoted to a detailed analysis of the structure of the sets of optimal strategies of a matrix game. The final sections are devoted to a description of the method of fictitious play of Brown and to Robinson's proof that the method converges.

Chapter 8 is concerned first with a linear exchange model, equivalent versions of which seem to have been discovered independently by Frisch, Remak, and Bray. A complete analysis is given of the equilibria of such models. A dynamic theory of linear trade models is then treated along the lines of some work of Solow. The theorems here are exactly the same as those which occur in the theory of Markov chains in probability theory. The final sections of the chapter treat a particular model of price equilibrium.

Among the topics treated in the final chapter are Leontief models, including the Samuelson-Koopmans-Arrow substitutability theorem, the work of Koopmans on the relation between efficiency and profit maximization, and von Neumann's expanding linear model.

Terminology, Notation, Bibliography. We shall, of course, define all technical terms and symbols as they are introduced. For the most part we have adhered to standard terminology and notations when such things existed. On the other hand, we have exercised the mathematical equivalent of poetic license to institute an occasional "improvement," mostly in the interests of typographical simplicity. Thus the scalar product of two vectors is simply indicated by their juxtaposition, no unnecessary dots, parentheses, commas, or brackets. Also, we do not make the distinction between row and column vectors, though this seems still to be the vogue in many quarters, for what reason we cannot imagine. Perhaps we are carrying typographical economy too far when we denote the vector x with coordinates from ξ_1 to ξ_n by the symbol (ξ_i) instead of the conventional $(\xi_1, \ldots, \xi_n)$, but why not? After all, nobody objects to indicating a matrix A in terms of its coordinates by the symbol (α_{ij}). We have gone to considerable length to avoid hanging subscripts on subscripts. The general philosophy has been that a clean-looking page of symbols will have a good psychological effect on the reader, or to put it the other way, a tangled symbolism suggests a tangled argument and is likely to frighten rather than entice.

About the most radical innovation in terminology is the replacement of the universally used "nonsingular" by "regular" in describing a square matrix of maximal rank. We just didn't like the sound of the double negative. Vector spaces have a certain "rank" rather than "dimension" simply because there is no reason to use two words for the same thing. "Polyhedral cone" hasn't been around very long yet. Perhaps we can persuade others to join us in calling them "finite cones." It does sound better, and as Professor Coxeter has pointed out, "polyhedron" belongs to the 3-space just as "polygon" belongs to the plane. The correct n-dimensional word is "polytope," and this is the word that will be encountered here.

Our system for numbering displayed relations is admittedly unortho-
dox.   In each proof we start numbering the relations from the beginning starting with (1).   Thus, if we argue that a certain conclusion
follows from (3) we are referring to (3) in that same proof.

If the reader disagrees with some of the liberties we have taken we
hope he will simply attribute them to temperament and forgive us.
To ensure against the possibility of serious confusion we have included
a table of notations at the front of the book and an index of terms at
the back.

Finally, a word concerning the bibliography.   We have listed con-
scientiously at the end of each chapter all sources which were actually
used in its preparation.   We have, however, made no attempt at
bibliographical completeness, as this is not generally done in textbooks.
The people whose names appear in the bibliography at the end of the
book represent but a fraction of those who have made significant contributions to the subject—an ever-dwindling fraction since new
investigators are constantly entering the field.   For the reader who
is interested in bibliographical matters we recommend the very complete "Bibliography on Linear Programming and Related Techniques"
by Riley and Gass (Johns Hopkins Press, Baltimore, 1958).

Acknowledgments

This book evolved in three distinct stages.   The initial stage
involved a course given in the academic year 1956–1957 to a group
of graduate students in pure and applied mathematics at Brown
University.   From this course my assistant Edmund Eisenberg and
I assembled a set of mimeographed notes which were made available
to the public in a limited supply.   This enterprise was carried out in
part under a contract with the Logistics Branch of the Office of Naval
Research, to which I am indebted not only for financial support but
also for encouragement and interest in the project.

Because of the favorable response to the course notes I decided to
expand them into a textbook.   Most of this work was done while I
was working as a consultant to the Mathematical Analysis Division of
The RAND Corporation in 1957–1958.   RAND not only supplied me with
all the physical equipment needed for this operation but, even more

important, enabled me to do the work in the place having the highest concentration of contributors to the subject about which I was writing. For this stimulating atmosphere I am ultimately indebted to the United States Air Force, whose Project RAND contract has enabled The RAND Corporation to undertake its broad program of scientific research. Part of this volume was given limited circulation in three Project RAND research memoranda. I will not even attempt to list all the people at RAND who have helped me in one way or another on various portions of the exposition, but should like to give special thanks to J. D. Williams, head of the Mathematics Division, who made it possible for me to come to RAND.

The final stages of writing were completed at Brown University in the fall of 1958, again with the support of the Logistics Branch of the Office of Naval Research.

Finally, I should like to thank Professor E. Barankin of the University of California whose suggestions based on a critical reading of the mimeographed course notes led me to make fairly extensive revisions in my original organization of material.

To all the above groups and individuals let me convey my gratitude and express the hope that the finished product presented herewith will to some extent justify their support.

David Gale

List of Notations

Below are listed the principal mathematical notations used in this book. The notations are listed in the order in which they occur in the text.

$\alpha, \beta, \gamma, \ldots, \xi, \eta, \zeta$, and other Greek letters represent numerical quantities also referred to as *scalars*

$a, b, c, \ldots, x, y, z$, and other italic letters represent vector quantities

$x = (\xi_i)$ the vector whose ith coordinate is ξ_i

$b = (\beta_j)$ the vector whose jth coordinate is β_j

$y = (\eta_1, \ldots, \eta_n)$ the vector whose coordinates are $\eta_1, \ldots, \eta_n$

F^n the set of all n-vectors over the field F

R^n n *space*, the set of all real n-vectors

u, v the *unit vectors* all of whose coordinates are one

$u_i, (v_j)$ the *i*th (*j*th) *unit vector* whose *i*th (*j*th) coordinate is one and whose other coordinates are zero

λx product of scalar λ with vector x

ε symbol for set-theoretic membership, "is an element of"

xy *scalar product* of vectors x and y

$A = (\alpha_{ij})$ the *matrix* whose ijth coordinate is α_{ij}

$a_i = (\alpha_{i1}, \ldots, \alpha_{in})$ the ith *row vector* of the matrix A

$a^j = (\alpha_{1j}, \ldots, \alpha_{mj})$ the jth *column vector* of the matrix A

$xA, (Ay)$ the product of the matrix A with the vector $x(y)$

L linear subspace of a vector space

L^* orthogonal or *dual* subspace of L

$x \geqq 0$ vector x is *nonnegative*

$x \geq 0$ vector x is *semipositive*

$x > 0$ vector x is *positive*

$M = \{1, \ldots, m\}, N = \{1, \ldots, n\}$ the set of positive integers from 1 to m and 1 to n, respectively

$\subset, \supset$ set-theoretic inclusion, "is contained in" and "contains," respectively

$\{x|P\}$ the set of all x such that x has property P

$\cup$ set-theoretic *union*

$\cap$ set-theoretic *intersection*

C convex cone

$C_1 + C_2$ algebraic *sum* of convex cones

C^* *dual cone* of C

P the *positive orthant*, all nonnegative vectors

(b) the *halfline* generated by the vector b

$(b)^*$ the *halfspace* generated by the vector b

$(a_1) + \cdots + (a_m)$ the finite cone generated by $a_1, \ldots, a_m$

K convex set

$<X>$ the *convex hull* of the set X

$<x_1, \ldots, x_n>$ the convex hull of vectors $x_1, \ldots, x_n$

$I = (\delta_{ij})$ the *identity matrix*

A^{-1} the *inverse* of the matrix A

A^* the *transpose* of the matrix A

$x \succ 0$ x is *lexicographically positive*

(N, k) *capacitated network* with *nodes* N and *capacity function* k

(x, y) *edge* from node x to node y

$g(A)$ values of function on nodes A of N given by $g(A) = \sum_{x \varepsilon A} g(x)$

$h(A, B)$ value of function on edges from A to B given by $h(A, B) = \sum_{x \varepsilon A, y \varepsilon B} h(x, y)$

s *source* in a network

s' *sink* in a network

(S, S') a *cut* in a network

∞ symbol for infinity

Γ two-person zero-sum game

P_1, P_2 first and second player

s, t *strategies* for first and second players

S, T *strategy sets* for first and second players

$(S, T; \phi)$ game with strategy sets S and T and *payoff* ϕ

σ, τ *mixed strategies* for first and second players

$<S>, <T>$ sets of mixed strategies for first and second players

$\bar{\sigma}, \bar{\tau}$ *optimal* mixed strategies

ω *value* of a game

$(\bar{\sigma}, \bar{\tau}; \omega)$ *solution* of a game in mixed strategies

$\bar{x}, \bar{y}$ *optimal strategies* for a matrix game

$U_m = \{u_1, \ldots, u_m\}$ set of *pure strategies* for a matrix game

$<U_m> = <u_1, \ldots, u_m>$ set of *mixed strategies* for a matrix game

$\bar{X}, \bar{Y}$ set of *optimal strategies* for a matrix game

$(\bar{X}, \bar{Y}; \omega)$ *solution* of a matrix game

$x_k \to x$ sequence x_k *converges* to x

$|x|$ *norm* of x

Contents

Linear Programming: Examples, Definitions, and Statement of the Principal Theorems

Maximum and minimum problems occur frequently in many branches of pure and applied mathematics. In economic applications such problems are especially natural. Firms try to maximize profits or minimize costs. Social planners attempt to maximize the welfare of the community. Consumers wish to spend their income in such a way as to maximize their satisfaction.

Linear programming is concerned with special classes of maximum and minimum problems which come up very frequently in economic applications. It is our purpose in this chapter to describe and define these problems in a precise manner. We shall then present the main theoretical results concerning them. The proofs of the results will be given in Chap. 3 after we have developed the necessary algebraic machinery in the next chapter.

It will be our policy here and throughout the book to introduce general concepts by means of concrete examples. Accordingly, the next section will be devoted to discussion of some specific instances of linear programs which will serve to guide us in formulating the general definitions which follow.

1. Examples

Example 1. The Diet Problem. This problem has become the classical illustration in linear programming and is treated in virtually every exposition of the subject. It is concerned with the problem of feeding, say, an army in the most economical way while at the same time satisfying certain nutritional requirements. Let us be specific. A dietitian is confronted with n different foods which will be labeled $F_1, F_2, \ldots, F_n$. From these he is to select a *diet*, that is, he must determine the amount of each food which is to be consumed annually by a person or group of persons. This yearly menu is required to supply certain amounts of various nutritional elements such as proteins, calories, minerals, vitamins, and the like. We shall refer to these types of nutritive elements simply as *nutrients* of which there will be m varieties denoted by $N_1, \ldots, N_m$. We suppose that each man is required to consume at least γ_1 units of N_1, γ_2 units of N_2, $\ldots$, γ_m units of N_m, per year. In order to meet these requirements the dietitian must know exactly how much of each nutrient is contained in each of the foods. Let us denote by α_{ij} the amount of the ith nutrient contained in one unit of the jth food. The information which the dietitian needs is then conveniently presented in the following table or *matrix*:

	F_1	$F_2 \cdots F_n$	
N_1	α_{11}	α_{12}	α_{1n}
N_2	α_{21}	α_{22}	α_{2n}
.			
.	$\cdots$	$\cdots$	$\cdots$
.			
N_m	α_{m1}	α_{m2}	α_{mn}

The entry in the ith row and the jth column of the matrix is the number α_{ij}, giving the amount of N_i in one unit of F_j. We shall refer to the table above as the *nutrition matrix* of the problem.

Suppose now that the dietitian has chosen a diet. This means that he has determined that η_1 units of F_1, η_2 units of F_2, etc., shall be consumed per man per year. How does he now check that the nutritional requirements are satisfied by this diet? Obviously, he simply calculates the amount of each nutrient in the diet and compares it with the prescribed amount. Consider the nutrient N_1. Each unit of F_1 contains α_{11} units of N_1, and since there are η_1 units of F_1 in the diet, we get $\eta_1\alpha_{11}$ units of N_1 from F_1. Similarly we get $\eta_2\alpha_{12}$ units of N_1

from F_2, and in general $\eta_j \alpha_{1j}$ units of N_1 from F_j.   The total amount of N_1 in this diet is then

$$\eta_1 \alpha_{11} + \eta_2 \alpha_{12} + \cdots + \eta_n \alpha_{1n}$$

and this amount is required to be at least equal to γ_1.   Thus the requirement on N_1 simply states that the numbers $\eta_1, \ldots, \eta_n$ must satisfy the inequality

$$\sum_{j=1}^{n} \eta_j \alpha_{1j} \geq \gamma_1$$

The requirements on the remaining nutrients take exactly the same form, and the condition that the diet satisfy all requirements is that the numbers η_j satisfy simultaneously the m inequalities

$$\sum_{j=1}^{n} \eta_j \alpha_{ij} \geq \gamma_i \qquad \text{for } i = 1, 2, \ldots, m \qquad (1)$$

A diet for which conditions (1) are satisfied will be termed a *feasible diet*.

As yet no maximum or minimum problem has been described, but we have already mentioned that the dietitian must choose the most economical diet consistent with the requirement (1).   We are assuming then that a *price* is associated with each food.   Let π_j be the price of one unit of the food F_j.   It follows that the cost of the diet described by the numbers η_j is given by the expression

$$\pi_1 \eta_1 + \pi_2 \eta_2 + \cdots + \pi_n \eta_n = \sum_{j=1}^{n} \pi_j \eta_j \qquad (2)$$

We can now give a complete statement of the diet problem.   *Among all diets satisfying conditions* (1) *find one such that expression* (2) *is a minimum.*

The problem which we have just described in perhaps tedious detail is a typical linear programming problem.   The word "linear" is used because both the inequalities (1) and the function to be minimized (2) are linear.

A diet which satisfies both (1) and (2) is called an *optimal* diet. Mathematically the diet problem can be broken into two parts: first, that of finding a feasible diet and, second, if a feasible diet exists, of finding an optimal diet. It is easy to see that a feasible diet will always exist provided each nutrient N_i occurs in at least one food F_j, for then by using a sufficient amount of the foods one can always satisfy the requirements. It is quite clear in this case that an optimal diet also exists. A rigorous proof of this fact will have to wait, however, until a later chapter.

Example 2. The Transportation Problem. Let a certain commodity, say steel, be produced at each of m plants, $P_1, \ldots, P_m$, and let σ_i (σ = supply) be the yearly output of the ith plant. Suppose now that steel is required at each of n markets, $M_1, \ldots, M_n$, and let the annual demand at the jth market be δ_j. Finally, let γ_{ij} be the cost of shipping one unit from P_i to M_j.

The problem is now to determine a *shipping schedule* such that (1) the demand δ_j at the market M_j will be satisfied, (2) the supply σ_i at the plant P_i will not be exceeded, and (3) the total shipping cost will be a minimum. A shipping schedule consists simply of mn nonnegative numbers ξ_{ij}, where ξ_{ij} represents the amount to be shipped from P_i to M_j. The total amount shipped into M_j is thus $\sum\limits_{i=1}^{m} \xi_{ij}$, and condition (1) becomes

$$\sum_{i=1}^{m} \xi_{ij} \geqq \delta_j \tag{1}$$

The total amount shipped out of P_i is $\sum\limits_{j=1}^{n} \xi_{ij}$, and condition (2) is therefore

$$\sum_{j=1}^{n} \xi_{ij} \leqq \sigma_i \tag{2}$$

and, finally, we are required to minimize

$$\sum_{i,j} \gamma_{ij}\xi_{ij} \tag{3}$$

It will be noted that this problem is of the same general form as the diet problem. We are seeking certain nonnegative numbers ξ_{ij} which satisfy the system of *linear inequalities* (1) and (2) and minimize the *linear function* (3). In analogy with terminology used in the diet problem, we shall say that a shipping schedule is *feasible* if the numbers ξ_{ij} satisfy inequalities (1) and (2). It is immediately clear that a necessary condition for the problem to be feasible is the requirement that total supply be at least as large as the total demand, that is,

$$\sum_{i=1}^{m} \sigma_i \geqq \sum_{j=1}^{n} \delta_j \qquad (4)$$

Conversely, we leave it to the reader to prove that if (4) is satisfied then there exists a feasible shipping schedule (see Exercise 1).

The next two examples are of quite general importance and include many others as special cases. These involve the important idea of a *linear production model*, which we now describe. Consider a production system, say a factory, in which n goods $G_1, \ldots, G_n$ are involved either as inputs to the productive process or as final goods. For instance, these goods might include steel, labor, automobiles, etc. Goods are produced by *linear processes* or *activities* which are to be thought of as "recipes" giving the proportions of the various goods required in a given mode of production. An ordinary cookbook recipe provides a typical example. Thus, if the goods are, say, eggs, butter, salt, milk, cheese, the *soufflé activity* is completely described by stating how many parts of butter, eggs, etc., are required to produce one unit of soufflé. The statement that this process is *linear* simply means that multiplying all ingredients by any constant multiplies the amount of soufflé by the same constant. Note that this assumption of linearity is a rather severe restriction on the types of processes to be considered. If in the culinary example above we had included labor among the goods, the linearity feature would have been lost, for it is certainly not true in general that preparing a double portion of soufflé requires twice the cooking labor.

A formal definition of an activity is now easily given.

Definition. An *activity* P involving n goods corresponds to a set of n numbers, $\alpha_1, \ldots, \alpha_n$. The good G_j is called an *input* to the activity if α_j is negative, and an *output* of the activity if α_j is positive.

A *linear production model* P involving n goods consists of a set of such activities $P_1, \ldots, P_m$. Such a model is completely described by an array of mn numbers α_{ij}, where α_{ij} is the amount of G_j produced (or consumed if α_{ij} is negative) when P_i is operated at unit level. This array of numbers is called the *production matrix* of the model.

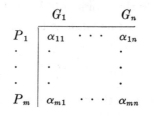

$$
\begin{array}{c|ccc}
 & G_1 & & G_n \\
\hline
P_1 & \alpha_{11} & \cdots & \alpha_{1n} \\
\cdot & \cdot & & \cdot \\
\cdot & \cdot & & \cdot \\
\cdot & \cdot & & \cdot \\
P_m & \alpha_{m1} & \cdots & \alpha_{mn}
\end{array}
$$

Now, in order to describe completely how the production model behaves it is necessary to specify the inputs and outputs of each of the activities. We shall say the activity P_i is being *operated at the level* or *intensity* ξ_i if its inputs and outputs are given by the numbers $\xi_i\alpha_{i1}, \xi_i\alpha_{i2}, \ldots, \xi_i\alpha_{in}$. A *production schedule* for P is defined to be a set of nonnegative intensities $\xi_1, \ldots, \xi_m$ for the activities P_i. Given these numbers ξ_i we see that the total amount of G_j produced is the sum of the amounts produced by each of the activities and is given by the expression

$$\xi_1\alpha_{1j} + \xi_2\alpha_{2j} + \cdots + \xi_m\alpha_{mj}$$

where, of course, this quantity may be negative, which simply means that the jth good is being consumed rather than produced.

We are now prepared to present the two examples.

Example 3. Production to Meet Given Demand at Minimum Cost. Assume we have a linear production model and it is required that we produce at least δ_j units of G_j (δ = demand). Suppose further that the cost of operating the process P_i at unit level is γ_i; hence the cost of operating P_i at level ξ_i is $\xi_i\gamma_i$, where we are again making the rather restrictive assumption that the cost of operating an activity is proportional to the level at which it is operated. The problem is then to choose a production schedule which will satisfy the demands δ_j and minimize the total cost. Thus, we seek nonnegative numbers $\xi_1, \ldots, \xi_m$ which

$$\text{minimize} \sum_{i=1}^{m} \xi_i\gamma_i \tag{1}$$

subject to the requirements that

$$\sum_{i=1}^{m} \xi_i \alpha_{ij} \geqq \delta_j \qquad \text{for } j = 1, \ldots, n \qquad (2)$$

Some remarks are in order here. Recall that the numbers α_{ij} may be either positive or negative according as G_j is produced or consumed by the process P_i. Similarly, the demands δ_j may be negative. A negative demand is economically a supply, for if δ_j is negative, the inequality

$$\sum_{i=1}^{m} \xi_i \alpha_{ij} \geqq \delta_j$$

means that we must not consume more than the amount $-\delta_j$. Thus, both supplies and demands are taken account of in this model.

The question of feasibility is no longer a simple one in this example. It may easily happen that it is not technologically possible to satisfy the given demands with the given resources, for (2) may be any system of linear inequalities and such systems need not have solutions. If, however, a feasible schedule does exist, it is intuitively clear that there is an *optimal* schedule since the cost of a given schedule is bounded below by zero. A proof of this fact will be given in Chap. 3.

Example 4. Production to Maximize Income from Given Resources. This example is essentially the same as the previous one except for a change of sign. Again we consider a linear production model but instead of associating a cost with each activity we let $\gamma_i \geqq 0$ be the rate of *return* or *income* associated with the activity P_i, obtained, say, from selling the outputs of the activity. Assume further that there is a given fixed supply σ_j of the jth good. The problem is now to find a production schedule $\xi_1, \ldots, \xi_m$ which will maximize the total income without exceeding the given supplies. In symbols, we wish to

$$\text{maximize } \sum_{i=1}^{m} \xi_i \gamma_i \qquad (1)$$

subject to the conditions

$$-\sum_{i=1}^{m} \xi_i \alpha_{ij} \leqq \sigma_j \qquad (2)$$

The reason for the negative sign in (2) is that we are here taking supplies as positive and thus the amount of G_j consumed in production is not to exceed σ_j.

With the four examples before us it is not difficult to see what elements they have in common, and we can give our first basic definition.

Definition. A *standard linear programming problem* is that of finding nonnegative numbers $\xi_1, \ldots, \xi_m$ which either maximize or minimize a given linear function, that is,

$$\sum_{i=1}^{m} \xi_i \gamma_i \text{ is to be maximum or minimum} \tag{1}$$

where the numbers ξ_i are also required to satisfy a set of linear inequalities.

$$\sum_{i=1}^{m} \xi_i \alpha_{ij} \leq \beta_j \quad j = 1, \ldots, n \tag{2}$$

We shall later define a more general kind of linear program. For the present the reader should observe that all our examples fall under the definition above. In accordance with previous terminology we shall call numbers ξ_i which satisfy (2) a *feasible solution* of the problem, and we shall call a problem *feasible* if it has a feasible solution. A feasible solution which maximizes or minimizes (1) will be called an *optimal solution*. The number giving the maximum or minimum will then be called the *value* of the linear program.

2. Duality and Prices

We begin this section by considering a specific maximum problem.

Example 5. Find nonnegative numbers $\xi_1, \xi_2, \xi_3, \xi_4$ such that

$$2\xi_1 + 4\xi_2 + \xi_3 + \xi_4 \text{ is a maximum} \tag{1}$$

subject to the conditions

$$\begin{aligned}
\xi_1 + 3\xi_2 \quad\quad + \xi_4 &\leq 4 \\
2\xi_1 + \xi_2 \quad\quad\quad &\leq 3 \\
\xi_2 + 4\xi_3 + \xi_4 &\leq 3
\end{aligned} \tag{2}$$

We assert: An optimal solution of this problem is given by

$$\xi_1 = 1 \qquad \xi_2 = 1 \qquad \xi_3 = \tfrac{1}{2} \qquad \xi_4 = 0$$

The reader will verify by direct substitution that these numbers are feasible; i.e., they satisfy the inequalities (2) above. Substituting the numbers in (1) we obtain

$$2 \cdot 1 + 4 \cdot 1 + \tfrac{1}{2} + 0 = 6\tfrac{1}{2}$$

and it is our claim that $6\tfrac{1}{2}$ is in fact the desired maximum. How do we know this and how can we be sure that some other choice of the numbers ξ_i will not give us a larger value of (1) and still satisfy (2)? In the paragraphs that follow we are going to prove to the reader that the feasible solution above is actually optimal. In order to do this we turn for a moment to the general problem of finding *nonnegative numbers* $\xi_1, \ldots, \xi_m$ *which*

$$maximize \sum_{i=1}^{m} \xi_i \gamma_i \qquad (3)$$

subject to the inequalities

$$\sum_{i=1}^{m} \xi_i \alpha_{ij} \leqq \beta_j \qquad j = 1, \ldots, n \qquad (4)$$

The fundamental fact about linear programming is that to the maximum problem above corresponds the following standard minimum problem: *find nonnegative numbers* $\eta_1, \ldots, \eta_n$ *which*

$$minimize \sum_{j=1}^{n} \eta_j \beta_j \qquad (3)^*$$

subject to the inequalities

$$\sum_{j=1}^{n} \eta_j \alpha_{ij} \geqq \gamma_i \qquad i = 1, \ldots, m \qquad (4)^*$$

Problem $(3)^*$, $(4)^*$ is called the *dual* of problem (3), (4) and the central results of linear programming theory concern the relationship between a problem and its dual. We shall shortly give a precise statement of this relationship. At this time we make the following observation.

Lemma 1.1. Let $\xi_1, \ldots, \xi_m$ be a feasible solution of a standard maximum problem [thus, a nonnegative solution of inequalities (4)] and let $\eta_1, \ldots, \eta_n$ be a feasible solution of the dual problem [a nonnegative solution of inequalities (4)*]. *Then*

$$\sum_{i=1}^{m} \xi_i \gamma_i \leqq \sum_{i,j} \xi_i \eta_j \alpha_{ij} \leqq \sum_{j=1}^{n} \eta_j \beta_j \tag{5}$$

Proof. Multiplying the *j*th inequality of (4) by η_j and summing on *j* gives

$$\sum_{j=1}^{n} \eta_j \beta_j \geqq \sum_{j=1}^{n} \eta_j \sum_{i=1}^{m} \xi_i \alpha_{ij} = \sum_{i,j} \xi_i \eta_j \alpha_{ij} \tag{6}$$

Multiplying the *i*th inequality of (4)* by ξ_i and summing on *i* gives

$$\sum_{i=1}^{m} \xi_i \gamma_i \leqq \sum_{i=1}^{m} \xi_i \sum_{j=1}^{n} \eta_j \alpha_{ij} = \sum_{i,j} \xi_i \eta_j \alpha_{ij} \tag{7}$$

and (6) and (7) together yield (5).

As a consequence of this lemma we have our first important result.

Theorem 1.1 (optimality criterion). *If there exist feasible solutions $\xi_1, \ldots, \xi_m$ and $\eta_1, \ldots, \eta_n$ for the maximum problem above and its dual such that*

$$\sum_{i=1}^{m} \xi_i \gamma_i = \sum_{j=1}^{n} \eta_j \beta_j \tag{8}$$

then these feasible solutions are, in fact, optimal solutions of their respective problems.

Proof. Let $\xi'_1, \ldots, \xi'_m$ be any other feasible solution of the maximum problem. Then from the lemma

$$\sum_{i=1}^{m} \xi'_i \gamma_i \leq \sum_{j=1}^{n} \eta_j \beta_j \tag{9}$$

and combining this with (8) gives

$$\sum_{i=1}^{m} \xi'_i \gamma_i \leqq \sum_{i=1}^{m} \xi_i \gamma_i$$

showing that $\xi_1, \ldots, \xi_m$ is an optimal solution. A symmetrical argument proves the optimality of $\eta_1, \ldots, \eta_n$.

Let us immediately apply this result to our numerical problem. The dual of this problem is seen to be that of finding nonnegative numbers η_1, η_2, η_3 such that

$$4\eta_1 + 3\eta_2 + 3\eta_3 \text{ is a minimum subject to} \qquad (1)^*$$

$$\begin{aligned}
\eta_1 + 2\eta_2 \qquad &\geq 2 \\
3\eta_1 + \eta_2 + \eta_3 &\geq 4 \\
4\eta_3 &\geq 1 \\
\eta_1 + \qquad \eta_3 &\geq 1
\end{aligned} \qquad (2)^*$$

Now, one verifies by direct substitution that

$$\eta_1 = {}^{11}\!\!/_{10} \qquad \eta_2 = {}^{9}\!\!/_{20} \qquad \eta_3 = \tfrac{1}{4}$$

provides a nonnegative solution of $(2)^*$, hence a feasible solution of the dual problem. Furthermore, evaluating $(1)^*$ gives

$$4 \cdot {}^{11}\!\!/_{10} + 3 \cdot {}^{9}\!\!/_{20} + 3 \cdot \tfrac{1}{4} = {}^{130}\!\!/_{20} = 6\tfrac{1}{2}$$

which is the same as the value obtained from the feasible solution of the original maximum problem. It follows from Theorem 1.1 that we have found optimal solutions for both the original problem and its dual.

We have now fulfilled our promise of proving to the reader that the feasible solution which we exhibited at the beginning of this section is optimal. This was possible because we were able to find a feasible solution of the dual problem which together with the original solution satisfied the optimality criterion. A natural question which has now perhaps occurred to the reader is this: Was it just a fortunate accident that we were able to find a suitable solution of the dual problem in this case, or can we expect such solutions to exist in general? The central fact in the theory of linear programming is that the phenomenon noted in this example holds for all linear programming problems. In precise terms the converse of Theorem 1.1 is also true; if we have optimal solutions of a problem and its dual then the values of the two problems are equal. This result is known as the fundamental duality theorem of linear programming, which we state as follows:

Fundamental Duality Theorem. *If a standard maximum or minimum problem and its dual are both feasible then they both have optimal solutions and both have the same value. If either problem is not feasible then neither has an optimal solution.*

This rather remarkable result, which seems to have been noted first by von Neumann, is basic not only in the theory of linear programming but also in two-person game theory and a number of other branches of linear economic theory. The proof is not simple and will have to be put off until the necessary algebraic machinery has been developed in the next chapter. We shall devote the rest of this chapter to interpreting the result in economic terms and to deducing some of its consequences.

In order to gain further understanding of the significance of the duality theory let us return to the numerical problem of Example 5 and interpret this example as a production problem of the type described in Example 4. We assume we have 4 activities P_1, P_2, P_3, and P_4. The income from operating P_1 at unit level is 2, that for P_2 is 4, etc. There are 3 goods G_1, G_2, and G_3 and the activity P_1 requires as inputs 1 unit of G_1 and 2 units of G_2, while P_2 requires 3 units of G_1, 1 unit of G_2, and 1 unit of G_3, etc. There are available 4 units of G_1, 3 units of G_2, and 3 units of G_3. At what levels shall the processes be operated so as to maximize the total income?

We have given a typical interpretation of the problem (1), (2), but how are we to interpret the dual problem (1)*, (2)*? First note that the right-hand side of the inequalities (2)* is income and is therefore measured in monetary units, say in dollars. The coefficients on the left-hand side of (2)* are in units of goods. It follows that the numbers η_j have the units of dollars per unit of goods, that is, the η_j are *unit prices* of the goods G_1, G_2, and G_3. With this interpretation of the unknowns η_j what is the meaning of the inequalities (2)*? Let us consider the first inequality

$$1 \cdot \eta_1 + 2 \cdot \eta_2 \geqq 2$$

The coefficients 1 and 2 on the left are the amounts of G_1 and G_2 required to operate activity P_1 at unit level. Since η_1 and η_2 are the corresponding prices the left-hand side above is the *cost* of operating

P_1 at unit level, and the inequality states that this cost must be at least as great as the income received from the activity. The same analysis applies to the other inequalities (2)*, whose meaning can now be summarized by the simple economic statement:

The prices η_j must be such that no activity P_i makes a positive profit.

Finally (1)* is seen to be the requirement that the total value of the resources be minimized. It is now possible to give a verbal argument justifying Theorem 1.1. It runs like this: We have found prices η_j with the property that the return from each activity will be no greater than the cost of the activity. Therefore, the total return from operating the model is at most equal to the total cost of the available resources. But we have found a way of operating the model in which the return is equal to this total cost, and therefore this mode of operation must be optimal.

3. Further Interpretation of Duality

We have now stated the fundamental duality theorem and shown how it can be used to prove that a given feasible solution of a program is optimal. In this section we shall look again at the examples of linear programs given in Sec. 1 and interpret the duality theorem in each case.

1. The Diet Problem. We shall not rewrite the problem formally but simply remind the reader that it concerned selecting a diet satisfying certain requirements on nutrients and minimizing total cost. The dual problem can be described as follows: to assign values or "prices" to each nutrient N_i in such a way that the sum of the values of the nutrients in one unit of the jth food F_j does not exceed its unit cost π_j, and such that the total value of the amounts of nutrients required by the diet is a maximum. It is recommended that the reader verify formally the above verbal statement.

An important nonmathematical question now arises. Is there any way of looking at this dual problem so that it makes sense economically? It is quite clear why a dietitian would want to minimize the cost of an adequate diet, but why would anyone want to maximize the value of the nutrients in such a diet? We are about to describe a simple situation in which such a maximization has an economic meaning. The description may seem artificial at first, but it will appear less so as we go on to consider other examples. The situation requires that we introduce a new character into our gastronomic drama, a seller of pills—vitamin pills, iron capsules, and so forth. This salesman is, in fact, able to provide the dietitian with all the nutrients the latter needs in some concentrated form. The dietitian, whose sole aim is to minimize costs, will willingly substitute pills and capsules for steak and potatoes provided this will save money (a certain lack of realism in the original problem is becoming increasingly apparent, but this is, of course, beside the point for present purposes). Suppose then that the pill salesman sets the prices of a unit of N_i (the ith nutrient) at some value ξ_i, making sure that

$$\sum_{i=1}^{m} \xi_i \alpha_{ij} \leqq \pi_j \qquad \text{for all } j, \text{ where } \alpha_{ij} \text{ is the amount of } N_i \text{ in } F_j \quad (2)^*$$

This means that the total value of the nutrients in a unit of F_j is no greater than the unit cost of F_j. It is now clear that, no matter what diet he chooses, it will always be at least as economical for the dietitian to buy pills since the cost of each food is at least as great as the cost of the nutrients it contains. The pill man will, however, now charge the dietitian as much as possible subject to the constraints $(2)^*$. Since the adequate diet calls for γ_i units of N_i, he sets prices ξ_i so as to maximize

$$\sum_{i=1}^{m} \xi_i \gamma_i \qquad\qquad\qquad (1)^*$$

and this is precisely the dual problem.

We can be somewhat less concrete in our description of the dual problem by saying that the nutrient prices ξ_i are those which enable the pill man to realize the maximum return and still compete favorably with the grocer. It is this idea of *competitive* prices which is characteristic of the interpretation of the duality theorem.

2. The Transportation Problem. In order to determine the dual here it is convenient to write out the relations without the summation symbols.   Recall that we wish to choose numbers ξ_{ij} which minimize the shipping cost

$$
\begin{aligned}
& \xi_{11}\gamma_{11} + \xi_{12}\gamma_{12} + \cdots + \xi_{1n}\gamma_{1n} \\
+ {}& \xi_{21}\gamma_{21} + \xi_{22}\gamma_{22} + \cdots + \xi_{2n}\gamma_{2n} \\
+ {}& \cdots \cdots \cdots \cdots \cdots \cdots \cdots \\
+ {}& \xi_{m1}\gamma_{m1} + \xi_{m2}\gamma_{m2} + \cdots + \xi_{mn}\gamma_{mn}
\end{aligned}
\tag{1}
$$

subject to the inequalities (see Sec. 1, Example 2)

$$
\begin{aligned}
-\xi_{11} - \cdots - \xi_{1n} && \geqq -\sigma_1 \\
-\xi_{21} - \cdots - \xi_{2n} && \geqq -\sigma_2 \\
\cdots \cdots \cdots \cdots && \\
-\xi_{m1} - \cdots - \xi_{mn} & \geqq -\sigma_m \\
\xi_{11} \qquad + \xi_{21} + \cdots \qquad + \xi_{m1} & \geqq \delta_1 \\
\cdots \cdots \cdots \cdots && \\
\xi_{1n} \qquad + \xi_{2n} + \cdots \qquad + \xi_{mn} & \geqq \delta_n
\end{aligned}
$$

where σ_i is the supply at plant P_i and δ_j is the demand at market M_j.

The dual problem now becomes: to determine nonnegative numbers $\pi_i,\ i = 1, \ldots, m$, and $\pi'_j,\ j = 1, \ldots, n$, such that $\pi'_j - \pi_i \leqq \gamma_{ij}$ for all i and j, and such that $\sum_{j=1}^{n} \pi'_j \delta_j - \sum_{i=1}^{m} \pi_i \sigma_i$ is a maximum.   The reader should verify that this is the correct statement of the dual problem.

How shall we interpret this dual problem?   First, notice that since we have the relations $\pi'_j - \pi_i \leqq \gamma_{ij}$ we are forced once again to measure the variables π'_j and π_j in units of money.   Let us consider now that the numbers γ_{ij} represent the established transportation costs which confront, say, a steel manufacturer who is in the act of trying to decide on a shipping schedule.   He is interrupted by a visit from a representative of the new Fly-By-Nite Transportation Company, who makes him the following proposition: "I will buy all your steel, paying π_i for each unit of steel at plant P_i.   I will guarantee to deliver the steel to the markets M_j in the quantities δ_j and I will then sell it back to you, charging π'_j for each unit at M_j.   Please notice that

$$
\pi'_j - \pi_i \leqq \gamma_{ij} \qquad \text{for all } i \text{ and } j \tag{2}*
$$

so you will pay no more than you would if you paid the normal transportation costs." The manufacturer is forced to agree on this point and the deal is therefore closed to the satisfaction of the Fly-By-Nite man as well, for he has shrewdly set the prices so as to maximize his profit $\Sigma \pi'_j \delta_j - \Sigma \pi_i \sigma_i$ subject only to (2)* above.

Because of the duality theorem, it will turn out that the manufacturer doesn't actually save any money by this maneuver (though he is saved the trouble of calculating the minimal shipping schedule).

Let us illustrate the duality theory for the transportation problem by a numerical example.

Example 6. The diagram in Fig. 1.1 gives a schematic representation of a transportation problem with two plants and three markets.

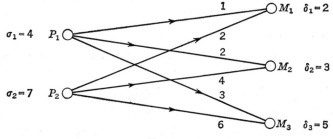

FIG. 1.1

This graphical representation is almost self-explanatory. The vertices of the graph represent the plants and markets, and the corresponding supplies σ_i and demands δ_j are indicated. The lines connecting plants and markets represent the various routes and the number above each line gives the cost of the corresponding route. The *cost matrix* is seen to be

$$
\begin{array}{c|ccc}
 & M_1\ M_2\ M_3 \\
\hline
P_1 & 1\ \ 2\ \ 3 \\
P_2 & 2\ \ 4\ \ 6 \\
\end{array}
$$

where the *ij*th entry above is the unit shipping cost from P_i to M_j.

We now claim that a solution to the above problem is given by

$$\xi_{11} = 0 \qquad \xi_{12} = 0 \qquad \xi_{13} = 4$$
$$\xi_{21} = 2 \qquad \xi_{22} = 3 \qquad \xi_{23} = 1$$

and the minimum cost is given by

$$0 \cdot 1 + 0 \cdot 2 + 4 \cdot 3 + 2 \cdot 2 + 3 \cdot 4 + 1 \cdot 6 = 12 + 4 + 12 + 6 = 34$$

In order to prove that this is a minimum, we exhibit the following feasible prices for the dual problem:

$$\pi_1 = 3 \qquad \pi_2 = 0$$
$$\pi'_1 = 2 \qquad \pi'_2 = 4 \qquad \pi'_3 = 6$$

To verify feasibility, we must check that $\pi'_j - \pi_i$ is not greater than the ijth entry in the cost matrix. The following figure will facilitate this verification:

$$\pi'_1 = 2 \quad \pi'_2 = 4 \quad \pi'_3 = 6$$

$\pi_1 = 3$	1	2	3
$\pi_2 = 0$	2	4	6

One easily checks that each entry in the cost matrix is not less than the difference between the numbers at the head of its column and row.

Finally we see that our solutions of the dual problems are optimal for we compute

$$\Sigma \pi'_j \delta_j - \Sigma \pi_i \sigma_i = 2 \cdot 2 + 4 \cdot 3 + 5 \cdot 6 - 3 \cdot 4 - 0 \cdot 7 = 34$$

and since this is the same as the shipping cost computed above we have solved the problem.

The solution can also be written down in tabular form as a *shipping matrix*

0	0	4
2	3	1

where the ijth entry is the amount shipped from P_i to M_j. Comparing the shipping matrix with the cost matrix we note that in our solution the cheapest route, that from P_1 to M_1, is not used, while the most expensive route, that from P_2 to M_3, is used. This fact is perhaps somewhat surprising and shows that it is not easy to guess the solution of a transportation problem in advance.

3. Production to Meet Given Demand at Minimum Cost. The interpretation of the dual here is very similar to that of the diet problem. The details are left to the reader.

4. Production to Maximize Return from Given Resources.

This is the problem treated in the previous section. The dual consists in assigning prices π_j to the various goods G_j in such a way that

$$\sum_{j=1}^{n} \pi_j \sigma_j \text{ is minimized} \qquad (1)^*$$

subject to

$$-\sum_{j=1}^{n} \pi_j \alpha_{ij} \geqq \gamma_i \qquad (2)^*$$

Interpretation. A competitor believes he has a more efficient way of utilizing the given resources and wants to buy out the producer. He therefore offers to pay the producer the amount π_j for each unit of G_j, where the numbers π_j satisfy $(2)^*$ above. The competitor quickly convinces the producer that the amount of money offered is at least as much as he could obtain from any production schedule, "for," says the competitor, "if you operate P_i at level ξ_i your return will be

$$\sum_{i=1}^{m} \xi_i \gamma_i \qquad (3)$$

where, of course, because of your limited supplies,

$$-\sum_{i=1}^{m} \xi_i \alpha_{ij} \leqq \sigma_j \qquad (4)$$

But if you sell to me, your return will be

$$\sum_{j=1}^{n} \pi_j \sigma_j$$

and
$$\sum_j \pi_j \sigma_j \geqq -\sum_j \pi_j \sum_i \xi_i \alpha_{ij} \qquad \text{[from (4)]} \qquad (5)$$

$$= -\sum_i \xi_i \sum_j \pi_j \alpha_{ij} \geqq \sum_i \xi_i \gamma_i \qquad \text{[from (2)*]}$$

so you will be at least as well off." Conclusion: The producer accepts the offer and the competitor buys him out at the lowest possible figure [i.e., condition $(1)^*$ subject to $(2)^*$].

4. Price Equilibrium

In this section we shall present a result which is a rather simple consequence of the duality theorem. It is, however, of considerable economic importance, providing our first example of an "equilibrium theorem," a terminology which will be explained shortly.

We return to consideration of the standard maximum problem of finding nonnegative numbers $\xi_1, \ldots, \xi_m$ which

$$\text{maximize} \sum_{i=1}^{m} \xi_i \gamma_i \tag{1}$$

subject to

$$\sum_{i=1}^{m} \xi_i \alpha_{ij} \leqq \beta_j \qquad j = 1, \ldots, n \tag{2}$$

and the dual problem of finding nonnegative numbers $\eta_1, \ldots, \eta_n$ which

$$\text{minimize} \sum_{j=1}^{n} \eta_j \beta_j \tag{1*}$$

subject to

$$\sum_{j=1}^{n} \eta_j \alpha_{ij} \geqq \gamma_i \qquad i = 1, \ldots, m \tag{2*}$$

Assuming the duality theorem to be true we shall now prove the following result.

Theorem 1.2 (equilibrium theorem). *The feasible solutions $\xi_1, \ldots, \xi_m$ and $\eta_1, \ldots, \eta_n$ of (2) and (2)*, respectively, are optimal solutions if and only if*

$$\eta_j = 0 \qquad whenever \qquad \sum_{i=1}^{m} \xi_i \alpha_{ij} < \beta_j \tag{3}$$

and

$$\xi_i = 0 \qquad whenever \qquad \sum_{j=1}^{n} \eta_j \alpha_{ij} > \gamma_i \tag{3*}$$

Proof. First, suppose conditions (3) and (3)* hold. Multiplying the jth inequality of (2) by η_j and summing on j and making use of (3) gives

$$\sum_{j=1}^{n} \eta_j \beta_j = \sum_{j=1}^{n} \eta_j \sum_{i=1}^{m} \xi_i \alpha_{ij} = \sum_{i,j} \xi_i \eta_j \alpha_{ij} \qquad (4)$$

Similarly, from (2)* and (3)* we get

$$\sum_{i=1}^{m} \xi_i \gamma_i = \sum_{i=1}^{m} \xi_i \sum_{j=1}^{n} \eta_j \alpha_{ij} = \sum_{i,j} \xi_i \eta_j \alpha_{ij} \qquad (5)$$

and (4) and (5) show that

$$\sum_{i=1}^{m} \xi_i \gamma_i = \sum_{j=1}^{n} \eta_j \beta_j$$

whence from Theorem 1.1 the ξ_i and η_j are optimal solutions.

Conversely, if the ξ_i and η_j provide optimal solutions then from the duality theorem we know that

$$\sum_{i=1}^{m} \xi_i \gamma_i = \sum_{i,j} \xi_i \eta_j \alpha_{ij} = \sum_{j=1}^{n} \eta_j \beta_j$$

From the first equation we have

$$\sum_{i=1}^{m} \xi_i \left(\gamma_i - \sum_{j=1}^{n} \eta_j \alpha_{ij} \right) = 0$$

but since the numbers η_j are feasible it follows that the terms $\left(\gamma_i - \sum_{j=1}^{n} \eta_j \alpha_{ij} \right)$ are nonpositive and hence for each i

$$\xi_i \left(\gamma_i - \sum_{j=1}^{n} \eta_j \alpha_{ij} \right) = 0$$

from which (3)* follows at once. A symmetrical argument proves condition (3).

We shall now interpret the above result economically and justify the use of the word "equilibrium." For this purpose let us think of (1), (2) above as the production problem of Example 4. We have already seen that it is natural to interpret the dual variables η_j as prices, and we have also seen that the feasibility conditions (2)* correspond to the requirement that no activity makes a positive profit.

Condition (3)* has a very obvious interpretation. It says that if the cost of an activity exceeds the income derived from it then it will not be used; i.e., it will be operated at level zero. Conditions (2)* and (3)* together may be thought of as *stability conditions* in the following sense. If the model is operating at activity levels $\xi_1, \ldots, \xi_m$ and these conditions are satisfied then there will be no incentive to change the activity levels since there is no way of increasing income. Looked at the other way, if conditions (2)* or (3)* failed to hold then activity levels would be unstable, for the producer could increase his income by changing the production levels.

As to conditions (2) and (3), the first is simply the technological requirement that the available supply must not be exceeded. Condition (3) states that, if there are goods of which there is a *surplus*, that is, whose supply is not exhausted, then the price of these goods must be zero. This is also a stability condition, this time on prices rather than on activity levels. Recall that according to the classical "law of supply and demand" if the supply of a good exceeds the demand for it then its price will drop. On the other hand, prices cannot drop below zero and therefore a good which is oversupplied even when income is being maximized must become a *free good*.

As a second illustration of the equilibrium theorem, let us see what it says for the case of the transportation problem. Recall that a feasible shipping schedule is one which satisfies the given demands without exceeding the given supplies, and a feasible set of dual variables are prices at each plant and market with the property that the difference between market price and plant price does not exceed the shipping cost from plant to market. The equilibrium conditions now become:

(3)* If the difference between the price at a particular market and a particular plant is less than the corresponding shipping cost, then no goods will be shipped from that plant to that market.

Interpretation. "The company" will lose money if it costs more to ship from plant to market than what can be realized by sales at the market. Such unprofitable routes will not be used.

(3) If the amount shipped out of some plant is less than the supply at that plant then the price at that plant must be zero.

Interpretation. As in the previous discussion, if there is a surplus at some plant, the price there must drop to zero.

One of the most important uses of the equilibrium theorem is in connection with numerical computation. We have already seen that if feasible solutions of the primal and dual problems are given they can easily be checked for optimality. Now, using the equilibrium theorem we can often find the solution to the dual problem when the solution to the primal is given. Let us return to the numerical Example 5 in which the inequalities were

$$
\begin{aligned}
\xi_1 + 3\xi_2 \quad\quad + \xi_4 &\leqq 4 \\
2\xi_1 + \xi_2 \quad\quad\quad &\leqq 3 \\
\xi_2 + 4\xi_3 + \xi_4 &\leqq 3
\end{aligned}
\tag{2}
$$

and the proposed optimal solution was

$$
\xi_1 = 1 \quad\quad \xi_2 = 1 \quad\quad \xi_3 = \tfrac{1}{2} \quad\quad \xi_4 = 0
$$

According to the equilibrium theorem the dual inequalities must in fact be equations for the cases $i = 1, 2, 3$; so we must solve

$$
\begin{aligned}
\eta_1 + 2\eta_2 \quad\quad &= 2 \\
3\eta_1 + \eta_2 + \eta_3 &= 4 \\
4\eta_3 &= 1
\end{aligned}
$$

and this is a simple system of 3 equations in 3 unknowns whose unique solution is easily seen to be the one given in Sec. 2. Thus, knowing only the solution of the original problem we are able to find the solution of the dual.

Let us apply the equilibrium theorem to solving the transportation problem of Example 6. The proposed solution was given by the shipping matrix

$$
\begin{vmatrix}
0 & 0 & 4 \\
2 & 3 & 1
\end{vmatrix}
$$

We wish to find the prices π_1, π_2 and π'_1, π'_2, and π'_3. Note first that the supply σ_2 at P_2 is 7, but only 6 units are shipped out of P_2. According to the equilibrium theorem, therefore, the price $\pi_2 = 0$. Next, corresponding to the nonzero entries in the shipping matrix above we must have equations in the dual problem. These are

$$\pi_1' - \pi_2 = \pi_1' = 2$$
$$\pi_2' - \pi_2 = \pi_2' = 4$$
$$\pi_3' - \pi_1 \quad\;\;= 3$$
$$\pi_3' - \pi_2 = \pi_3' = 6$$

so $\pi_1' = 2$, $\pi_2' = 4$, $\pi_3' = 6$, and $\pi_1 = 3$, which is the answer given in the previous section.

Bibliographical Notes

The term "linear programming" came into being about 1947–1948. The earliest published work containing these words in the title is due to Dantzig [1], *Programming* in a *Linear* Structure (italics mine), 1949. An early formulation and discussion of the diet problem was given by Stiegler [1] and of the transportation problem by Hitchcock [1].   The duality theorem was known to von Neumann [2] at least as early as 1947 and is contained in a set of privately circulated notes, but the proof as given there is incomplete.   The first published proof based on von Neumann's notes is due to Gale, Kuhn, and Tucker [2].   The explicit statement of the equilibrium theorem is due to Goldman and Tucker [2] in a paper that contains a very complete treatment of linear programming theory.

Exercises

1. Prove that a transportation problem is feasible if and only if the total supply is at least equal to the total demand, that is,

$$\sum_{i=1}^{m} \sigma_i \geqq \sum_{j=1}^{n} \delta_j$$

2. Find a feasible shipping schedule for the transportation problem with 5 plants and 5 markets where the supplies and demands are given by

$$\sigma_1 = 120 \qquad \sigma_2 = 75 \qquad \sigma_3 = 205 \qquad \sigma_4 = 145 \qquad \sigma_5 = 90$$
and $\quad \delta_1 = 235 \qquad \delta_2 = 50 \qquad \delta_3 = 115 \qquad \delta_4 = 80 \qquad \delta_5 = 150$

3. Show that the following standard maximum problem is not feasible: Find nonnegative numbers ξ_1 and ξ_2 which

$$\text{maximize } 3\xi_1 - 2\xi_2 \tag{1}$$

subject to

$$2\xi_1 + 5\xi_2 \leq 3 \tag{2}$$
$$-3\xi_1 + 8\xi_2 \leq -5$$

4. Show that the following linear program is feasible but has no optimal solution: Find ξ_1, $\xi_2 \geq 0$ such that

$$\xi_1 + \xi_2 \text{ is a maximum} \tag{1}$$

subject to

$$-3\xi_1 + 2\xi_2 \leq -1 \tag{2}$$
$$\xi_1 - \xi_2 \leq 2$$

5. Write the dual problem of the problem given in Exercise 4. In view of the result of Exercise 4 and the duality theorem what must be true of this dual problem? Verify this directly.

6. Construct a standard maximum problem involving two inequalities and two unknowns which has more than one optimal solution although not every feasible solution is optimal.

7. Consider the standard minimum problem of finding nonnegative numbers $\xi_1, \ldots, \xi_m$ which

$$\text{minimize} \sum_{i=1}^{m} \xi_i \gamma_i \tag{1}$$

subject to

$$\sum_{i=1}^{m} \xi_i \alpha_{ij} \geq \beta_j \qquad \text{for } j = 1, \ldots, n \tag{2}$$

If $\alpha_{ij} \geq 0$ for all i, j show that the problem is feasible if and only if

$$\beta_j \leq 0 \qquad \text{whenever} \qquad \alpha_{1j} = \alpha_{2j} = \cdots = \alpha_{mj} = 0$$

Interpret this result for the case of the diet problem.

8. Write out the dual of the problem of Exercise 7. Assuming that the conditions of Exercise 7 hold, show from the duality theorem that both the original problem and its dual have optimal solutions if $\gamma_i \geq 0$ for all i.

9. Verify that the dual of the diet problem is correctly described by the statement of Sec. 3, Subsec. 1.

10. Verify that the dual of the transportation problem is correctly given by the relations in Sec. 3, Subsec. 2.

11. Give an economic interpretation of the dual of the problem of "production to meet a given demand at minimum cost."

12. Consider the following standard maximum problem:

$$\text{maximize } \xi_1 + \xi_2 + \xi_3 + \xi_4 \tag{1}$$

subject to

$$
\begin{aligned}
\xi_1 + \xi_2 \qquad\qquad &\leqq 3 \\
\xi_3 + \xi_4 &\leqq 1 \\
\xi_2 + \xi_3 \qquad &\leqq 1 \\
\xi_1 \qquad + \xi_3 \qquad &\leqq 1 \\
\xi_3 + \xi_4 &\leqq 3
\end{aligned} \tag{2}
$$

Show that this problem has the optimal solution

$$\xi_1 = 1 \qquad \xi_2 = 1 \qquad \xi_3 = 0 \qquad \xi_4 = 1$$

by finding a solution of the dual problem making use of the equilibrium theorem.

13. By the methods of Exercise 12 show that

$$\xi_1 = 4 \qquad \xi_2 = 1$$

is an optimal solution of the problem

$$\text{maximize } \xi_1 - \xi_2 \tag{1}$$

subject to

$$
\begin{aligned}
-2\xi_1 + \xi_2 &\leqq 2 \\
\xi_1 - 2\xi_2 &\leqq 2 \\
\xi_1 + \xi_2 &\leqq 5
\end{aligned} \tag{2}
$$

14. The cost matrix for a transportation problem with 3 plants and 4 markets is

	M_1	M_2	M_3	M_4
P_1	4	4	9	3
P_2	3	5	8	8
P_3	2	6	5	7

The supplies and demands are

$$\sigma_1 = 3 \qquad \sigma_2 = 5 \qquad \sigma_3 = 7 \qquad \delta_1 = 2 \qquad \delta_2 = 5 \qquad \delta_3 = 4 \qquad \delta_5 = 4$$

We claim that the following shipping matrix gives an optimal solution:

0	0	0	3
0	5	0	0
2	0	4	1

Verify this by finding the prices in the dual solution, given the fact that the prices at P_2 and P_3 are zero.

15. Let $P_0, P_1, \ldots, P_n$ be a set of geographical points. A certain good is produced at P_0 and desired at P_n. For each pair of points P_i and P_j there is a nonnegative number c_{ij} called a *capacity*, which measures the maximum amount that can be shipped from P_i to P_j in one year. Formulate algebraically a linear program for maximizing the amount which can be received at P_n in a year. Show that the program is always feasible. (This is called the *maximum-flow problem*.) (Hint: Since goods are produced only at P_0 the flow out of P_i must not exceed the flow into P_i for $i > 0$.)

16. Write out the dual of the maximum-flow problem above. How many inequalities and unknowns does it contain? Show that this dual is always feasible if P_0 is distinct from P_n. In view of the duality theorem what does this imply for the original problem?

17. In a certain plant there are n different job openings $J_1, \ldots,$ J_n and m individuals $I_1, \ldots, I_m$ are available for working the various jobs. An efficiency expert has tested each individual at each job and has found that the *rating* of I_i for the job J_j is given by the nonnegative number α_{ij}. The problem is to determine what fraction of time I_i should work at job J_j assuming only one person can work at a given job at a time, in order to maximize the sum of the ratings. Formulate this problem algebraically as a linear program and show that it is always feasible. (This is called the *optimal-assignment* problem.)

18. Write out the dual of the optimal-assignment problem. Show that it has $m + n$ unknowns and mn inequalities. Using the duality theorem, prove that the optimal-assignment problem always has an optimal solution.

19. The following is the *rating matrix* for an optimal-assignment problem:

	J_1	J_2	J_3	J_4	J_5
I_1	12	9	10	3	8
I_2	6	6	2	2	9
I_3	6	8	10	11	9
I_4	6	3	4	1	1
I_5	11	1	10	9	12

We maintain that a solution to this problem is given by

I_1 works full time on J_1

I_2 works full time on J_5

I_3 works full time on J_4
I_4 works full time on J_2
I_5 works full time on J_3

Also, the 5 dual unknowns $\pi'_1, \ldots, \pi'_5$ corresponding to $J_1, \ldots, J_5$ in an optimal solution are

$$\pi'_1 = 3 \qquad \pi'_2 = 0 \qquad \pi'_3 = 1 \qquad \pi'_4 = 0 \qquad \pi'_5 = 3$$

Verify optimality by first finding the dual unknowns $\pi_1, \ldots, \pi_5$ corresponding to $I_1, \ldots, I_5$.

CHAPTER TWO

Real Linear Algebra

In this chapter we shall develop all the mathematical machinery needed for the applications in the remainder of the book. The first four sections contain basic material which is needed for an understanding of all subsequent chapters. The last three sections are of a somewhat more technical nature and contain material that will be used only occasionally for particular applications. Depending on his objectives, the reader may or may not wish to work through these sections on first reading (in this connection see the section on How to Use the Book in the Preface).

The presentation of this chapter of necessity represents a compromise. We shall give more than a mere recital of the facts. Fortunately, linear algebra is closely related to analytic geometry and we shall when it seems desirable insert suggestive pictures as aids to the reader's mathematical digestion. Another device we shall adopt is that of giving our main theorems names as well as numbers in order to underline their content. Undoubtedly it would have been possible to give more descriptive material, but it was felt that this would expand the chapter disproportionately. It need hardly be mentioned here that one exercise worked by the reader is worth three paragraphs of explanation from us. A selection of such exercises will be found as usual at the chapter's end.

As a guide to the reader let us survey briefly the program to be followed in these sections. Our subject is the theory of linear equations and inequalities in real numbers. These objects are so familiar that one would expect them to be standard material in any text on algebra. This is not the case. We know of only one text (see Bibliographical Notes) at the present time which attempts a systematic treatment of inequality theory. Even more surprising is the fact that it is only in relatively recent times that this theory has become part of the working equipment of research mathematicians. As a striking illustration of this fact, it was more than twenty years between the time von Neumann first proved the minimax theorem of game theory (1928) and the discovery of a simple algebraic proof based on inequality theory (1950).

Our presentation is divided into three parts. The first is concerned with the classical theory of linear equations presented in the language of vectors and matrices. By the classical theory is meant the theory which holds over any field of numbers, real, rational, complex, finite fields, etc. This theory is, of course, treated in every text on algebra. It has seemed advisable, nevertheless, to develop the subject here essentially from the beginning rather than refer the reader to outside sources. The difficulty is that all these sources contain much more material than we shall need, and as a result, the parts of the theory which we do need are likely to become obscured by the great bulk of irrelevant material. For example, the theory of determinants is usually given an extensive treatment in most texts. We know of no instances where this theory is useful for economic problems and there is therefore no need to spend time treating this rather intricate subject.

The second part of our presentation, Secs. 3 and 4, gives the basic existence theorems for the theory of inequalities. As already mentioned, this material is not standard subject matter in algebra texts, though we venture to predict that it will become so in the near future. In any case, we had no choice but to develop it here from the beginning, since it represents the mathematical core on which most of the later applications are based. The final sections give a more detailed analysis of solutions of inequalities and introduce a number of important geometric notions which will be used occasionally in later chapters.

Although the material on vectors and matrices is essentially self-contained, we are assuming most of our readers have some familiarity with these objects, and we shall therefore make only very brief mention of their elementary properties and the corresponding geometric ideas. We shall be considerably more explicit about these matters when we come to the sections on inequalities.

1. Vectors

The results of this section deal with certain properties of algebraic objects called *fields*. For our purposes we need not give the abstract definition. When we talk of a field F the reader may think of any set of real or complex numbers which is closed under the operations of addition, subtraction, multiplication, and division; that is, if two elements a and b belong to F so also does $a + b$, $a - b$, ab, and a/b, this last provided $b \neq 0$. The elements of F will be referred to as *scalars* or *numbers*.

Definition. An *m-vector* x is an ordered set of m numbers ξ_1, ξ_2, . . . , ξ_m. The number ξ_i is called the *ith coordinate* of x. We shall use the notation $x = (\xi_i)$, meaning x is the vector whose ith coordinate is ξ_i.

The set of all m-vectors is called *m-space* and is denoted by F^m.

Among the vectors of F^m we wish to single out certain ones which will play an important role in the theory to follow.

Definition. The *unit vector* in F^m is the vector all of whose coordinates are 1. We shall denote unit vectors by the letter u or v.

The *ith unit vector* is the vector whose ith coordinate is 1 and whose other coordinates are zero. We denote the ith unit vector by the symbol u_i or v_i.

We now define two algebraic operations on the vectors x of F^m.

Addition. If $x = (\xi_i)$ and $y = (\eta_i)$ are m-vectors, their *sum $x + y$* is the vector $(\xi_i + \eta_i)$.

Scalar Multiplication. If $x = (\xi_i)$ is an m-vector and λ is a number, the *product λx* is the vector $(\lambda \xi_i)$.

We remind the reader of the familiar "pictures" of the vector operations. Let F^3 be thought of as 3-space of analytic geometry; a vector $x = (\xi_1, \xi_2, \xi_3)$ corresponds to a directed line segment from the origin to the point whose coordinates are ξ_1, ξ_2, ξ_3; vectors are added by completing the "parallelogram of forces." Multiplying a vector by λ "stretches" it by the amount λ (reversing the sense in case λ is negative).

We now list a number of properties of addition and scalar multiplication which follow immediately from the definition, as the reader will easily verify. We shall use these properties freely in what follows without giving explicit reference after each use.

For addition we have

A1: $(x + y) + z = x + (y + z)$ (associative law)

A2: $x + y = y + x$ (commutative law)

A3: For any x and y there is a z such that

$$x + z = y \qquad \text{(law of subtraction)}$$

For multiplication we have

M1: $\lambda(x + y) = \lambda x + \lambda y$ (vector distributive law)

M2: $(\lambda + \mu)x = \lambda x + \mu x$ (scalar distributive law)

M3: $\lambda(\mu x) = (\lambda\mu)x$ (scalar associative law)

M4: $1x = x$ (identity law)

For many of the theorems to be proved here it is sufficient to use only properties A1 to A3 and M1 to M4 above and never refer back to the original definition of F^m. In fact, the properties listed may be taken as axioms for an abstract algebraic system. Such systems are called *vector spaces*.

We shall use the symbol 0 ambiguously to denote either the number zero or the vector all of whose coordinates are zero. It will always be clear from the context which is meant.

Notation. It is convenient at this point to introduce the set-theoretic symbol ε, to be read "is an element of." The statements "x is an m-vector," "λ is a scalar" become "$x \varepsilon F^m$" and "$\lambda \varepsilon F$." We shall consistently use Greek letters for scalars and italic letters for vectors.

We proceed to develop the fundamental properties of vector spaces.

Definitions.   A subset L in a vector space U is called a *linear sub-space* or simply a *subspace* if it is closed under the operations of addition and scalar multiplication; that is,

$$\text{if } x, y \, \varepsilon \, L \qquad \text{then } x + y \, \varepsilon \, L \tag{1}$$

$$\text{if } x \, \varepsilon \, L, \, \lambda \, \varepsilon \, F \qquad \text{then } \lambda x \, \varepsilon \, L \tag{2}$$

A set of vectors $x_1, \ldots, x_n$ in U is *linearly dependent*, or simply *dependent*, if there exist numbers $\lambda_1, \ldots, \lambda_n$, not all zero, such that

$$\sum_{i=1}^{n} \lambda_i x_i = 0$$

If the vectors are not dependent they are called *independent*.

A vector y is a *linear combination* of the vectors $x_1, \ldots, x_n$ if

$$y = \sum_{i=1}^{n} \lambda_i x_i$$

for some numbers λ_i.

We recall the geometric pictures corresponding to these definitions. In ordinary 3-space the subspaces correspond to lines and planes through the origin, the whole of 3-space, or the origin alone. Two vectors are linearly dependent if they lie on the same line through the origin; three vectors are dependent if they lie in the same plane through the origin.

We are now prepared to give a basic result of the theory of vector spaces.

Theorem 2.1 (fundamental theorem of vector spaces).   *If each of the vectors $y_0, y_1, \ldots, y_n$ in a vector space U is a linear combination of the vectors $x_1, \ldots, x_n$, then the y_i are dependent.*

Proof (by induction on n).   If $n = 1$ then $y_0 = \lambda_0 x_1$, $y_1 = \lambda_1 x_1$. If both λ_1 and λ_0 are zero then $y_1 = y_0 = 0$ and the conclusion is immediate. If not, say $\lambda_0 \neq 0$. Then $\lambda_0 y_1 - \lambda_1 y_0 = \lambda_0 \lambda_1 x_1 - \lambda_1 \lambda_0 x_1 = 0 x_1 = 0$, giving the desired dependence.

Now, assume the theorem holds for $n = k - 1$ and let us prove it for $n = k$. By hypothesis we have

$$y_j = \sum_{i=1}^{k} \lambda_{ij} x_i \qquad j = 0, \ldots, k$$

Again if all λ_{ij} are zero the proof is immediate; so assume this is not the case. Then at least one number λ_{ij} is not zero, say $\lambda_{10} \neq 0$. Define

$$z_j = y_j - \frac{\lambda_{1j}}{\lambda_{10}} y_0 = \sum_{i=2}^{k} \left(\lambda_{ij} - \frac{\lambda_{1j}}{\lambda_{10}} \lambda_{i0} \right) x_i$$

for $j = 1, \ldots, k$. Then each of the k vectors z_j is a linear combination of the $k - 1$ vectors $x_2, \ldots, x_k$; so by the induction hypothesis, the z_j are dependent, that is, there exist numbers $\mu_1, \ldots, \mu_k$, not all zero, such that

$$0 = \sum_{j=1}^{k} \mu_j z_j = \sum_{j=1}^{k} \mu_j y_j - \frac{1}{\lambda_{10}} \left(\sum_{j=1}^{k} \mu_j \lambda_{1j} \right) y_0$$

but this shows that the y_j are dependent, as asserted.

Corollary 1. *Any set of $m + 1$ vectors in F^m is dependent.*

Proof. Let u_i be the ith unit vector. Then any vector x in F^m is a combination of the u_i, for if $x = (\xi_i)$ then $x = \sum_{i=1}^{m} \xi_i u_i$. The conclusion now follows from the theorem above.

Corollary 2. *Any system of n homogeneous linear equations in $n + 1$ unknowns has a nonzero solution.*

Proof. Let

$$\sum_{j=0}^{n} \alpha_{ij} \lambda_j = 0 \qquad i = 1, \ldots, n \tag{1}$$

be the equations for the unknown λ_j in terms of the given α_{ij}. Let a^j be the n-vector defined by $a^j = (\alpha_{1j}, \ldots, \alpha_{nj})$ for $j = 0, \ldots, n$. Then the a^j are a set of $n + 1$ vectors in n-space; hence by the above corollary they are dependent; so there exist numbers λ_j not all zero such that

$$\sum_{j=0}^{n} \lambda_j a^j = 0$$

and these λ_j give the desired solution of (1).

Theorem 2.1 and its corollaries form the basis for the entire **theory** of linear equations. Note that the proof of the theorem is actually *constructive;* that is, given $m + 1$ vectors in F^m, the theorem shows how to compute the λ's which exhibit the linear dependence. The computation is nothing more than the familiar method of elimination.

We next introduce an important algebraic concept.

Definition. Let S be a subset of vector space U. The *rank r* of S is the maximum number of independent vectors which can be chosen from S.

If r is the rank of S a set of r independent vectors of S is called a *basis* for S.

For general vector spaces it may be possible to choose infinitely many vectors from S which are independent. However, if $U = F^m$, Corollary 1 above shows that the rank of S is at most equal to m.

For the special case in which the subset S is a linear subspace most texts refer to the rank of S as its *dimension*. We prefer to reserve the term dimension for use later on. However, for the case of subspaces, our notions of rank and dimension will coincide.

In ordinary 3-space, the linear subspaces of rank 0, 1, 2, and 3 are, respectively, the origin, any line through the origin, any plane through the origin, and the whole of 3-space.

A linear subspace of F^m whose rank is $m - 1$ is called a *hyperplane*, being the obvious analogue of the plane in 3-space.

Corollary 3. F^m has rank m.

Proof. We have just observed that the rank of F^m is at most m. On the other hand, the unit vectors $u_1, \ldots, u_m$ are independent since $\sum\limits_{i=1}^{m} \lambda_i u_i = (\lambda_1, \ldots, \lambda_m)$ and this vector is zero only if $\lambda_i = 0$ for all i.

Theorem 2.2 (basis theorem). *The independent vectors $x_1, \ldots, x_r$ in S are a basis for S if and only if every vector y in S is a linear combination of the x_i.*

Proof. Suppose every y in S is a linear combination of the x_i. Then S contains no larger set of independent vectors, for any set of more than r vectors must be dependent since they are combinations of the x_i. Therefore, S has rank r and the x_i are a basis.

Conversely, suppose the x_i are a basis. Then by definition, S has rank r; so if $y \, \varepsilon \, S$ the vectors $x_1, \ldots, x_r$ and y are dependent; thus[1]

$$\Sigma \lambda_i x_i + \lambda y = 0$$

and, in fact, $\lambda \neq 0$, for otherwise the x_i would be dependent. Therefore, we have

$$y = -\frac{1}{\lambda} \sum \lambda_i x_i$$

giving the desired linear combination.

2. Scalar Product, Matrices, Linear Equations

We now introduce a third operation in F^m.

Scalar Product. If $x = (\xi_i)$ and $y = (\eta_i)$ are vectors in F^m, we define their *product* xy to be the number $\displaystyle\sum_{i=1}^{m} \xi_i \eta_i$.

Some immediate properties of the scalar product are

S1: $\qquad\qquad xy = yx$ $\qquad$ (commutative law)
S2: $\qquad\qquad (\lambda x)y = \lambda(xy)$ $\qquad$ (mixed associative law)
S3: $\qquad\qquad (x + y)z = xz + yz$ $\qquad$ (distributive law)

The reader is reminded of the geometric interpretation of the scalar product in ordinary analytic geometry. The scalar product of two vectors in this case is the product of the lengths of the vectors times the cosine of the angle between them. In particular, the scalar product of a pair of vectors is positive, negative, or zero, according as the vectors make an acute, obtuse, or right angle with each other. We shall not prove these facts since they will never be needed. It is nevertheless important for the reader to keep them in mind in order to visualize the algebraic facts to be presented.

The scalar product is useful as a notational device for writing linear equations. The system of equations

$$\sum_{j=1}^{n} \alpha_{ij} \eta_j = \alpha_i \qquad i = 1, \ldots, n$$

can now be written in the more compact vector form

---

[1] Henceforth, we shall omit writing explicitly the range of the summation index i when there is no possibility of ambiguity.

$$a_i y = \alpha_i \qquad i = 1, \ldots, n$$

where $a_i = (\alpha_{i1}, \ldots, \alpha_{in})$ and $y = (\eta_1, \ldots, \eta_n)$.

In scalar-product notation, Corollary 2 of the previous section becomes

Corollary 2.   If $a_1, \ldots, a_{m-1}$ are vectors in F^m, then the equations

$$a_i x = 0 \qquad i = 1, \ldots, m - 1$$

have a solution $x \neq 0$.

We next introduce the very convenient matrix notation.

Definition. An $m \times n$ *matrix* is a rectangular array of numbers $\alpha_{ij}, i = 1, \ldots, m, j = 1, \ldots, n$.   Thus,

$$A = \begin{pmatrix} \alpha_{11}, & \cdots, & \alpha_{1n} \\ \cdots & \cdots & \cdots \\ \cdots & \cdots & \cdots \\ \alpha_{m1}, & \cdots, & \alpha_{mn} \end{pmatrix}$$

Instead of writing out the above tableau, we shall simply write $A = (\alpha_{ij})$, to be read, "A is the matrix whose ijth *coordinate* is α_{ij}."

The n-vector $a_i = (\alpha_{i1}, \ldots, \alpha_{in})$ is called the *ith row vector* of A. The m-vector $a^j = (\alpha_{1j}, \ldots, \alpha_{mj})$ is called the *jth column vector* of A. The rank of the set of row vectors (column vectors) of A is called the *row rank (column rank)* of A. As a first important property of matrices, we show that these two ranks are, in fact, equal.

Theorem 2.3 (rank theorem).   *For any matrix A, the row rank and column rank are equal.*

Proof.   Let $r = $ row rank A, $s = $ column rank A, and suppose that $r < s$. Now, choose a row basis for A which we may assume consists of the rows $a_1, \ldots, a_r$ (reordering rows or columns of A clearly does not affect its row or column rank), and a column basis which we assume consists of columns $a^1, \ldots, a^s$. Let $\hat{a}_i = (\alpha_{i1}, \ldots, \alpha_{is})$ and note that the equations

$$\hat{a}_i y = 0 \qquad i = 1, \ldots, r \tag{1}$$

being r equations in s unknowns have a nonzero solution $\bar{y}$. Also, since $a_1, \ldots, a_r$ are a row basis, it follows from the basis theorem that, for all k, $a_k = \sum_{i=1}^{r} \mu_{ik} a_i$ for some numbers μ_{ik}; hence

$$\hat{a}_k = \sum_{i=1}^{r} \mu_{ik}\hat{a}_i \tag{2}$$

and so
$$\hat{a}_k\bar{y} = \sum_{i=1}^{r} \mu_{ik}(\hat{a}_i\bar{y}) = 0 \qquad \text{for all } k \tag{3}$$

but writing $\bar{y} = (\bar{\eta}_1, \ldots, \bar{\eta}_s)$, we may rewrite (3) as

$$\sum_{j=1}^{s} \bar{\eta}_j a^j = 0 \tag{4}$$

giving a dependence among the a^j, $j \leq s$, contradicting the assumption that they were a basis. The contradiction shows that $r \geq s$, and a symmetrical argument interchanging the roles of rows and columns gives the reverse inequality, completing the proof.

In view of this theorem, we are now justified in referring simply to the *rank of A*.

An immediate consequence of the rank theorem is this result on linear equations:

Corollary. If the vectors $a_1, \ldots, a_r$ are independent in F^n, then there exists a vector y such that

$$a_i y = \alpha_i \qquad i = 1, \ldots, r \tag{1}$$

for any numbers $\alpha_1, \ldots, \alpha_r$.

Proof. Let A be the $r \times n$ matrix with rows $a_1, \ldots, a_r$. By the rank theorem, the columns a^j of A have rank r, and thus if, say, $a^1, \ldots, a^r$ are a column basis we have r independent vectors in F^r and hence the vector $a = (\alpha_1, \ldots, \alpha_r)$ is a linear combination of them (from the basis theorem); that is,

$$a = \sum_{j=1}^{r} \eta_j a^j$$

and hence the vector $y = (\eta_1, \ldots, \eta_r, 0, \ldots, 0)$ satisfies (1).

We next introduce a multiplication between vectors and matrices which will be much used from here on.

Matrix-Vector Product. Let $A = (\alpha_{ij})$ be an $m \times n$ matrix, let $x = (\xi_i)$ be an m-vector, and let $y = (\eta_j)$ be an n-vector. The *product* xA of x and A is an n-vector,

$$xA = \xi_1 a_1 + \cdots + \xi_m a_m = (a^1 x, \ldots, a^n x)$$

The second equality above follows from the definitions of the vector operations. The *product* Ay of A and y is an m-vector, where

$$Ay = \eta_1 a^1 + \cdots + \eta_n a^n = (a_1 y, \ldots, a_m y)$$

Some immediate properties of this product are

P1: $(x + x')A = xA + x'A$ $A(y + y') = Ay + Ay'$
(distributivity)

P2: $(\lambda x)A = \lambda(xA)$ $A(\lambda y) = \lambda(Ay)$ (homogeneity)

P3: $(xA)y = x(Ay)$ (associativity)

To verify, for instance, P3, we write

$$(xA)y = (\Sigma \xi_i a_i)y = \Sigma \xi_i (a_i y)$$
$$= x(a_1 y, \ldots, a_m y) = x(Ay)$$

The matrix-vector product is actually a special case of the more general multiplication of two matrices. This operation and its properties will be developed in the exercises and used occasionally in later chapters. For the present development the operation just introduced suffices.

The matrix-vector product allows us to write linear equations in an extremely compact manner. Thus the equations

$$xa^j = \beta_j \qquad j = 1, \ldots, n \tag{1}$$

become $$xA = b \tag{2}$$

where A is the matrix whose jth column is a^j and $b = (\beta_j)$. Also the equation

$$\sum_{i=1}^{m} \xi_i a_i = b \tag{3}$$

becomes $$xA = b \tag{4}$$

where A is the matrix whose ith row is a_i and $x = (\xi_i)$.

Using matrix notation we now give the principal theorems concerning solvability of linear equations. We first consider the *homogeneous* case $xA = 0$. We have already seen (Corollary 2 of Theorem 2.1) that if A has more rows than columns then this equation has at least one nonzero solution.   The next theorem generalizes this by showing precisely how large the set of solutions is.

Theorem 2.4 (solutions of homogeneous equations).   *Let A be an $m \times n$ matrix of rank r.   Then the set X of all solutions of the equation*

$$xA = 0 \tag{1}$$

is a linear subspace of rank $m - r$.

Proof.   The fact that X is a subspace follows at once from properties P1 and P2 of the matrix product.   To complete the proof, we shall exhibit a basis for X consisting of $m - r$ vectors.

We may suppose (reordering if necessary) that the rows $a_1, \ldots, a_r$ form a row basis for A, so that for $k > r$ we have

$$a_k = \sum_{i=1}^{r} \mu_{ik} a_i \qquad k = r + 1, \ldots, m \tag{2}$$

Now define

$$b_k = (-\mu_{1k}, \ldots, -\mu_{rk}, 0, \ldots, 1, \ldots, 0)$$

for $k = r + 1, \ldots, m$, where the kth coordinate of b_k is 1.   In view of (2), each b_k is a solution of (1), and also the b_k are independent, for the linear combination

$$b = \Sigma \lambda_k b_k$$

has λ_k as its kth coordinate; hence $b = 0$ only if $\lambda_k = 0$ for all k.

It remains to show that every vector in X is a linear combination of the b_k.   Let $x = (\xi_i)$ be a solution of (1).   Then so also is

$$x - \sum_{k=r+1}^{m} \xi_k b_k = x' = (\xi_i') \tag{3}$$

but we see that $\xi_i' = 0$ for $i = r + 1, \ldots, m$ and hence

$$\sum_{i=1}^{r} \xi_i' a_i = 0$$

which means $\xi_i' = 0$ for all i, since $a_1, \ldots, a_r$ were assumed independent.   Thus $x' = 0$ and (3) gives

$$x = \sum_{k=r+1}^{m} \xi_k b_k$$

as asserted.

We remark that the theorem is constructive in that it indicates how one may go about finding *all* solutions of a set of homogeneous equations, by finding in a systematic manner a basis for the set of solutions.

The above theorem has an illuminating geometric interpretation.

Definition. If L is a subspace of F^m the set of all vectors y such that $xy = 0$ for all x in L is called the *orthogonal* or *dual subspace* of L and is denoted by L^*. In geometric language, L^* consists of all vectors perpendicular to L.

The above theorem amounts to the statement

$$\operatorname{rank} L + \operatorname{rank} L^* = m$$

Thus, in 3-space, the subspace of vectors perpendicular to a plane is a line and vice versa. The proof of the relation above is left as an exercise (see Exercise 11).

The final theorem of this section gives a criterion for the solvability of a general (not necessarily homogeneous) set of linear equations. From now on unless the contrary is explicitly stated, A will denote an $m \times n$ matrix, x an m-vector with coordinates ξ_i, and y an n-vector with coordinates η_j.

Before stating the theorem, let us make some simple preliminary observations. Consider the set of equations

$$xa^j = \beta_j \qquad j = 1, \ldots, n \tag{1}$$

We wish to find conditions which guarantee the solvability of (1). Instead of looking for such conditions, however, let us try to find conditions under which (1) will not be solvable. Now note that if x satisfies (1) and $\eta_1, \ldots, \eta_n$ are any numbers, then x must also satisfy

$$x \left(\sum_{j=1}^{n} \eta_j a^j \right) = \sum_{j=1}^{n} \eta_j \beta_j \tag{2}$$

If, therefore, we can find numbers η_j such that $\Sigma \eta_j a^j = 0$, while $\Sigma \eta_j \beta_j = 1$, then (2) becomes the impossible statement "zero equals one;" hence (1) can have no solution. The existence theorem we are about to prove states that, if the situation just described does not occur, then, indeed, the system (1) has a solution.

Theorem 2.5 (solvability of linear equations). *Exactly one of the following alternatives holds. Either the equation*

$$xA = b \tag{1}$$

has a solution or the equations

$$Ay = 0 \qquad by = 1 \tag{2}$$

have a solution.

Proof. We have already seen above that (1) and (2) cannot both be true. It remains to show that if (1) is false then (2) is true.

Let $a_1, \ldots, a_r$ be a row basis for A. Then these vectors together with b are independent since otherwise b would be a linear combination of the a_i giving a solution of (1). From the corollary to the rank theorem, there exists a vector y such that $a_i y = 0$ for $i \leqq r$ and $by = 1$. But for all k we have $a_k = \sum_{i=1}^{r} \lambda_i a_i$, since the a_i were a row basis, and hence $a_k y = 0$ for all k; thus

$$Ay = 0 \qquad \text{and} \qquad by = 1$$

as asserted.

The importance of this theorem like those of the next section is due to the fact that it gives a positive criterion for determining when a set of equations has *no* solution. In order to demonstrate the unsolvability of system (1), one need only produce a solution of system (2).

The theorem above has a simple geometric interpretation. If (1) above has no solution, this means that the vector b does not lie in the subspace L consisting of linear combinations of the row vectors a_i. In this case, the theorem asserts we can find a vector perpendicular to L and making an acute angle with b. In 3-space a picture makes this fact intuitively evident.

Finally, the theorem also has the following geometric consequence.

Corollary. *If L is a subspace of F^m then $L^{**} = L$.*

Proof. It is immediate that L is contained in L^{**} for if $y \, \varepsilon \, L^*$ and $b \, \varepsilon \, L$ then $by = 0$, but then from the definition $b \, \varepsilon \, L^{**}$.

Conversely, suppose $b \notin L$.   Let $a_1, \ldots, a_r$ be a basis for L.   Then the equation

$$\Sigma \lambda_i a_i = b$$

has no solution, and therefore by the theorem there is a vector y such that $a_i y = 0$ for all i and $by = 1$.   But we see that $y \varepsilon L^*$, for if $x \varepsilon L$ then $x = \displaystyle\sum_{i=1}^{r} \alpha_i a_i$ since the a_i are a basis and hence $xy = \Sigma \alpha_i (a_i y) = 0$. Finally, since $by = 1$, b is not in L^{**}.   Thus L^{**} lies in L, completing the proof.

The reader will readily construct illustrations of this result in 3-space.

3. Real Linear Equations and Inequalities

We come now to the material representing the mathematical heart of this book, for the great bulk of the theory to follow will depend on it. A solid understanding of these results is therefore a prerequisite to virtually all the remaining topics, and for this reason the importance of thorough familiarity at this point cannot be too strongly emphasized.

The results of this section apply to vector spaces in which the field of scalars is the real numbers or, more generally, any subfield of the real numbers.   Accordingly, we shall from now on denote the field by the letter R rather than F.   The important additional fact about the field R is that its elements are *ordered*, and thus the notions of positive, negative, maximum, and minimum are applicable.   Also for the vector space R^m we have an additional important property of the scalar product.   Denoting by x^2 the product of the vector x with itself we have

S4: $x^2 \geqq 0$ for all x in R^m and $x^2 = 0$ if and only if $x = 0$

We remind the reader that $x^2 = \displaystyle\sum_{i=1}^{m} \xi_i^2$, and thus the square root $\sqrt{x^2}$ is the usual distance of x from the origin of analytic geometry. Property S4 then asserts that this distance is always positive, as any well-behaved distance must be.

We shall be concerned at the moment principally with two questions, solvability of linear inequalities and existence of positive solutions of linear equations.   For this, the following notational conventions will be useful.

Definition.   If $x = (\xi_i)$ in R^m, then

x is *nonnegative*, written $x \geq 0$, if $\xi_i \geq 0$ for all i

x is *positive*, written $x > 0$, if $\xi_i > 0$ for all i

x is *semipositive*, written $x \geq 0$, if $x \geq 0$ but $x \neq 0$

If $x, y \, \varepsilon \, R^m$, we write $x \geq y$, $x > y$, or $x \geq y$ according as $x - y$ is nonnegative, positive, or semipositive.

The relations $\geq$, $\geq$, and $>$ define what is called a *partial ordering* on the vectors of R^m.   The following properties of the ordering can be verified directly from the definitions and will be used from here on without giving explicit reference after each use.   The letter R stands for any one of the three relations:

O1:   if xRy and yRz then xRz

O2:   if x_1Ry_1 and x_2Ry_2 then $(x_1 + x_2)$R$(y_1 + y_2)$

O3:   if xRy and $\lambda > 0$ then λxRλy

        if xRy and $\lambda < 0$ then λyRλx

Of especial importance is the following:

O4:   if $x \geq y$ and $a > 0$ then $ax > ay$

        if $x > y$ and $a \geq 0$ then $ax > ay$

The reader should verify this (see Exercise 15).

Consider now the problem of finding a nonnegative solution of the equations

$$xa^j = \beta_j \qquad \text{for } j = 1, \ldots, n \qquad (1)$$

and as before, let us look for obvious conditions under which (1) will have no solutions.   This will clearly be the case if there exist numbers $\eta_1, \ldots, \eta_n$ such that $\Sigma \eta_j a^j \geq 0$ and $\Sigma \eta_j \beta_j < 0$, for any solution of (1) must also satisfy

$$x(\Sigma \eta_j a^j) = \Sigma \eta_j \beta_j$$

but the right side of this equation is negative while the left is not, a contradiction.   We shall show, just as in the solvability theorem of the last section, that if the situation just described does not occur then, indeed, the system (1) has a nonnegative solution. Stated formally, we have

Theorem 2.6 (nonnegative solutions of linear equations). *Exactly one of the following alternatives holds. Either the equation*

$$xA = b \tag{1}$$

has a nonnegative solution or the inequalities

$$Ay \geqq 0 \qquad by < 0 \tag{2}$$

have a solution.

This result is actually the key to a whole series of existence theorems which we shall need for later applications. Unfortunately, the proof

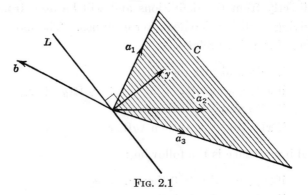

Fig. 2.1

is rather formal and does not make clear why the theorem "works." For this reason, we shall give first a geometric picture which makes the validity of the result intuitively plausible.

Let us consider the row vectors a_i of A as points in R^n. The set of all nonnegative linear combinations of the a_i forms a cone-shaped region C, the shaded region of Fig. 2.1.

The statement that (1) above has no nonnegative solution means that the vector b does not lie in C. In this case, the theorem asserts the existence of a vector y which makes an obtuse angle with b and a nonobtuse angle with each of the vectors a_i. This means that the hyperplane L orthogonal to y has the cone C on one side and the point b on the other. For this reason, the theorem is often referred to as the "theorem of the separating hyperplane."

Proof of Theorem. We have already argued that (1) and (2) cannot both have solutions, for if so, taking the scalar product of Eq. (1) with y gives

$$xAy = by$$

and taking the scalar product of inequality (2) with x gives

$$xAy \geqq 0$$

since x is nonnegative. But these two relations together contradict the condition $by < 0$.

Assuming now that (1) has no nonnegative solution, we shall show that (2) has a solution. If (1) has no solution at all, then by Theorem 2.5 there exists y such that $Ay = 0$ and $by = -1$; hence y satisfies (2). We suppose then that (1) has a solution but no nonnegative solution, and proceed by induction on m, the number of rows of A.

If $m = 1$ then (1) becomes

$$\xi a_1 = b$$

and we assume there is a solution $\xi < 0$. Then let $y = -b$ and note that

$$by = -b^2 < 0 \qquad \text{and} \qquad a_1 y = \frac{by}{\xi} = \frac{-b^2}{\xi} > 0$$

so y is a solution of (2).

Now assume the theorem true when the number of rows of A is less than m. If (1) has no nonnegative solution, then certainly neither does the equation

$$\sum_{i=1}^{m-1} \xi_i a_i = b$$

so by the inductive hypothesis, there exists y_1 such that $a_i y_1 \geqq 0$ for $i < m$ and $by_1 < 0$. If also $a_m y_1 \geqq 0$ then y_1 satisfies (2) and the theorem is proved. If $a_m y_1 < 0$, let

$$\bar{a}_i = (a_i y_1)a_m - (a_m y_1)a_i \qquad \text{for } i < m \tag{3}$$
$$\bar{b} = (by_1)a_m - (a_m y_1)b$$

Now the equation

$$\sum_{i=1}^{m-1} \xi_i \bar{a}_i = \bar{b} \tag{4}$$

can have no nonnegative solution, for if so, substituting (3) in (4) gives

$$\frac{1}{-a_m y_1} \left[\sum_{i=1}^{m-1} \xi_i(a_i y_1) - b y_1 \right] a_m + \sum_{i=1}^{m-1} \xi_i a_i = b$$

and we would have a nonnegative solution of (1) contrary to assumption. In view of this, we apply the inductive assumption to (4) and get a vector $\bar{y}$ such that $\bar{a}_i \bar{y} \geq 0$ for $i < m$ and $\bar{b} \bar{y} < 0$. Now let

$$y = (a_m \bar{y}) y_1 - (a_m y_1) \bar{y}$$

and verify that

$$a_i y = \bar{a}_i \bar{y} \geq 0 \quad \text{for } i < m$$
$$b y = \bar{b} \bar{y} < 0 \quad \text{and}$$
$$a_m y = 0$$

so that y satisfies (2) and the theorem is proved.

We turn next to the problem of the solvability of linear inequalities, and our theorem will take the same form as those we have just proved. Thus the set of inequalities

$$a_i y \geq \gamma_i \quad i = 1, 2, \ldots, m$$

obviously can have no solution if there exist nonnegative numbers ξ_i such that

$$\Sigma \xi_i a_i = 0 \quad \text{and} \quad \Sigma \xi_i \gamma_i = 1$$

for then we would get the contradiction

$$0y \geq 1$$

Our theorem states that, barring this possibility, solutions to the inequalities will always exist.

Theorem 2.7 (solutions of linear inequalities). *Exactly one of the following alternatives holds.*

Either the inequality

$$Ay \geq c \tag{1}$$

has a solution or the equations

$$xA = 0 \quad xc = 1 \tag{2}$$

have a nonnegative solution.

Proof. As seen above, (1) and (2) cannot hold simultaneously. Next, letting $c = (\gamma_1, \ldots, \gamma_m)$ we rewrite (2) in the form

$$\sum_{i=1}^{m} \xi_i a_i = 0$$

$$\sum_{i=1}^{m} \xi_i \gamma_i = 1$$

and if these equations have no nonnegative solution, then the previous theorem asserts that there exists an n-vector y and a number η such that

$$a_i y + \gamma_i \eta \geqq 0 \qquad \text{for } i = 1, \ldots, m$$

and
$$0y + \eta = \eta < 0$$

but this means that $a_i(y/-\eta) \geqq \gamma_i$, and $-y/\eta$ gives the desired solution of (1).

The following theorem is important in the theory of linear programming to be taken up in the next chapter.

Theorem 2.8 (nonnegative solutions of linear inequalities). *Exactly one of the following alternatives holds.*

Either the inequality

$$xA \leqq b \tag{1}$$

has a nonnegative solution, or the inequalities

$$Ay \geqq 0 \qquad by < 0 \tag{2}$$

have a nonnegative solution.

Proof. The reader will verify at once that (1) and (2) cannot both have solutions. On the other hand, suppose (1) has no nonnegative solution. This means the equation

$$\sum_{i=1}^{m} \xi_i a_i + \sum_{j=1}^{n} \lambda_j v_j = b \tag{3}$$

has no nonnegative solution, $\xi_1, \ldots, \xi_m, \lambda_1, \ldots, \lambda_n$, where v_j is the jth unit vector in R^n. From Theorem 2.6, then, there exists y such that

$$a_i y \geqq 0 \qquad \text{for } i = 1, 2, \ldots, m \tag{4}$$
$$v_j y \geqq 0 \qquad \text{for } j = 1, \ldots, n \tag{5}$$

and $$by < 0 \qquad (6)$$

From (5) above, y is nonnegative and from (4) and (6) it satisfies (2).

The two theorems which follow give conditions for the solvability of homogeneous equations and inequalities. They are of the same form as the preceding results.

Theorem 2.9 (semipositive solutions of homogeneous equations). *Exactly one of the following alternatives holds.*

Either the equation

$$xA = 0 \qquad (1)$$

has a semipositive solution or the inequality

$$Ay > 0 \qquad (2)$$

has a solution.

Proof. That the two possibilities are incompatible is immediate [multiply (1) on right by y, (2) on left by x; contradiction]. On the other hand, if (1) has no semipositive solution, then the equations

$$\Sigma \xi_i a_i = 0$$
$$\Sigma \xi_i = 1$$

have no nonnegative solution and hence by Theorem 2.6 there exists a vector y and number η such that

$$a_i y + \eta \geqq 0 \qquad \text{for all } i$$

and
$$0y + \eta = \eta < 0$$

which means $a_i y \geqq -\eta > 0$ for all i, and this shows that (2) has a solution.

Theorem 2.9 has a natural geometric interpretation. Let L be a subspace of R^n and let L^* be its dual.

Corollary 1. *Either the subspace L contains a positive vector or L^* contains a semipositive vector.*

Proof. Let $a^1, \ldots, a^r$ be a basis for L. To say that L contains no positive vector means that there are no numbers $\eta_1, \ldots, \eta_r$ such that $\Sigma \eta_j a^j > 0$, or if A is the matrix whose jth column is a^j, this asserts that the inequality $Ay > 0$ has no solution. According to the theorem, then, there exists $x \geq 0$ such that $xA = 0$, that is, $xa^j = 0$ for all j; hence $x \, \varepsilon \, L^*$.

The conclusion of the corollary is intuitively obvious in two and three dimensions, as illustrated in Fig. 2.2.

Corollary 2 (positive solutions of homogeneous equations). *Exactly one of the following alternatives holds.*

Either the equation

$$xA = 0 \qquad (1)$$

has a positive solution, or the inequality

$$Ay \geq 0 \qquad (2)$$

has a solution.

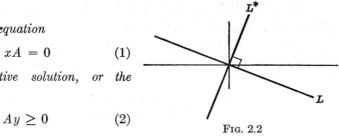

FIG. 2.2

The proof follows from Corollary 1. The details are left to the reader (see Exercise 22).

A final result along these lines is the following.

Theorem 2.10 (semipositive solutions of homogeneous inequalities). *Exactly one of the following alternatives holds.*

Either the inequality

$$xA \leq 0 \qquad (1)$$

has a semipositive solution, or the inequality

$$Ay > 0 \qquad (2)$$

has a nonnegative solution.

Proof. The incompatibility of (1) and (2) is seen at once. Now, suppose (1) has no semipositive solution. Then the inequalities

$$\Sigma \xi_i a_i \leq 0$$
$$-\Sigma \xi_i \leq -1$$

have no nonnegative solutions. From Theorem 2.8, therefore, there exist $y \geq 0$ and $\eta \geq 0$ such that $a_i y - \eta \geq 0$ and $-\eta < 0$; thus $a_i y \geq \eta > 0$ and $Ay > 0$, as asserted.

4. Basic Solutions of Equations

The fundamental existence theorems for solutions of linear equations and inequalities were given in the previous section. In the next section, we shall present a more detailed study of the structure and properties of these solutions. The present section is concerned with one particular result on the structure of solutions, which is of sufficient importance to warrant a separate treatment.

At this point, it is convenient to introduce some notations which will be used frequently from here on.

Notation. The letters M and N shall denote the set of positive integers from 1 to m and 1 to n, respectively. This is written

$$M = \{1, \ldots, m\}$$
$$N = \{1, \ldots, n\}$$

The statement "S is a subset of M" is written in familiar set-theoretic notation, $S \subset M$.

Now let $a_1, \ldots, a_m$ be vectors in R^n, and let S be a subset of M.

Definition. A solution $x = (\xi_i)$ of the equation

$$\sum_{i=1}^{m} \xi_i a_i = b \tag{1}$$

is said to *depend on the set S* if $\xi_i = 0$ for i not in S.

A solution x of (1) is called a *basic solution* if it depends on a set S such that the vectors a_i are independent for i in S.

It is easily seen that, if (1) has a solution, then it has a basic solution (see Exercise 13). We now prove an important extension of this result.

Theorem 2.11 (basic solutions). *If the equation (1) above has a nonnegative solution, it has a basic nonnegative solution.*

Proof. We proceed by induction on m. For $m = 1$ the result is immediate. Suppose the result holds for $k < m$ and let $x = (\xi_i)$ be a nonnegative solution of (1). If any coordinate ξ_i is zero, then we are immediately reduced to the case $k = m - 1$; hence the only case to consider is that in which x is positive; so we have

$$\sum_{i=1}^{m} \xi_i a_i = b \qquad \xi_i > 0 \qquad \text{for } i = 1, \ldots, m \tag{2}$$

Now if the vectors a_i are independent, then x is already basic and there is nothing to prove.   Suppose, therefore, that the a_i are dependent so that for some λ_i not all zero we have

$$\Sigma \lambda_i a_i = 0 \qquad (3)$$

and we may in fact assume that λ_i is positive for some i [if not, simply multiply (3) by -1].

Now let $\theta = \max_i \lambda_i / \xi_i$, say $\theta = \lambda_1 / \xi_1 > 0$ (reordering if necessary). Multiplying (3) by $1/\theta$ and subtracting from (2) gives

$$\frac{1}{\theta} \sum_{i=1}^{m} \left(\theta - \frac{\lambda_i}{\xi_i} \right) \xi_i a_i = b \qquad (4)$$

but by the definition of θ the first coefficient in (4) is zero, and the rest are nonnegative.   Thus we have a nonnegative solution of (1) depending on $a_2, \ldots, a_m$ and we have again reduced the proof to the case of fewer than m vectors.

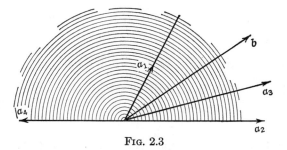

FIG. 2.3

The geometric picture corresponding to this theorem is given in Fig. 2.3.   Since b lies in the shaded region, it is a nonnegative linear combination of the a_i, and one easily sees that it is in fact expressible as a combination of two independent a_i, either a_1 and a_3, a_1 and a_2, or a_3 and a_4.

5. Geometry of Linear Inequalities.   Convex Cones

For most of the applications of subsequent chapters, the material contained in the preceding sections of this chapter is sufficient.   The more detailed results of this section will be used only occasionally, as in part of the analysis of games. The reader may therefore wish to omit details of proof on first reading. He should, however, become familiar with the definitions of this section, as they will be used repeatedly in the sequel.

It will be convenient at this point to introduce some of the standard symbolism of set theory which will be used without further explanatory comment from here on.

Definitions, Notations. Let X be a given abstract set of elements x, and let P be some statement about elements of X. Then the symbol $\{x|P\}$ is to be read, "the set of all x in X such that P."

Example. If X is the set of real numbers then $\{x|x > 0\}$ represents the set of all positive real numbers.

If A and B are subsets of X then the *union* $A \cup B$ of A and B is the set consisting of all elements belonging to either A or B. In the above notation,

$$A \cup B = \{x|x \,\varepsilon\, A \text{ or } x \,\varepsilon\, B\}$$

The *intersection* $A \cap B$ of A and B is the set of all x belonging to both A and B; thus

$$A \cap B = \{x|x \,\varepsilon\, A \text{ and } x \,\varepsilon\, B\}$$

The set A is *contained* in B, written $A \subset B$, if every element of A is also an element of B, and A *contains* B, written $A \supset B$, if B is contained in A.

We next introduce a new and very important geometric concept which generalizes the notion of linear subspace.

Definition. A subset C of R^m is called a *convex cone* if it is closed under the operations of addition and multiplication by nonnegative scalars, that is,

$$\text{if } x, y \,\varepsilon\, C \text{ then } x + y \,\varepsilon\, C \tag{1}$$
$$\text{if } x \,\varepsilon\, C \text{ and } \lambda \geqq 0 \text{ then } \lambda x \,\varepsilon\, C \tag{2}$$

Examples

1. Any linear subspace L is obviously a special case of a convex cone.

2. The set of all nonnegative vectors P of R^m is a convex cone, called the *nonnegative orthant* of R^m. Note, however, that the set of

positive vectors is not a cone but becomes one if the origin is adjoined.

3. For any vector b in R^m the set of vectors of the form λb, $\lambda \geq 0$ is a convex cone, called a *halfline* and denoted by (b). Thus

$$(b) = \{x|x = \lambda b, \qquad \lambda \geq 0\}$$

4. The set of all solutions of the inequality $xb \leq 0$ is a convex cone, called a *halfspace* and denoted by $(b)^*$. Formally, we have

$$(b)^* = \{x|xb \leq 0\}$$

5. As a generalization of 4, the set of all solutions of the homogeneous inequality $xA \leq 0$, for any matrix A, forms a convex cone.

The reader should verify at this point that each of the examples above does indeed satisfy the definition of a convex cone.

Definitions. We now define three operations on convex cones.

Addition. If C_1 and C_2 are convex cones, their *sum* $C_1 + C_2$ is defined by

$$C_1 + C_2 = \{x|x = x_1 + x_2, \qquad x_1 \, \varepsilon \, C_1, \qquad x_2 \, \varepsilon \, C_2\}$$

Clearly $C_1 + C_2$ is again a convex cone.

Intersection. If C_1 and C_2 are convex cones, their *intersection* $C_1 \cap C_2$ is again a convex cone.

Dual. If C is a convex cone, the *dual cone* C^* is defined by

$$C^* = \{y|xy \leq 0 \qquad \text{for all } x \, \varepsilon \, C\}$$

The geometric pictures corresponding to the sum, intersection, and dual are illustrated by Figs. 2.4, 2.5, and 2.6 respectively.

The pictures of sum and intersection are self-explanatory and require no comment. The dual of the cone C is seen to consist of all vectors making a nonacute angle with all vectors of the cone C.

Let us determine the dual cone for each of the five examples above. If C is a subspace, then the dual cone C^* is simply the dual subspace, for let L^* be the dual subspace of C. Then for any y in L^*, $yx = 0$ for all x in C and hence y is in C^*. On the other hand, if y is in C^* then $yx \leq 0$ for all x in C, but since C is a subspace, if x is in C so is $-x$; hence also $y(-x) \leq 0$ or $yx \geq 0$, and therefore $yx = 0$ so that

$y \, \varepsilon \, L^*$ and so $L^* = C^*$. This shows that the "star" notation introduced here is consistent with that of the previous sections.

The dual of the nonnegative orthant P is the set of all nonpositive vectors, the *nonpositive orthant* N. We leave the proof of this to the reader.

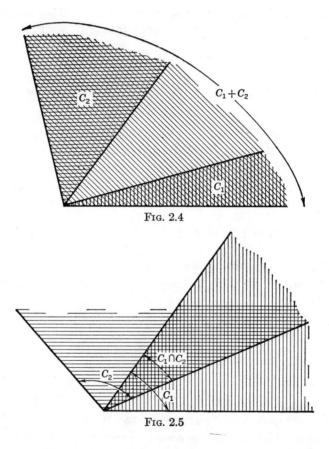

Fig. 2.4

Fig. 2.5

The dual of the halfline (b) of Example 3 is by definition the halfspace $(b)^*$ of Example 4 (thus our notation is again consistent). Conversely, the dual of the halfspace $(b)^*$ is the halfline (b). This is, in fact, a special case of the situation of Example 5. Let C be the set of solutions of the inequality $xA \leqq 0$ which we rewrite as $xa^j \leqq 0$ for $j = 1, \ldots, n$. Now for any nonnegative numbers $\lambda_1, \ldots, \lambda_n$ the vector $y = \Sigma\lambda_j a^j$ is clearly in C^* since for x in C, $x(\Sigma\lambda_j a^j) = \Sigma\lambda_j(xa^j) \leqq 0$.

It will be shown shortly that, conversely, every vector of C^* is such a nonnegative combination of the vectors a^j.

We now list some properties of the operations on cones.

$$\text{if } C_1 \subset C_2 \text{ then } C_2^* \subset C_1^* \tag{1}$$

$$(C_1 + C_2)^* = C_1^* \cap C_2^* \tag{2}$$

$$C_1^* + C_2^* \subset (C_1 \cap C_2)^* \tag{3}$$

$$C \subset (C^*)^* \tag{4}$$

These properties follow easily from the definitions. Let us verify (2).

Suppose $x \varepsilon C_1^* \cap C_2^*$; then $xy_1 \leq 0$ for all $y_1 \varepsilon C_1$ and $xy_2 \leq 0$ for all $y_2 \varepsilon C_2$. But now if $y \varepsilon C_1 + C_2$, we have $y = y_1 + y_2$, where $y_1 \varepsilon C_1$, $y_2 \varepsilon C_2$; so $xy = xy_1 + xy_2 \leq 0$ and therefore $x \varepsilon (C_1 + C_2)^*$.

Conversely, if $x \varepsilon (C_1 + C_2)^*$ then $xy \leq 0$ for $y = y_1 + y_2$, $y_1 \varepsilon C_1$, $y_2 \varepsilon C_2$. In particular, if $y_2 = 0$, we get $xy_1 \leq 0$ for all $y_1 \varepsilon C_1$ and if $y_1 = 0$ we get $xy_2 \leq 0$ for all $y_2 \varepsilon C_2$, and therefore $x \varepsilon C_1^*$ and $x \varepsilon C_2^*$; i.e., $x \varepsilon C_1^* \cap C_2^*$, as was to be shown.

In general, the "contained in" relations of properties (3) and (4) cannot be strengthened to equalities (see Exercise 28).

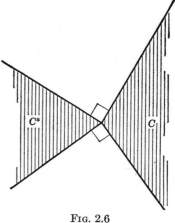

Fig. 2.6

As the title of this section indicates, convex cones were introduced as a means of studying solutions of inequalities. For this purpose, it is desirable to specialize the notion of cones as follows.

Definition. The convex cone C is called a *finite cone* if it is the sum of a finite number of halflines, that is,

$$C = (a_1) + \cdots + (a_n) \tag{1}$$

The vectors $a_1, \ldots, a_n$ are called *generators* of C.

Equivalently, C is a finite cone if for some matrix A

$$C = \{y | y = xA \quad \text{for } x \geq 0\} \tag{2}$$

For finite cones, we have the following important relation.

Theorem 2.12 (duality theorem). *If C is a finite cone, then* $C^{**} = C.$

Proof. We leave to the reader the automatic verification that $C \subset C^{**}$. Suppose, conversely, that b is not in C. Since C is of the form (2) above, this means the equation $b = xA$ has no nonnegative solution; hence by Theorem 2.6 there is a vector y such that $Ay \leq 0$ and $by > 0$. The first relation shows that y is in C^* since it implies $xAy \leq 0$ for all $x \geq 0$. But since $by > 0$ it follows that b is not in C^{**}, completing the proof.

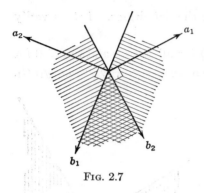

FIG. 2.7

Corollary. Let $C = \{x | xA \leq 0\}$. Then $C^* = \{x | x = Ay, y \geq 0\}$.

Proof. Let $K = \{x | x = Ay, y \geq 0\}$. We must show that $K = C^*$. Now clearly $C = K^*$, for $x \varepsilon K^*$ if and only if $xAy \leq 0$ for all $y \geq 0$ and this is true if and only if $xA \leq 0$ (why?). But if $C = K^*$ then $C^* = K^{**} = K$ from the theorem. This corollary establishes the assertion made about the dual cone for Example 5.

The fundamental property which we wish now to establish is the fact that the set C of solutions of the inequality $xA \leq 0$ is a finite cone. This result is geometrically rather obvious, for if we write the inequality in the form

$$xa^j \leq 0 \qquad j = 1, \ldots, n$$

then C is the intersection of halfspaces, that is,

$$C = (a^1)^* \cap \cdots \cap (a^n)^*$$

The situation in two dimensions is illustrated in Fig. 2.7. The cone C represented by the doubly shaded area is the intersection of the shaded areas $(a_1)^*$ and $(a_2)^*$. It is also the sum of the halflines (b_1) and (b_2).

This property of homogeneous inequalities is also useful from a practical point of view, for it means that in order to find all solutions of a set of inequalities, it suffices to find a certain finite set of solutions. Then all the rest will be nonnegative combinations of these.

The fundamental property will be established first for two special cases.

Lemma 2.1.   *A linear subspace L is a finite cone.*

Proof.   If $a_1, \ldots, a_r$ is a basis for L then clearly

$$L = (a_1) + \cdots + (a_r) + (-a_1) + \cdots + (-a_r)$$

Lemma 2.2.   *The set of all nonnegative solutions of*

$$xA = 0 \tag{1}$$

is a finite cone.

Proof.   We proceed by considering the related equations

$$\sum_{i=1}^{m} \xi_i a_i = 0$$

$$\sum_{i=1}^{m} \xi_i = 1 \tag{2}$$

$$\xi_i \geqq 0$$

Now, every semipositive solution of (1) is a positive multiple of some solution of (2). We shall show that every solution of (2) is a nonnegative combination of basic solutions (recall the definition and Theorem 2.11). Further, there are only a finite number of such basic solutions since there are but a finite number of independent subsets of the vectors a_i, and thus the theorem will be proved.

Assume inductively that every solution of (2) which depends on fewer than m vectors is a nonnegative combination of basic solutions (this is obvious for $m = 1$ and $m = 2$). Suppose now that $x = (\xi_i)$ is positive and solves (2). Let $\hat{a}_i$ be the $(n + 1)$-vector whose first n coordinates are a_i and whose last coordinate is 1. If the $\hat{a}_i$ are independent, then x is basic and there is nothing to prove. If the $\hat{a}_i$ are dependent, then from the theorem on basic solutions we can find a basic solution $x' = (\xi_i')$ where $\xi_i' = 0$ for at least one index i. It follows that $\xi_i' > \xi_i$ for some i since $\Sigma \xi_i = \Sigma \xi_i' = 1$. Let $\gamma = \max \xi_i'/\xi_i$, say $\gamma = \xi_1'/\xi_1$. Then $\gamma > 1$ and we may define

$$x'' = \frac{1}{\gamma - 1} (\gamma x - x') \tag{3}$$

Then $x'' = (\xi_i'')$ is nonnegative and satisfies (2), as one verifies directly, but note that $\xi_1'' = 0$ so that x'' depends on at most $m - 1$ vectors a_i and hence by induction hypothesis x'' is a nonnegative combination of basic solutions. But from (3)

$$x = \frac{1}{\gamma} x' + \left(1 - \frac{1}{\gamma}\right) x''$$

as one again verifies, and since x' is basic and x'' is a nonnegative combination of basic solutions the same is true for x and the theorem is proved.

Corollary. *The intersection of any subspace L with the nonnegative orthant P is a finite cone.*

Proof. Let $b_1, \ldots, b_s$ be a basis for L^* and let C be all nonnegative solutions of the equations $b_i x = 0$, $i = 1, \ldots, s$. From the lemma, C is a finite cone, and clearly if $x \varepsilon L \cap P$ then $x \varepsilon C$. On the other hand, if $x \varepsilon C$ then $x b_i = 0$ for all i; so $x \varepsilon L^{**} = L$; hence $C = L \cap P$.

Theorem 2.13. *The set of solutions of*

$$xA \leqq 0 \tag{1}$$

is a finite cone.

Proof. Let L be the subspace defined by

$$L = \{y \mid y = xA, \; x \varepsilon R^m\}$$

From the previous corollary $L \cap P$ is a finite cone; hence

$$L \cap P = (y_1) + \cdots + (y_r) \tag{2}$$

Now choose $x_1, \ldots, x_r$ such that $-y_i = x_i A$. Finally, let X' be the linear subspace of solutions of $xA = 0$. From Lemma 2.1,

$$X' = (x_1') + \cdots + (x_s') \tag{3}$$

for some vectors x_i'. We now assert that the set C of solutions of (1) is given by

$$C = (x_1) + \cdots + (x_r) + (x_1') + \cdots + (x_s')$$

for suppose $xA \leqq 0$. Then $-xA \varepsilon L \cap P$; so from (2),

$$xA = -\sum_{i=1}^{r} \lambda_i y_i = \sum_{i=1}^{r} \lambda_i (x_i A)$$

where $\lambda_i \geq 0$; thus $\left(x - \sum_{i=1}^{r} \lambda_i x_i\right) A = 0$; hence from (3)

$$x - \sum_{i=1}^{r} \lambda_i x_i = \sum_{i=1}^{s} \mu_i x_i' \qquad \mu_i \geq 0$$

and then
$$x = \sum_{i=1}^{r} \lambda_i x_i + \sum_{i=1}^{s} \mu_i x_i'$$

The following theorem sums up the algebraic properties of finite cones in a comprehensive manner.

Theorem 2.14. *If C and C' are finite cones, so also are*

$$C + C' \tag{1}$$
$$C \cap C' \tag{2}$$
$$C^* \tag{3}$$

and the following relations hold:

$$(C + C')^* = C^* \cap C'^* \tag{4}$$
$$(C \cap C')^* = C^* + C'^* \tag{5}$$
$$C^{**} = C \tag{6}$$

Proof. Property (1) follows from the definition, (4) has already been proved for arbitrary convex cones, and (6) is exactly the statement of the duality theorem. To prove (3), let $C = (a_1) + \cdots + (a_n)$. Then C^* is the set of all solutions of the inequalities $a_i y \leq 0$, $i = 1, \ldots, m$, which we have just seen is a finite cone. Next, (2) follows from (3), for if C and C' are finite cones, so are C^* and C'^* and $C \cap C' = C^{**} \cap C'^{**} = (C^* + C'^*)^*$ from (4), but this last expression is a finite cone from (1) and (3). Finally, we have (5), for

$$C^* + C'^* = (C^* + C'^*)^{**} = (C^{**} \cap C'^{**})^* = (C \cap C')^*$$

Virtually all the theorems of this and the previous section can be obtained quickly from the general result above. As an example, let us re-prove Theorem 2.10, which stated: "Exactly one of the following alternatives holds. Either the inequality

$$xA \leqq 0 \tag{1}$$

has a semipositive solution, or the inequality

$$Ay > 0 \tag{2}$$

has a nonnegative solution."

Proof. Let $C = (a^1) + \cdots + (a^n)$. If (1) does not hold, this means $C^* \cap P = 0$. Taking duals gives

$$C + P^* = C + N = (0)^* = R^m$$

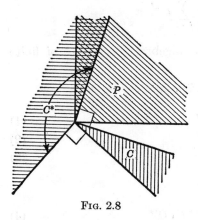

In particular, some positive vector u lies in $C + N$; thus $u = c - p$, where $u > 0$, where $p \geqq 0$, and $c \varepsilon C$, but then $c = u + p > 0$ and since $c = \sum_{j=1}^{n} \eta_j a^j$, the vector $y = (\eta_j)$ satisfies (2).

FIG. 2.8

Geometrically, this theorem states that, if a given finite cone does not contain a positive vector, then its dual contains a semipositive vector (see Fig. 2.8). This generalizes the situation already noted for subspaces (Corollary 1 of Theorem 2.9, Fig. 2.3).

6. Extreme Vectors and Extreme Solutions

In this section, we continue the study of solutions of inequalities, inhomogeneous as well as homogeneous. The results we obtain will be used in the analysis of solutions of matrix games and linear production models. A number of the important facts will be left for the reader to work out as part of the exercises at the end of the chapter.

We have seen in the previous section that the solutions of the homogeneous inequalities

$$xA \leqq 0 \tag{1}$$

form a finite cone

$$C = (x_1) + \cdots + (x_k)$$

Thus, in order to know all solutions of (1), it suffices to find some finite set of solutions $x_1, \ldots, x_k$, the remaining solutions being non-negative combinations of these x_i. We now look into the question of how to find the solutions x_i. The situation is illustrated in Fig. 2.9.

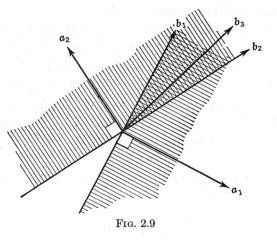

Fig. 2.9

In the figure, we wish to solve

$$xa_1 \geqq 0$$
$$xa_2 \geqq 0$$

The doubly shaded region gives the cone C of solutions, and this is easily seen to be the finite cone "generated" by the vectors b_1 and b_2; thus

$$C = (b_1) + (b_2)$$

Of course, the cone C could be written in many other ways. Thus, if b_3 is any vector in C, we could also write

$$C = (b_1) + (b_2) + (b_3)$$

but this is clearly redundant as the vector b_3 is unnecessary for describing C. On the other hand, it is clear from the picture that any way of writing C as a finite cone must use the "extreme" vectors b_1 and b_2, since neither of these is expressible as a nonnegative combination of other vectors in C. We proceed to make these notions precise.

Definition. A vector $x \neq 0$ in a convex cone C is called an *extreme vector* of C if x cannot be written in the form

$$x = x_1 + x_2 \qquad x_1, \, x_2 \, \varepsilon \, C$$

where x_1 and x_2 are independent.

If C is the cone of solutions of the inequality $xA \leqq 0$, an extreme vector x in C is called an *extreme solution.*

In the example of Fig. 2.9, it is seen that the vectors b_1 and b_2 are extreme vectors and they generate the cone C. It would be pleasant if we could say that every finite cone is generated by its extreme vectors. This is unfortunately not the case. In fact, there are cones which have no extreme vectors. Any subspace or halfspace (except in two dimensions) is an example of this. However, for cones which are "pointed" like the one in the figure, the assertion is true, as we shall now see.

Definition. The vectors $a_1, \, \ldots, \, a_m$ are called *positively independent* if the equation

$$\sum_{i=1}^{m} \xi_i a_i = 0$$

has no semipositive solution.

Geometrically, the vectors a_i are positively independent if the cone they generate contains no subspace except 0; hence the term *pointed.*

Lemma 2.3. If $a_1, \, \ldots, \, a_m$ are positively independent, then the cone

$$C = \sum_{i=1}^{m} (a_i) \ \textit{is the sum of its extreme halflines.}$$

Proof. From the set of vectors $a_1, \, \ldots, \, a_m$ delete any vector which is expressible as a nonnegative combination of the remaining vectors. If this is possible, then from the remaining $m - 1$ vectors one may again delete any vector which is a nonnegative combination of the other $m - 2$. Continuing in this way, it is clear that we shall eventually arrive at a set of vectors, say $a_1, \, \ldots, \, a_r$, with the properties that

$$C = \sum_{i=1}^{r} (a_i) \tag{1}$$

no vector in the set is a nonnegative combination of the others (2)

We shall show that all vectors in this set are extreme. Suppose then that, say, a_1 is not extreme. Then $a_1 = \sum_{i=1}^{r} \lambda_i a_i$, where each $\lambda_i \geqq 0$. Now, if $\lambda_1 \geqq 1$, then we would have

$$(\lambda_1 - 1)a_1 + \sum_{i=2}^{r} \lambda_i a_i = 0$$

contradicting the positive independence of the set a_i. On the other hand, if $\lambda_1 < 1$ then we would have

$$a_1 = \frac{1}{1 - \lambda_1} \sum_{i=2}^{r} \lambda_i a_i$$

contrary to the conditions on the set $a_1, \ldots, a_r$. Therefore a_1, and thus all a_i, are extreme, completing the proof.

We can now apply the lemma to solutions of inequalities.

Theorem 2.15 (extreme solutions of inequalities). *If A has rank m then every solution of*

$$xA \leqq 0 \tag{1}$$

is a nonnegative combination of extreme solutions.

Proof. Let $C = (b_1) + \cdots + (b_k)$ be the cone of all solutions of (1) and suppose the b_i are positively dependent, that is,

$$\sum_{i=1}^{k} \lambda_i b_i = 0$$

where $\lambda_i \geqq 0$. Now if, say, $\lambda_1 > 0$ then

$$-b_1 = \frac{1}{\lambda_1} \sum_{i=2}^{k} \lambda_i b_i$$

and therefore $-b_1 A = (1/\lambda_1)\Sigma\lambda_i(b_i A) \leqq 0$, or $b_1 A \geqq 0$. But since $b_1 \varepsilon C$ this means that $b_1 A = 0$ so that the rows of A are dependent contrary to the assumption that rank $A = m$. Since, therefore, the b_i are positively independent, it follows from the lemma that C is the sum of its extreme vectors as asserted.

The next question is how to recognize the extreme solutions of a set of inequalities.   Before stating the result, let us consider a simple numerical example.   Consider the system of four inequalities in three unknowns,

$$\xi_1 \leqq 0 \qquad \xi_2 \leqq 0 \qquad \xi_3 \leqq 0 \qquad \xi_1 - \xi_2 + \xi_3 \leqq 0 \qquad (1)$$

or, in vector notation,

$$xu_1 \leqq 0 \qquad xu_2 \leqq 0 \qquad xu_3 \leqq 0 \qquad xa \leqq 0$$

where $a = u_1 - u_2 + u_3$.   The figure below gives a representation of the situation in 3-space.

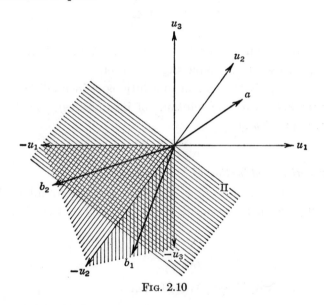

Fig. 2.10

We have shaded in the region corresponding to the cone C of solutions and we assert that extreme vectors of C are the vectors $-u_1$, $-u_3$, $b_1 = -u_3 - u_2$, and $b_2 = -u_1 - u_2$.   The points b_1 and b_2 are located geometrically by taking the plane Π perpendicular to the vector a and finding its intersection with the negative orthant.   The solutions of (1) are, in fact, all points of the negative orthant which are "behind" the plane Π.   The vectors b_1 and b_2 lie in the intersection of the plane Π with the u_2, u_3 plane and the u_1, u_2 plane, respectively.   Thus b_1 satisfies the first and fourth of the inequalities as equations, while b_2 satisfies the third and fourth as equations. Also $-u_1$ satisfies the second and third inequalities and $-u_3$ satisfies the first and second inequalities as equations. Thus the extreme vectors turn out to be those solutions of the inequalities which yield equality in two equations.

This geometric picture suggests the following general statement: A solution of a system of inequalities in m unknowns is extreme if it lies on $m - 1$ independent hyperplanes. In algebraic terms the result takes the simple form:

Theorem 2.16 (characterization of extreme solutions). *The solution $\bar{x}$ of the inequality*

$$xA \leqq 0 \tag{1}$$

is extreme if and only if the set of columns a^j for which $\bar{x}a^j = 0$ has rank $m - 1$.

Proof. Let $S \subset \{1, \ldots, n\}$ be the indices j such that $\bar{x}a^j = 0$ and let S' be the complementary set such that $\bar{x}a^j < 0$. Suppose first that the vectors a^j, $j \,\varepsilon\, S$ have rank $m - 1$. Then $\bar{x}$ is extreme, for suppose $\bar{x} = x' + x''$. Then clearly $a^j x' = a^j x'' = 0$ for $j \,\varepsilon\, S$; but, from Theorem 2.4 on solutions of homogeneous equations, we know that the set of solutions of these equations has rank 1 so that x' and x'' are dependent and hence $\bar{x}$ is extreme.

Conversely, suppose $\bar{x}$ is a solution of (1) and let $S \subset N$ be all indices j such that $\bar{x}a^j = 0$. If $\bar{x} \neq 0$ this set of vectors has rank less than m. If its rank is less than $m - 1$ then again by Theorem 2.4 we can find a second solution x of the equations $xa^j = 0$, $j \,\varepsilon\, S$, which is independent of $\bar{x}$. But now choose $\lambda \neq 0$ with $|\lambda|$ so small that $x' = (\bar{x} + \lambda x)/2$ and $x'' = (\bar{x} - \lambda x)/2$ satisfy $xa^j < 0$ for j in S'. Then x' and x'' satisfy (1) and are independent (why?) but $\bar{x} = x' + x''$ and hence $\bar{x}$ is not extreme.

The theorems of this section are important in that they give us a constructive means, in principle, for computing all solutions to a set of homogeneous inequalities, at least if the rank of the system is m (if not, some additional modification is necessary). Namely, one simply solves all subsystems of equations of rank $m - 1$. Those solutions (unique up to multiplication by a scalar) which also satisfy the original inequalities comprise all extreme solutions of the system and thus we have found all solutions. (From the standpoint of practical computation, such a scheme would be enormously time-consuming, and indeed much faster methods exist and will be discussed in a later chapter.)

7. Convex Sets and Polytopes

The notion of convex sets which we now introduce plays a central role in the mathematical theory of games and in many other economic models. Roughly speaking, convex sets bear the same relation to inhomogeneous inequalities that convex cones bear to homogeneous inequalities. We shall not develop the whole theory of inequalities here but shall leave a number of the key theorems for the reader to work out as exercises.

Definition. A subset K of R^m is called *convex* if for any vectors x and x' in K and any number λ, $0 \leq \lambda \leq 1$, the vector $\lambda x + (1 - \lambda)x'$ is in K.

Recall from analytic geometry that the line through two points x and x' consists of all points of the form $\lambda x + (1 - \lambda)x'$. Thus a set is convex if whenever it contains two points it contains the *segment* connecting them.

The reader will at once verify that the sum and intersection (but not the union) of convex sets is convex. We shall proceed rather rapidly to present a few of the essential properties of convex sets. The geometric pictures are similar to those for the case of cones, and it is suggested that the reader try to visualize the results as they are presented. (See Fig. 2.11 below.)

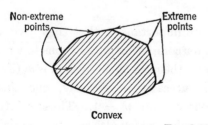
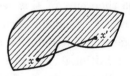

Convex   Non-convex

Fig. 2.11

Definition. The vector x in R^m is a *convex combination* of the vectors $x_1, \ldots, x_k$ if

$$x = \Sigma \lambda_i x_i$$

where $\lambda_i \geqq 0$ for all i, and $\displaystyle\sum_{i=1}^{k} \lambda_i = 1$.

If X is any subset of R^m the *convex hull* of X or simply the *convex* of X, written $<X>$, is the set of all convex combinations of points of X.

If X is a finite set, then $<X>$ is called a *convex polytope*. (The word "polytope" is the m-dimensional extension of the two- and three-dimensional words "polygon" and "polyhedron.")

The following lemma justifies the terminology of this definition.

Lemma 2.4. *If X is a subset of R^n then $X = <X>$ if and only if X is convex.*

Proof. That $<X>$ is convex follows at once from the definition, for if x and x' are in $<X>$ then

$$x = \Sigma \lambda_i x_i \qquad \lambda_i \geqq 0 \qquad \Sigma \lambda_i = 1 \qquad x_i \, \varepsilon \, X$$
$$x' = \Sigma \lambda_i' x_i' \qquad \lambda_i' \geqq 0 \qquad \Sigma \lambda_i' = 1 \qquad x_i' \, \varepsilon \, X$$

and $\lambda x + (1 - \lambda)x' = \Sigma \mu_i x_i + \Sigma \mu_i' x_i'$, where $\mu_i = \lambda \lambda_i$, $\mu_i' = (1 - \lambda)\lambda_i'$, so that $\Sigma \mu_i + \Sigma \mu_i' = \lambda + 1 - \lambda = 1$.

Conversely, if X is convex, we show that, for any $x_i \, \varepsilon \, X$ and $\lambda_i \geqq 0$ and $\displaystyle\sum_{i=1}^{n} \lambda_i = 1$, we have

$$x = \sum_{i=1}^{n} \lambda_i x_i \, \varepsilon \, X \qquad (1)$$

From the definition, (1) holds for $n = 2$; so let us assume it holds for fewer than n vectors x_i. We may suppose $\lambda_n < 1$, for if not, $x = x_n$ and there is nothing to prove. Let $x' = \displaystyle\sum_{i=1}^{n-1} \lambda_i x_i / (1 - \lambda_n)$. Then by assumption, $x' \, \varepsilon \, X$ since $\displaystyle\sum_{i=1}^{n-1} \lambda_i / (1 - \lambda_n) = 1$, but $x = \lambda_n x_n + (1 - \lambda_n)x'$, which is in X by definition of convexity.

The lemma suggests an alternative way of defining convexity. Given points $x_1, \ldots, x_n$ in X, we may imagine associating with each point x_i a certain mass $\lambda_i \geq 0$. The physical center of mass is then the point

$$x = \frac{1}{\lambda} \sum \lambda_i x_i$$

where $\lambda = \Sigma \lambda_i$, and convexity requires that this center of mass shall lie in the set X.

Definition. A vector x in a convex set K is called an *extreme point* or a *vertex* of K if, for any x', $x'' \varepsilon K$ and $0 < \lambda < 1$, $x = \lambda x' + (1 - \lambda)x''$ implies $x = x' = x''$. In geometric terms, an extreme point of K is a point which is not an interior point of any segment of K (see Fig. 2.11).

A convex set need not have any extreme points even if it is bounded. An example is the interior of the disk $\xi_1^2 + \xi_2^2 < 1$ in the plane. However, if the set is a polytope, we have the following key fact.

Theorem 2.17. *If K is a convex polytope and $\dot{K}$ is its set of extreme points then $K = <\dot{K}>$.*

Let $K = <x_1, \ldots, x_n>$. Then any extreme point of K is one of the points x_i, as one sees directly from the definitions of vertex and convex hull. From among the x_i choose a minimal subset (as few elements as possible) whose convex hull is K. Suppose this is the set $\{x_1, \ldots, x_r\}$. Then each of these points is extreme, for if, say,

$$x_r = \lambda x + (1 - \lambda)x' \qquad 0 < \lambda < 1 \tag{1}$$

we shall show that $x = x' = x_r$. Writing x and x' in terms of the x_i gives

$$x = \sum_{i=1}^{r} \lambda_i x_i \tag{2}$$

$$x' = \sum_{i=1}^{r} \lambda_i' x_i \tag{3}$$

and substituting (2) in (1) we get x_r as a convex combination of the x_i,

$$x_r = \sum_{i=1}^{r} \mu_i x_i \tag{3}$$

but if $\mu_r < 1$, then we would have

$$x_r = \frac{1}{1 - \mu_r} \sum_{i=1}^{r-1} \mu_i x_i$$

contrary to the minimality of the set $\{x_1, \ldots, x_r\}$. On the other hand, if $\mu_r = 1$, then $\mu_i = 0$ for $i \neq r$, or

$$\lambda \lambda_i + (1 - \lambda)\lambda'_i = 0$$

for $i \neq r$, which means $\lambda_i = \lambda'_i = 0$ for $i \neq r$ so that $x = x' = x_r$, as asserted.

Bibliographical Notes

We shall make no attempt here to trace the history of the material on equations and inequalities presented in this chapter, except to mention that the earliest investigations that we know of are those of Fourier in 1823 [1]. For a fairly complete bibliography of the subject, see Kuhn and Tucker [1]. Among recent expositions of the subject are those given by Kuhn [2], Goldman and Tucker [1], and Thrall and Tornheim [1], this last being a chapter in a textbook on matrix algebra.

Exercises

On Sections 1 and 2

1. Let $a_1, \ldots, a_m$ be m-vectors. Prove that the equations

$$a_i y = \beta_i \qquad i = 1, \ldots, m$$

have a unique solution y if and only if the equations

$$a_i y = 0 \qquad i = 1, \ldots, m$$

have no nonzero solution.

2. Exhibit the linear dependence between the vectors

$$a_1 = (0, 1, -2), a_2 = (1, 1, 1), a_3 = (1, 2, 3), a_4 = (2, 0, 3)$$

3. A function f from F^m into F is called a *linear function* if

$$f(x + y) = f(x) + f(y) \qquad \text{for all } x, y \, \varepsilon \, F^m \qquad (1)$$
$$f(\lambda x) = \lambda f(x) \qquad \text{for all } x \, \varepsilon \, F^m, \lambda \, \varepsilon \, F \qquad (2)$$

Show that, if f is a linear function, there exists a vector a in F^m such that $f(x) = xa$ for all x in F^m.

4. A function f from F^m to F^n is called a *linear transformation* if it satisfies (1) and (2) of Exercise 3. Show that, if f is a linear transformation, then there is an $m \times n$ matrix A such that $f(x) = xA$ for all x in F^m.

5.* If $A = (a_{ij})$ is an $m \times n$ matrix and $B = (\beta_{ij})$ is a $n \times p$ matrix, their *product* AB is an $m \times p$ matrix $AB = (\gamma_{ij})$, where $\gamma_{ij} = \sum_{k=1}^{n} \alpha_{ik}\beta_{kj}$. Show that scalar multiplication, scalar product, and the matrix-vector product are all special cases of matrix multiplication.

6.* If A is $m \times n$, B is $n \times p$, C is $p \times q$, prove

$$(AB)C = A(BC) \qquad \text{(associative law)}$$

7.* If $A = (\alpha_{ij})$ and $B = (\beta_{ij})$ are $m \times n$ matrices, their sum is defined by $A + B = (\alpha_{ij} + \beta_{ij})$. Prove if C is an $n \times p$ matrix then

$$(A + B)C = AC + BC \qquad \text{(distributive law)}$$

8.* The $n \times n$ *identity matrix* $I = (\delta_{ij})$ is the matrix such that

$$\begin{aligned} \delta_{ij} &= 0 \qquad \text{for } i \neq j \\ &= 1 \qquad \text{for } i = j \end{aligned}$$

Show that if A is $m \times n$ and B is $n \times p$ then $AI = A$ and $IB = B$.

9.* An $m \times m$ matrix is called *regular* if it has rank m (otherwise *singular*). Show that if A is regular then there exists an $m \times m$ matrix A^{-1} called the *inverse* of A, such that $AA^{-1} = A^{-1}A = I$.

10. Find all solutions of the equations

$$\begin{aligned} 2x + 3y - z + w &= 0 \\ x - 5y + 2z &= 0 \end{aligned}$$

11. Prove for any linear subspace L in F^m, rank L + rank $L^* = m$.

12. Use Theorem 2.5 to show that the following equations have no solution:

$$\begin{aligned} 2x + 3y &= 1 \\ x - 3y &= 1 \\ -x + y &= 0 \end{aligned}$$

---

* Exercises marked with an asterisk contain results which will be used in subsequent chapters. For a complete understanding of what follows it is therefore essential that the reader work these problems.

13. If A is an $m \times n$ matrix with $m \geq n$, then if the equation $xA = b$ has a solution it has one with at most n nonzero coordinates.

14. A subset S of F^m is called an *affine subspace* if (a) $x, y \, \varepsilon \, S$ implies $\lambda x + (1 - \lambda)y \, \varepsilon \, S$ for all λ; or (b) $S = w + L$, where w is a vector, L a linear subspace; or (c) S is the set of all solutions of an equation $xA = b$. Prove that definitions (a), (b), and (c) are equivalent.

On Sections 3 and 4

15. Verify property O4 of Sec. 3.

16. Use Theorem 2.6 to show that the following equations have no nonnegative solution:

$$\xi_1 + 3\xi_2 - 5\xi_3 = 2$$
$$\xi_1 - 4\xi_2 - 7\xi_3 = 3$$

17. Prove, using Theorem 2.7, that the following inequalities have no solution:

$$4\xi_1 - 5\xi_2 \geq 2$$
$$-2\xi_1 - 7\xi_2 \geq 2$$
$$-\xi_1 + 3\xi_2 \geq -1$$

18. Exhibit a solution of the inequalities

$$5\xi_1 - 4\xi_2 \leq 7$$
$$-3\xi_1 + 3\xi_2 \leq -5$$

but prove from Theorem 2.8 that there are no nonnegative solutions.

19. Do the following equations have a semipositive solution?

$$3\xi_1 - 5\xi_2 + 2\xi_3 = 0$$
$$2\xi_1 - 4\xi_2 + \xi_3 = 0$$

20. Show that a set of n homogeneous inequalities in n unknowns always has a nonzero solution.

21. The inequality $xA \leq b$ has a solution if and only if every set of $m + 1$ of the inequalities $xa^j \leq \beta_j$ has a solution (use Theorems 2.6, 2.7, 2.11).

22. Prove Corollary 2 of Theorem 2.9.

23. For any subspace L of R^n, $L + L^* = R^n$. [Remark: This is not true in general. If F is the complex numbers, let L be all multiples of the vector $(1, i)$ in F^2 and note that $L^* = L$.]

24. For any subspace L in R^n there exists $x \geq 0$, $x \, \varepsilon \, L$, $y \geq 0$, $y \, \varepsilon \, L^*$ such that $x + y > 0$.

25. An $m \times m$ matrix A is called *positive semidefinite* if $xAx \geq 0$ for all x in R^m. Prove that, if A is positive semidefinite, then the inequality

$$xA \geq 0$$

has a semipositive solution.

On Sections 5, 6, and 7

26. Show that a subspace of rank r can be expressed as the sum of $r + 1$ halflines.

27. If X is a subset of R^m and $x \ \varepsilon \ <X>$ show that x is a convex combination of some set of at most $m + 1$ points of X (use theorem on basic solutions).

28. Construct an example of a convex cone C (not finite) such that $C^{**} \neq C$. Construct cones C_1 and C_2 such that $(C_1 \cap C_2)^* \neq C_1^* + C_2^*$.

29. For any finite cone C in R^m show that $C + C^* = R^m$ (this generalizes Exercise 23).

30. For a finite cone $C \cap (-C^*) = 0$ if and only if C is a linear space.

31. The *transpose* $A^* = (\alpha_{ij}^*)$ of the matrix $A = (\alpha_{ij})$ is the matrix such that $\alpha_{ij}^* = \alpha_{ji}$. Using Exercise 30 above, show that the inequality $xA \leq 0$ has a nonzero solution if and only if the inequality $yA^*A \leq 0$ has a nonzero solution. (The last two problems are results of J. Gaddum [1].)

32. For any cone C there exists $x \geq 0$, $x \ \varepsilon \ C$, $y \geq 0$, $y \ \varepsilon \ C^*$ such that $x + y > 0$ (this generalizes Exercise 24).

33. The *lineality* of a convex cone C is the rank of the set of all vectors in C whose negatives also belong to C. Prove (a) for a convex cone in R^m, rank C + lineality $C^* = m$; (b) for finite cones, rank C^* + lineality $C = m$.

34. An *open halfspace* in R^m is the set of all vectors x such that $xa < 0$ for some fixed vector a. Show that, if S is a finite set in R^m such that every $m + 1$ points in S belong to some open halfspace, then there is an open halfspace containing all of S (use Theorem 2.9 and Exercise 27).

35. From Exercise 34 show that the inequality

$$xA < 0$$

has a solution if and only if every set of $m + 1$ of the inequalities

$$xa^j < 0$$

has a solution.

36. A set X in R^m is called a *solution set* if X is the set of all solutions of an inequality $xA \leq b$. Prove that every convex polytope K is a solution set. [Hint: Let $K = <x_1, \ldots, x_n>$, where $x_i = (\xi_{i1}, \ldots, \xi_{im})$. Define $\hat{x}_i = (\xi_{i1}, \ldots, \xi_{im}, 1)$, let $C = (\hat{x}_1) + \cdots + (\hat{x}_n)$, and consider C^*.]

37. A set X in R^m is *bounded* if there exists a number $\mu \geq 0$ such that for all $x = (\xi_i)$ in X, $|\xi_i| \leq \mu$. Show that the set of solutions of the inequality $xA \leq b$ is bounded if and only if the inequality $xA \leq 0$ has no nonzero solution.

38. From the last two exercises, show that the solution set X is a convex polytope if and only if X is bounded.

39. Show that every solution set can be expressed as the sum of a convex polytope and a finite cone, and conversely.

40.* If X is a solution set in R^m and A is an $m \times n$ matrix, then $Y = \{y | y = xA, x \, \varepsilon \, X\}$ is a solution set in R^n.

41. (Helly's theorem.) If $K_1, \ldots, K_r$ are a collection of convex polytopes in R^n such that every set of $n + 1$ of the K_i have a point in common, then all the K_i have a point in common. (Hint: Use Exercises 21 and 36.)

CHAPTER THREE

The Theory of Linear Programming

Using the algebraic machinery developed in the first four sections of the preceding chapter it will be a fairly simple matter now to develop the theory of linear programming. We recall that the standard maximum problem was defined in Chap. 1 as the problem of finding nonnegative numbers which satisfy certain linear inequalities and maximize a given linear function. In the vector matrix notation which we have introduced, this problem can be written in the following compact form: Given an $m \times n$ matrix A, an n-vector b, and an m-vector c, find a nonnegative m-vector x such that

$$xc \text{ is a maximum} \tag{1}$$

subject to

$$xA \leqq b \tag{2}$$

The dual problem is then that of finding a nonnegative n-vector y such that

$$yb \text{ is a minimum} \tag{1*}$$

subject to

$$Ay \geqq c \tag{2*}$$

We shall actually be interested in problems which are more general than standard maximum and minimum problems, and the next section will be devoted to defining and classifying the various types of problems which will be included under the general heading of linear programs.

1. Definitions

In the standard maximum and minimum problems which we have considered so far, the unknown vector x was required to be nonnegative and satisfy a linear inequality.   In many applications one wishes to impose conditions in the form of equations as well as inequalities. Also, there are numerous applications in which one does not require that solutions be nonnegative.   It is convenient to introduce the term *linear constraint* to mean either a linear equation or an inequality. We can then distinguish the various types of linear programs according to the nature of the constraints.

One type of program which is especially convenient in connection with computational methods, as we shall see in the next chapter, is that in which the unknown vector is required to be nonnegative but the constraints take the form of equations.

Definition.   Let A, b, and c be as before.   The *canonical maximum problem* is that of finding a nonnegative vector x which

$$\text{maximizes } xc \tag{1}$$

subject to

$$xA = b \tag{2}$$

The canonical minimum problem is defined in exactly the same way, replacing the word "maximize" by "minimize."

We shall now show that the standard and canonical problems are equivalent in the sense that either one can be transformed into the other in an obvious manner.   If we replace (2) above by the inequalities

$$\begin{aligned} xA &\leqq b \\ -xA &\leqq -b \end{aligned} \tag{2}$$

it is clear that we have rephrased the canonical problem as a standard problem.   On the other hand, to change a standard problem to a canonical one we replace the inequality

$$xA \leqq b \tag{3}$$

by the equation

$$xA + z = b \tag{4}$$

and the further requirement

$$z \geqq 0$$

We now have a problem whose constraints are equations, and clearly x and z are nonnegative and x maximizes (1) subject to (4) if and only if x satisfies (3) and maximizes (1).

We shall also consider the most general case in which some coordinates of x are required to be nonnegative while others may be arbitrary, and where the constraints include both equations and inequalities.

Definition. Let $a^1, \ldots, a^r, \bar{a}^1, \ldots, \bar{a}^s$, and c be m-vectors and let $\beta_1, \ldots, \beta_r, \bar{\beta}_1, \ldots, \bar{\beta}_s$ be numbers. The *general maximum problem* is that of finding an m-vector x such that

$$xc \text{ is a maximum} \tag{1}$$

subject to

$$\begin{aligned} xa^j &\leq \beta_j & \text{for } j = 1, \ldots, r \\ x\bar{a}^j &= \bar{\beta}_j & \text{for } j = 1, \ldots, s \end{aligned} \tag{2}$$

It is clear that both the standard and canonical problems are special cases of the general problem. Conversely, a simple trick permits us to transform the general problem into either of the others. To obtain a standard problem equivalent to the general problem above, we first obtain constraints involving only inequalities by replacing the equations in (2) above by the inequalities

$$\begin{aligned} x\bar{a}^j &\leq \bar{\beta}_j \\ -x\bar{a}^j &\leq -\bar{\beta}_j \end{aligned} \tag{3}$$

Next, introduce new unknown nonnegative m-vectors $x' = (\xi_i')$ and $x'' = (\xi_i'')$ and replace inequalities (2) and (3) by

$$\begin{aligned} (x' - x'')a^j &\leq \beta_j \\ (x' - x'')\bar{a}^j &\leq \bar{\beta}_j \\ -(x' - x'')\bar{a}^j &\leq -\bar{\beta}_j \end{aligned} \tag{4}$$

and require that

$$x'c - x''c \text{ be a maximum} \tag{5}$$

Now clearly, the $2m$-vector $z = (\xi_1', \ldots, \xi_m', \xi_1'', \ldots, \xi_m'')$ maximizes (5) subject to (4) if and only if the vector $x = x' - x''$ solves the original problem [the details are left as an exercise (see Exercise 3)],

and the equivalence of the standard and general maximum (and similarly, minimum) problem is demonstrated.

We have stated that the theory of linear programming centers
around the fundamental duality theorem for the standard maximum
and minimum problems. As one would probably expect, there are
also dual problems for the canonical and general problem. We shall
first give the dual of the general problem. The dual of the canonical
and standard problems will then drop out as special cases. For this
purpose it is convenient to reformulate the general problem.

Let A, b, and c have their usual meaning. We now use the notation
of Sec. 4 of Chap. 2, in which M and N denoted the indices 1 to m and
1 to n, respectively. Thus

$$M = \{1, \ldots, m\} \qquad N = \{1, \ldots, n\}$$

Let S be a subset of M and let S' be its *complement*, that is, all
indices in M but not in S. Let T be a subset of N and let T' be its
complement. We can now describe the general maximum problem as
follows: Find an m-vector $x = (\xi_i)$ such that

$$xc \text{ is a maximum} \tag{1}$$

subject to

$$\begin{aligned}
\xi_i &\geq 0 && \text{for } i \,\varepsilon\, S \\
xa^j &\leq \beta_j && \text{for } j \,\varepsilon\, T \\
xa^j &= \beta_j && \text{for } j \,\varepsilon\, T'
\end{aligned} \tag{2}$$

The dual of this problem is then defined as follows: Find an n-vector
$y = (\eta_j)$ such that

$$yb \text{ is a minimum} \tag{1*}$$

subject to

$$\begin{aligned}
\eta_j &\geq 0 && \text{for } j \,\varepsilon\, T \\
a_i y &\geq \gamma_i && \text{for } i \,\varepsilon\, S \\
a_i y &= \gamma_i && \text{for } i \,\varepsilon\, S'
\end{aligned} \tag{2*}$$

The symmetry in this duality is at once evident. To an inequality
in one system corresponds a nonnegative variable in the dual. To an
equation in one system corresponds an unrestricted variable in the dual.

Note that the standard maximum problem corresponds to the special
case of the general problem in which $S = M$ and $T = N$ so that S' and

T' are empty, and here the dual problem turns out to be the standard minimum problem as of course it must.   Observe, however, that the dual of a canonical maximum problem is not a canonical minimum problem, for this corresponds to the case where $S = M$ and T is empty. The dual is then the problem of finding an n-vector y (no restriction as to sign) such that

$$yb \text{ is a minimum} \tag{3}$$

subject to

$$Ay \geqq c \tag{4}$$

Concerning terminology, the words used in Chap. 1 all extend in an obvious manner to the other types of linear programs.   Thus:

Definitions.   A linear program is called *feasible* if there exists a vector satisfying the constraints.   Such a vector is called a *feasible vector* (rather than feasible solution as used in Chap. 1).

A feasible vector is called an *optimal vector* if it maximizes or minimizes the given linear form, and the value of this maximum or minimum is called the *value* of the program.

2. The Duality Theorems

In Chap. 1, we stated the duality theorem for the standard maximum and minimum problems.   An identical statement applies to the canonical and general problems.   Namely:

Theorem 3.1 (fundamental duality theorem).   *If both a program and its dual are feasible then both have optimal vectors and the values of the two programs are the same.   If either program is infeasible then neither has an optimal vector.*

We shall proceed by proving the duality theorem for the case of the standard program.   From this we shall get a proof for the general program.

Proof for Standard Program.   Suppose first that both the standard maximum problem and its dual are feasible.   We then have non-negative solutions x and y to the inequalities

$$xA \leqq b \tag{1}$$
$$Ay \geqq c \tag{2}$$

The theorem will be proved if we can find solutions of (1) and (2) which also satisfy

$$xc - yb \geq 0 \tag{3}$$

for we have seen in Lemma 1.1 that, if x and y satisfy (1) and (2) then $xc \leq yb$; so if (3) is also satisfied then $xc = yb$ and hence by Theorem 1.1 (page 10) x and y are both optimal.

Suppose then that the system (1), (2), and (3) has no nonnegative solution. This is precisely the situation to which Theorem 2.8 of the previous chapter applies (page 47). If we write out inequalities (1), (2), and (3) we get

$$\sum_i \xi_i \alpha_{ij} \leq \beta_j \qquad \text{for } j = 1, \ldots, n \tag{1'}$$

$$\sum_j \eta_j(-\alpha_{ij}) \leq -\gamma_i \qquad \text{for } i = 1, \ldots, m \tag{2'}$$

$$\sum_j \eta_j \beta_j - \sum_i \xi_i \gamma_i \leq 0 \tag{3'}$$

If these inequalities have no nonnegative solution then Theorem 2.8 states that there is a nonnegative n-vector $z = (\zeta_j)$ and a nonnegative m-vector $w = (\omega_i)$ and a number $\theta \geq 0$ such that

$$\sum_j \zeta_j \alpha_{ij} - \theta \gamma_i \geq 0 \qquad \text{for } i = 1, \ldots, m \tag{4'}$$

$$-\sum_i \omega_i \alpha_{ij} + \theta \beta_j \geq 0 \qquad \text{for } j = 1, \ldots, n \tag{5'}$$

and

$$\sum_j \zeta_j \beta_j - \sum_i \omega_i \gamma_i < 0 \tag{6'}$$

or in matrix vector form

$$Az \geq \theta c \tag{4}$$
$$wA \leq \theta b \tag{5}$$
$$zb - wc < 0 \tag{6}$$

Now θ is not zero, for if it were then choosing feasible vectors x and y, we would get from (4), (5), (1), and (2)

$$0 \leq xAz \leq zb$$

and
$$0 \geqq wAy \gneqq wc$$

which contradicts (6).

Now since θ is positive, w/θ and z/θ are a pair of feasible vectors so that, by Lemma 1.1,

$$\frac{w}{\theta} c \leqq \frac{z}{\theta} b \quad \text{or} \quad wc \leqq zb$$

which again contradicts (6). It follows that the original set of inequalities has a solution and this solution provides the desired pair of optimal vectors, as we have already observed.

Finally, suppose, say, (1) is not feasible. Then certainly the original maximum problem has no solution. Therefore, again by Theorem 2.8, there exists a nonnegative n-vector z such that

$$Az \geqq 0 \quad \text{and} \quad zb < 0 \tag{7}$$

But then if constraints (2) are feasible there exists a vector y such that

$$Ay \geqq c \tag{8}$$

and from (7), therefore, $y + \lambda z$ is also feasible for all positive λ, but since zb is negative this means the expression $(y + \lambda z)b$ can be made arbitrarily small; hence it has no minimum and the dual problem has no optimal vector. The proof for the standard program is now complete.

Proof for the General Linear Program. For this proof we transform the general problem into a standard program by the method of Sec. 1. We seek a vector $x = (\xi_i)$ such that

$$\sum_i \xi_i \gamma_i \text{ is a maximum} \tag{1}$$

subject to

$$
\begin{aligned}
\xi_i &\geqq 0 &&\text{for } i \,\varepsilon\, S \\
xa^j &\leqq \beta_j &&\text{for } j \,\varepsilon\, T \\
xa^j &= \beta_j &&\text{for } j \,\varepsilon\, T'
\end{aligned}
\tag{2}
$$

where S and T are subsets of M and N respectively.

Now for each i in S' we introduce two new nonnegative variables

ξ_i' and ξ_i'' and consider the standard problem of

$$\text{maximizing} \sum_{i \varepsilon S} \xi_i \gamma_i + \sum_{i \varepsilon S'} \xi_i' \gamma_i - \sum_{i \varepsilon S'} \xi_i'' \gamma_i \qquad (1')$$

subject to

$$\sum_{i \varepsilon S} \xi_i \alpha_{ij} + \sum_{i \varepsilon S'} \xi_i' \alpha_{ij} - \sum_{i \varepsilon S'} \xi_i'' \alpha_{ij} \leq \beta_j \qquad j \varepsilon T$$

$$\sum_{i \varepsilon S} \xi_i \alpha_{ij} + \sum_{i \varepsilon S'} \xi_i' \alpha_{ij} - \sum_{i \varepsilon S'} \xi_i'' \alpha_{ij} \leq \beta_j \qquad j \varepsilon T' \qquad (2')$$

$$- \sum_{i \varepsilon S} \xi_i \alpha_{ij} - \sum_{i \varepsilon S'} \xi_i' \alpha_{ij} + \sum_{i \varepsilon S'} \xi_i'' \alpha_{ij} \leq -\beta_j \qquad j \varepsilon T'$$

The dual of this standard program is to find nonnegative numbers η_j, $j \varepsilon T$, and η_j', η_j'', $j \varepsilon T'$ such that

$$\sum_{j \varepsilon T} \eta_j \beta_j + \sum_{j \varepsilon T'} \eta_j' \beta_j - \sum_{j \varepsilon T'} \eta_j'' \beta_j \qquad (1')*$$

is a minimum subject to

$$\sum_{j \varepsilon T} \eta_j \alpha_{ij} + \sum_{j \varepsilon T'} \eta_j' \alpha_{ij} - \sum_{j \varepsilon T'} \eta_j'' \alpha_{ij} \geq \gamma_i \qquad i \varepsilon S$$

$$\sum_{j \varepsilon T} \eta_j \alpha_{ij} + \sum_{j \varepsilon T'} \eta_j' \alpha_{ij} - \sum_{j \varepsilon T'} \eta_j'' \alpha_{ij} \geq \gamma_i \qquad i \varepsilon S' \qquad (2')*$$

$$- \sum_{j \varepsilon T} \eta_j \alpha_{ij} - \sum_{j \varepsilon T'} \eta_j' \alpha_{ij} + \sum_{j \varepsilon T'} \eta_j'' \alpha_{ij} \geq -\gamma_i \qquad i \varepsilon S'$$

Now the dual of problem (1), (2) is by definition that of finding a vector $y = (\eta_j)$ which

$$\text{minimizes} \sum_{j} \eta_j \beta_j \qquad (1)*$$

subject to

$$\eta_j \geq 0 \qquad \text{for } j \varepsilon T$$

$$\sum_{j} \eta_j \alpha_{ij} \geq \gamma_i \qquad \text{for } i \varepsilon S$$

$$\sum_{j} \eta_j \alpha_{ij} = \gamma_i \qquad \text{for } i \varepsilon S' \qquad (2)*$$

But, as we saw in Sec. 1, this problem is equivalent to problem $(1')*$, $(2')*$. It follows that if the original problem and its dual are feasible so also are the equivalent "primed" problems. But then from the standard duality theorem the dual primed problems have equal values and hence so do the original problems, completing the proof.

3. The Equilibrium Theorems

We have already stated the equilibrium theorem for standard programs in Chap. 1 and given a proof of this theorem from the standard duality theorem. There are also, as one might expect, equilibrium theorems for general and canonical programs. Because of its importance in future applications we shall state and prove the theorem for the canonical program. The statement and proof for the general program are left as an exercise (see Exercise 4).

Theorem 3.2 (canonical equilibrium theorem). *Let $x = (\xi_i)$ be a nonnegative solution of*

$$xA = b \tag{1}$$

and let $y = (\eta_j)$ be a solution of

$$Ay \geq c \tag{2}$$

Then x maximizes xc, and y minimizes yb if and only if

$$\xi_i = 0 \text{ whenever } a_i y > \gamma_i \tag{3}$$

Proof. If (3) is satisfied then we have

$$xc = \sum_i \xi_i \gamma_i = \sum_i \xi_i a_i y = \left(\sum_i \xi_i a_i \right) y = xAy = by \tag{4}$$

and therefore x and y are optimal vectors.

Conversely, if x and y are optimal then Eqs. (4) follow from the duality theorem, from which we get

$$\sum_i \xi_i (a_i y - \gamma_i) = 0 \tag{5}$$

and since all terms in this sum are nonnegative, condition (3) follows.

As with the standard equilibrium theorem, the above result can be used to verify the optimality of a proposed solution, as we show in the following illustration.

Example. 1. Find $x = (\xi_i) \geqq 0$ such that

$$\xi_1 + 6\xi_2 - 7\xi_3 + \xi_4 + 5\xi_5 \tag{1}$$

is a minimum, subject to

$$\begin{aligned}
5\xi_1 - 4\xi_2 + 13\xi_3 - 2\xi_4 + \xi_5 &= 20 \\
\xi_1 - \xi_2 + 5\xi_3 - \xi_4 + \xi_5 &= 8
\end{aligned} \tag{2}$$

It is asserted that the vector $\bar{x} = (0, \frac{4}{7}, \frac{12}{7}, 0, 0)$ is optimal for this problem, the corresponding value being

$$6 \times \tfrac{4}{7} - 7 \times \tfrac{12}{7} = -\tfrac{60}{7}$$

Let us look at the dual constraints:

$$\begin{aligned}
5\eta_1 + \eta_2 &\leqq 1 \\
-4\eta_1 - \eta_2 &\leqq 6 \\
13\eta_1 + 5\eta_2 &\leqq -7 \\
-2\eta_1 - \eta_2 &\leqq 1 \\
\eta_1 + \eta_2 &\leqq 5
\end{aligned} \tag{2*}$$

Since $\bar{\xi}_2$ and $\bar{\xi}_3$ are positive in the proposed solution, it follows from the equilibrium theorem that the second and third inequalities of (2)* must be satisfied as equations

$$\begin{aligned}
-4\eta_1 - \eta_2 &= 6 \\
13\eta_1 + 5\eta_2 &= -7
\end{aligned}$$

and hence $\qquad \eta_1 = -\tfrac{23}{7} \qquad \eta_2 = \tfrac{50}{7}$

To show that this is in fact a solution we need only check feasibility in the other three inequalities:

$$5\eta_1 + \eta_2 = \frac{-5 \times 23 + 50}{7} < 0 < 1$$

$$-2\eta_1 - \eta_2 = \frac{2 \times 23 - 50}{7} < 0 < 1$$

$$\eta_1 + \eta_2 = \frac{-23 + 50}{7} = \frac{27}{7} < 4 < 5$$

and hence $\bar{y} = (-\tfrac{23}{7}, \tfrac{50}{7})$ is feasible and therefore both $\bar{x}$ and $\bar{y}$ are optimal.   As a final check note that the value of the dual is

$$20\eta_1 + 8\eta_2 = \frac{-20 \times 23 + 8 \times 50}{7} = -\frac{60}{7}$$

so that the values of the two problems are the same, as they, of course, must be.

4. Basic Solutions

The problem of practical computation for linear programs will not be taken up until the next chapter.   We shall, however, prove here a theorem which shows that any such problem can be solved in a finite number of steps, though with the proposed procedure this number is too large to be useful in practical computations.

We recall that a solution of a set of linear equations is called basic if it depends on a linearly independent set of vectors (Chap. 2, Sec. 4). In a canonical linear program an optimal vector $\bar{x}$ is called *basic* if it is a basic solution of the constraint equation

$$xA = b \tag{1}$$

Theorem 3.3 (basic solutions of linear programs).   *If a canonical linear program has an optimal vector then it has a basic optimal vector.*

Proof.   Let x' be an optimal vector depending, say, on the vectors $a_1, \ldots, a_r$.   Now if $\bar{y}$ is any optimal vector for the dual problem we know from Theorem 3.2 that $a_i\bar{y} = \gamma_i$ for $i \leqq r$.   If the vectors $a_1, \ldots, a_r$ are independent, then x' is already the desired basic solution.   If not, then by Theorem 2.11 on basic solutions of equations, we can find another solution $\bar{x}$ of (1) above depending on an independent subset of the vectors $a_1, \ldots, a_r$.   But $\bar{x}$ will also be optimal since it too will satisfy condition (3) of Theorem 3.2 with respect to $\bar{y}$.

This theorem shows that a canonical problem can be solved by a finite set of trials.   For example, the problem of Example 1 could be solved in the following way: Since the constraints consist of two equations in five unknowns, we would examine the ten sets of basic solutions obtained by setting three of the unknowns equal to zero in all possible ways.   Among these ten feasible vectors the basic optimal vector is then the one which minimizes the given linear function. Clearly the method becomes impracticably time-consuming when the number of variables is large.

5. An Application: Allocation of Resources in a Competitive Economy

We conclude this chapter with a very important application of the theory which has just been developed.   The reader will observe that all the examples of linear programs which have been considered so far correspond to situations in which an individual or a group of individuals is working cooperatively toward the achievement of some well-defined goal.   Indeed, linear programming seems designed specifically for attacking this kind of "optimization problem."   We shall see in this section, however, that linear programming theory enables us to make significant statements about quite a different sort of situation in which individuals and groups not only are working toward different goals but are actually competing with each other.   We shall be considering the problem of equilibrium for a competitive economy, terms which will be explained in the paragraphs to follow.

As a starting point we recall the problem of Example 4, Chap. 1, of maximizing income from given resources.   A certain economic unit, which we shall from now on refer to as a *firm*, has at its disposal a number of activities which can be operated at various levels.   The return or income from operating an activity at unit level is given, and the firm seeks to maximize its total return subject to given limitations on the amount of supplies available as inputs to the activities.   In the example referred to, the activities were thought of as producing certain goods from other goods but the model applies to many other situations as well.   We shall think of firms as being involved in such diverse activities as running airlines, producing motion pictures, or supplying hydroelectric power as well as producing consumer goods. By an *economy* we shall mean simply a collection of such firms, say m of them, where the kth firm is represented by its activity matrix A_k. Now in the earlier income-maximization problem it was also assumed that one knew in advance the supplies available to the firm given by a supply vector s_k.   In studying the economy as a whole, however, we may no longer assume that the supplies for each firm are given. Indeed our main problem in this section will be to determine how the resources of the economy shall be distributed among its component firms, how much steel shall be used for automobiles, how much for bridges, how much of the railroad system shall carry freight, how much passengers, etc.   This is called the problem of *resource allocation*.   We shall show how it is solved by the mechanism of *free competition*. Before doing so we must give a more precise description of our model.

It is convenient to subdivide what we have loosely termed supplies above into two categories: *resources* such as raw materials which the various firms compete for, and *plant capacity* such as capital equipment which is rigidly attached to a given firm.   For a steel manufacturer iron ore belongs to the first category, blast furnaces to the second.   For a farmer feed and fertilizer belong to the first category, land to the second.[1]   It is easy to introduce this distinction into our linear model.   One method for doing this would be to assume that some coordinates of the supply vector correspond to resources and the rest to plant capacity.   An equivalent and notationally more convenient formulation is to split the activity matrix as well as the supply vector into two parts.   We first consider the case of plant capacity. Let x_k be an intensity vector for the kth firm.   This vector is limited by the available capacity according to the inequality

$$x_k B_k \leqq b_k \tag{1}$$

where b_k is a vector giving the amounts of various sorts of capacity (e.g., land, labor, blast furnaces) available to the kth firm.   The ijth coordinate of the matrix B_k gives the amount of the jth capacity element required to operate the ith activity at unit level.   From the economic interpretation it will be seen that both B_k and b_k may be taken to be nonnegative.

Subject to condition (1) above, the kth firm consumes or produces resources in a linear manner.   Algebraically this means that there is a

---

[1] The category to which an item belongs may depend on the particular application.   Thus, for some purposes one may wish to think of laborers as being rigidly attached to certain jobs; for others one may assume that industries are competing for the services of the labor force.

matrix A_k such that at intensities x_k the firm consumes (or produces) the vector of resources $x_k A_k$. The matrix A_k need not be nonnegative, and we shall choose our signs so that a positive coordinate of $x_k A_k$ corresponds to an amount consumed, a negative coordinate to an amount produced.

It should be noted that the categories of plant capacity and resources do not exhaust all types of commodities, for they do not include consumer goods like milk, eggs, automobiles, and theater tickets. These goods are taken care of in our model in an implicit manner. Nowhere in the model will one find, for instance, a quart of milk; but the model will include a dairy activity which produces milk among other things. The rate of income to this activity will come in part from selling milk; and this income rate, and therefore by implication the price of milk, is a given constant of the model. The same is true of all consumer goods and services. The prices of resources, on the other hand, are not given in advance but are to be determined by the competitive mechanism, as we shall see shortly.

There is now the important further constraint which states that the aggregate of all the firms must not use up more resources than the economy can provide. Let $s = (\sigma_j)$ be the vector such that σ_j is the maximum amount of the jth resource which is available in the economy. Then the desired condition takes the simple form

$$\sum_{k=1}^{m} x_k A_k \leqq s \qquad (2)$$

One further remark should be made concerning the nature of the resources, which are themselves of two kinds, first the so-called *primary goods* or *factors of production*, meaning things like land and labor which are available for use in the economy but are not produced by it; and second the *intermediate goods* like steel which are required resources for the production of automobiles and bridges but which must themselves be produced elsewhere in the economy. There is no mathematical necessity to distinguish between primary and intermediate goods in the analysis which follows, but it is important to keep the distinction in mind in order to appreciate the economic generality of the model. As an illustration, one of the firms might manufacture trucks for which steel is a necessary input. This steel in turn is an output of the steel-making firm which requires iron ore as an input. Now, depending on our purposes, either we may consider this ore as a primary good available in certain quantities annually, and never mind where it comes from, or the model may contain in it an iron-mining firm, in which case the ore becomes an intermediate good produced from the primary good, labor—and perhaps an additional necessary input to the mining operation would be trucks. Our seemingly simple model is thus seen to be capable of handling rather complicated situations. Mathematically, a primary good will show up as a positive coordinate of the supply vector s while an intermediate good will correspond to a zero coordinate of s.

Returning now to the resource-allocation problem we see that we are looking for a set of vectors x_k which satisfy the inequalities (1) and (2). This is, of course, not a linear programming problem since nothing is being optimized. In general there will be infinitely many possible solutions of these inequalities. We now describe how the mechanism of free competition acts to determine such a solution.

Let us begin by supposing that an arbitrary (nonnegative) set of prices $p = (\pi_j)$ has been assigned to the various resources of the economy. How then will the kth firm behave? As in Example 4 of Chap. 1, we let γ_i^k be the income to the kth firm from operating the ith activity at unit level. Then the *gross income* from operating the kth firm at levels given by the vector x_k is $x_k c_k$, where $c_k = (\gamma_i^k)$. The cost of this operation, on the other hand, is equal to $x_k A_k p$ (where a negative cost corresponds to additional income). Clearly the firm will try to act so as to maximize its *profit* given by the expression $x_k(c_k - A_k p)$. In other words, given the price vector p, the kth firm acts so as to solve the standard maximum problem of finding a nonnegative vector x_k such that

$$x_k(c_k - A_k p) \text{ is a maximum} \tag{3}$$

subject to condition (1).

But now observe that if each of the m firms acts so as to solve the above programming problem the vectors $x_k A_k$ obtained will in general not satisfy condition (2); that is, the inputs demanded by the various firms may not be compatible with the availability of resources, some of which will be "overdemanded," others "oversupplied." Classical economic doctrine now asserts that in accordance with "the law of supply and demand" the prices of the overdemanded goods will increase, thus reducing the demand for them, and eventually after a series of such price adjustments it is assumed that "equilibrium" prices will be found at which there is no excess demand for any resource. The distribution of resources induced by these equilibrium prices is what we have referred to as the solution of the allocation problem by means of free competition. Now if one is to have any faith in the competitive mechanism just described one must be convinced that the desired equilibrium prices actually exist. We shall use linear programming theory to prove the existence of such prices, a fact which is far from obvious in advance.

There is one additional requirement to be made on the equilibrium prices. We have remarked that the law of supply and demand requires the prices of overdemanded goods to increase. The same law also states traditionally that if a good is oversupplied then its price will drop. One might ask then for prices at which all resources are neither overdemanded nor oversupplied so that inequality (2) would become an equation. It turns out, however, that this is too much to ask and that such prices will not in general exist. It is easy to see why this should be. Imagine that in the production of gasoline one is forced also to produce petroleum jelly as a by-product. Suppose there is a much greater demand for gasoline than for petroleum jelly. Then in order to satisfy the demand for gasoline it may be necessary to over-produce petroleum jelly. Thus, because of the nature of the technology, it may happen that certain resources are not used up even at equilibrium. What then is to be done about the requirement that the price of oversupplied resources shall drop? The answer is the same as that given in discussing the equilibrium theorem of Chap. 1. We require that the equilibrium price of all oversupplied goods shall be zero. We are now prepared to formalize everything that has been said thus far.

Definition. A set of $m + 1$ vectors $(x_1, \ldots, x_m, p)$ is said to yield a *competitive equilibrium* if they satisfy relations (1), (2), and (3) and in addition

$$\sum_{k=1}^{m} x_k A_k v_j < \sigma_j \qquad \text{implies } \pi_j = 0 \qquad (4)$$

The vector p is called an *equilibrium price vector*.

We shall shortly prove the existence of a competitive equilibrium. Before doing so we make an important economic observation to the effect that if there is an equilibrium then resources will be distributed in such a way as to maximize the total gross return to the economy. Stated formally we have:

Theorem 3.4. *If (x_k, p) yields a competitive equilibrium then the vectors x_k maximize the function $\sum_{k=1}^{m} x_k c_k$ subject to constraints (1) and (2).*

Proof. Let x_k' be any set of vectors satisfying (1) and (2). Then from (3) we have

$$x_k(c_k - A_k p) \geqq x_k'(c_k - A_k p) \qquad \text{for all } k$$

Summing these inequalities on k gives

$$\Sigma x_k c_k - \Sigma x_k' c_k \geqq \Sigma x_k A_{kp} - \Sigma x_k' A_k p \qquad (5)$$

From (2) we know that $\Sigma x_k' A_k \leqq s$ so $\Sigma x_k' A_k p \leqq sp$. But from (2) and (4) it easily follows that $\Sigma x_k A_k p = sp$. Therefore, the right-hand side of (5) is nonnegative and hence $\Sigma x_k c_k \geqq \Sigma x_k' c_k$, proving the theorem.

We call attention to the remarkable economic content of this theorem. It says that if there is a competitive equilibrium (and we shall soon show that there is) then this equilibrium forces all firms to behave as though they all belonged to a single unit whose purpose was to maximize the gross value of output. Thus, while each firm is, as far as it is aware, acting in a purely selfish manner it is inadvertently cooperating with the rest of the economy to produce "as much as possible." A neater mathematical argument could hardly be found to support the philosophy that everything is for the best in this best of all possible, freely competitive, linear worlds!

In order to prove the existence of equilibrium we simply prove the converse of the above theorem and show that if vectors x_k solve the linear program of maximizing total gross return then the equilibrium prices appear in the solution of the dual problem. To use this approach we must know that the gross return cannot be made arbitrarily large. This is, of course, a very natural assumption to make. One way of assuring that it will be satisfied is to require that the set of solutions of inequalities (1) be bounded. This corresponds economically to assuming that because of plant capacity no activity can be operated at an arbitrarily high level. We now show:

Theorem 3.5. *If the total gross income of the economy is bounded above then there exists a competitive equilibrium.*[1]

Proof. We consider the standard maximum problem of finding nonnegative vectors x_k such that

$$\Sigma x_k c_k \text{ is a maximum} \tag{6}$$

subject to constraints (1) and (2), which for convenience we rewrite here:

$$x_k B_k \leqq b_k \qquad \text{for all } k \tag{1}$$

$$\sum_{k=1}^{m} x_k A_k \leqq s \tag{2}$$

Since (6) is bounded above, it attains its maximum for some set of vectors $\bar{x}_k$, and therefore the dual problem is also feasible. Hence from the duality theorem there exist nonnegative vectors $\bar{y}_1, \ldots, \bar{y}_m$ and p such that

$$B_k \bar{y}_k + A_k p \geqq c_k \qquad \text{for all } k \tag{7}$$

and

$$\Sigma \bar{y}_k b_k + ps = \Sigma \bar{x}_k c_k \tag{8}$$

[The inequalities (7) are simply the dual constraints to (1) and (2),

---

[1] For the benefit of readers familiar with such matters we point out that the competitive equilibrium described here is not a "general equilibrium" in the sense of Walras, for a general equilibrium would have to determine the prices of consumer goods as well as resources. Perhaps the most natural situation to which our theorem applies is that of a "semiplanned" economy in which the planners determine the prices of consumer goods but allow the competitive mechanism to determine the prices of resources. A rather spectacular consequence of our theorems is then the fact that the planners can effectively determine the output of the economy by suitably adjusting consumer prices and still preserve the profit motive as the incentive to individual firms!

as the reader will easily convince himself, while Eq. (8) is the condition that the two dual problems have the same value.]

We assert that the vectors $\bar{x}_k$ and p give the desired equilibrium. To show this, we must verify that $\bar{x}_k$ satisfies (3), that is, each $\bar{x}_k$ maximizes

$$x_k(c_k - A_k p)$$

subject to (1) above. The dual of this problem is that of finding a nonnegative y_k such that

$$y_k b_k \text{ is a minimum}$$

subject to

$$B_k y_k \geqq c_k - A_k p \tag{9}$$

Now the vector $\bar{x}_k$ is clearly feasible for this problem, and from (7) we see that $\bar{y}_k$ satisfies (9) and is therefore feasible for the dual problem. By the optimality criterion (Theorem 1.1, page 10) $\bar{x}_k$ will be optimal if

$$\bar{y}_k b_k = \bar{x}_k(c_k - A_k p) \tag{10}$$

To prove (10), note (Lemma 1.1, page 10) that $\bar{y}_k b_k \geqq \bar{x}_k(c_k - A_k p)$ or

$$0 \leqq \bar{y}_k b_k + \bar{x}_k A_k p - \bar{x}_k c_k \quad \text{for all } k \tag{11}$$

Summing (11) over all k gives

$$0 \leqq \Sigma \bar{y}_k b_k + (\Sigma \bar{x}_k A_k)p - \Sigma \bar{x}_k c_k \tag{12}$$

Now from (2) the right-hand side above is at most $\Sigma \bar{y}_k b_k + ps - \Sigma \bar{x}_k c_k$, but from (8) this expression is zero. It follows that equality holds in (12). But the right-hand side of (12) is the sum of the nonnegative terms on the right-hand side of (11). Therefore each such term is zero, which gives the desired equation (10).

Finally we note that the vectors $\bar{x}_k$ and p satisfy condition (4) concerning free goods, for this condition is precisely the statement of the equilibrium theorem applied to the constraints (2).

Let us summarize what has been shown. For a competitive economy in which each firm operates a set of linear activities it turns out that it is possible to assign prices to resources in such a way that, although each firm acts so as to maximize its profits, the demand for resources will not exceed the available supply.   Furthermore, at these prices the firms in maximizing their own profits will automatically be operating so as to maximize the value of the total output of the economy.

Bibliographical Notes

We have already given references in Chap. 1 for most of the material covered in this chapter.   The particular proof of the duality theorem given here is the same as that given by the author in [1].   The theorem on basic solutions is due to Dantzig [2].

The theorems on resource allocation and competitive equilibrium have not at the time of this writing appeared explicitly elsewhere in the literature, although the results themselves are probably familiar to many workers in the field.   A closely related result will be found in Koopmans [1], Theorem 5.12.

Exercises

1. Consider the linear program of finding a vector x unrestricted in sign such that

$$xc \text{ is a maximum} \tag{1}$$

subject to

$$xA = b \tag{2}$$

Show that the problem has a solution if and only if c is a linear combination of the columns of A.

2. Give an example of a standard 2×2 maximum problem in which neither the problem nor its dual is feasible.

3. Complete the proof of the equivalence of the standard and general maximum problems.

4. State and prove the equilibrium theorem for the general linear program.

5. Solve the following canonical maximum problem by computing all three of its basic solutions:

$$4\xi_1 + 2\xi_2 + \xi_3 = 4$$
$$\xi_1 + 3\xi_2 \quad\quad = 5$$
$$2\xi_1 + 3\xi_2 \quad\quad = \text{maximum}$$

Check by solving the dual.

6. Consider the canonical minimum problem of finding nonnegative numbers $\xi_0, \xi_1, \ldots, \xi_m$ which

$$\text{minimize } \xi_0 \tag{1}$$

subject to

$$\xi_0 b + \sum_{i=1}^{m} \xi_i a_i = b \tag{2}$$

Obtain a proof of Theorem 2.6 (page 44) by applying the duality theorem to this problem.

7. In Exercise 6 replace Eq. (2) by an inequality. Apply the duality theorem to obtain a proof of Theorem 2.8 (page 47).

8. Let X be the set of feasible vectors of a standard maximum problem and let $\bar{X}$ be the set of optimal vectors. Show that X and $\bar{X}$ are convex and if $\bar{x}$ is an extreme point of $\bar{X}$ it is also an extreme point of X.

The next two exercises depend on the following definition: Let φ be a function of two nonnegative vectors, x in R^m and y in R^n. The pair $(\bar{x}, \bar{y})$ is called a *saddle point* of the function if

$$\varphi(\bar{x}, y) \geq \varphi(\bar{x}, \bar{y}) \geq \varphi(x, \bar{y}) \qquad \text{for all } x, y \geq 0$$

9. If $\bar{x}$ and $\bar{y}$ are optimal vectors for a pair of dual standard programs show that $(\bar{x}, \bar{y})$ is a saddle point of the function defined by

$$\varphi(x, y) = xc + yb - xAy \qquad \text{for } x, y \geq 0$$

10. Prove that if $(\bar{x}, \bar{y})$ is a saddle point of the function φ of Exercise 9 then $\bar{x}$ and $\bar{y}$ are optimal vectors for the corresponding pair of dual standard programs.

11. Let (A, b, c) be a canonical maximum problem with value ω, and let c^k be a sequence of vectors approaching c [i.e., if $c^k = (\gamma_i^k)$ and $c = (\gamma_i)$ we assume that $\gamma_i^k \to \gamma_i$ for $i = 1, \ldots, m$]. Let ω_k be the value of the program (A, b, c^k). Show that ω_k approaches ω. (Hint: Use the fact that there are only a finite number of basic feasible vectors.)

12. In the previous exercise keep c fixed but let b^k be vectors approaching b. Prove again that ω_k approaches ω. (These exercises show that the value of a linear program depends *continuously* on the vectors b and c.)

13. Consider the following standard maximum problem: Find a nonnegative number ξ such that

$$\xi \text{ is a maximum} \tag{1}$$

subject to

$$\xi \leqq 1$$
$$\alpha\xi \leqq 0 \qquad (2)$$

where α is any nonnegative number. Show that, as α approaches zero, the value ω of the program changes *discontinuously*. (This shows that the value need not depend continuously on the matrix A.)

14. A function f of vectors x is called *subadditive* if

$$f(x_1 + x_2) \leqq f(x_1) + f(x_2) \qquad \text{for all } x_1, x_2$$

Prove that the value of a standard maximum problem is a subadditive function of the vector c.

15. The function f of the preceding exercise is called *superadditive* if

$$f(x_1 + x_2) \geqq f(x_1) + f(x_2) \qquad \text{for all } x_1, x_2$$

Prove that the value of a standard maximum problem is a super-additive function of the vector b.

16. Consider a diet problem in which it is required to satisfy each of the nutrient requirements exactly (as equations rather than inequalities), and suppose a certain optimal diet uses only the foods F_1, F_2, ... , F_k. Now suppose the requirements are changed but can still be satisfied by some diet using this same set of foods. Prove that this new diet is automatically optimal (use the equilibrium theorem).

17. Prove: If a diet problem with n foods and m nutrients has a solution, then there is an optimal diet using at most m foods.

18. Consider the following general maximum problem:

$$\text{to maximize } cx \qquad (1)$$

subject to

$$xA = b \qquad (2)$$

and

$$d \leqq x \leqq e \qquad \text{where } d = (\delta_i) \qquad e = (\epsilon_i) \qquad (3)$$

Prove that $\bar{x} = (\xi_i)$ is an optimal vector if and only if there exists a vector $\bar{y}$ such that

$$\text{if } a_i\bar{y} < \gamma_i \qquad \text{then } \xi_i = \epsilon_i \qquad (4)$$
$$\text{if } a_i\bar{y} > \gamma_i \qquad \text{then } \xi_i = \delta_i \qquad (5)$$

(Hint: First show that $\bar{x}$ is optimal if and only if there exists an n-vector $\bar{y}$ and nonnegative m-vectors $\bar{z}$ and $\bar{w}$ such that $A\bar{y} + \bar{z} - \bar{w} = c$ and $\bar{x}c = \bar{y}b + \bar{z}e - \bar{w}d$.)

19. Consider the general problem of maximizing xc where x is subject to arbitrary linear constraints. Now alter c by increasing γ_1

only.   If $x = (\xi_i)$ is optimal for the original problem and $x' = (\xi_i')$ is optimal for the altered problem, show that $\xi_1' \geq \xi_1$.

20. Consider an "economy" in which there are two goods and two firms each of which has at its disposal one activity given by the vectors a_1 and a_2, respectively, where

$$a_1 = (2, 1) \qquad a_2 = (2, 3)$$

and the respective rates of return are

$$\gamma_1 = 3 \qquad \gamma_2 = 4$$

and the available resources are

$$\sigma_1 = 3 \qquad \sigma_2 = 4$$

Because of limitations of plant capacity the activities are able to operate at maximum intensities of one unit.

Find a competitive equilibrium by giving (a) the equilibrium prices, (b) the values of the activity levels at equilibrium, (c) the total gross return to the economy at equilibrium.   Answer to (c): $5\frac{1}{2}$.

21. In an economy with three firms and three goods the activity vectors (one for each firm) are

$$a_1 = (-5, 2, 1) \qquad a_2 = (2, -3, 1) \qquad a_3 = (0, 2, -3)$$

and the rates of return are

$$\gamma_1 = 2 \qquad \gamma_2 = 0 \qquad \gamma_3 = 1$$

There are no external resources, and activities may be operated at a maximum intensity of 1.

Show that the intensities $\xi_1 = \frac{7}{8}$, $\xi_2 = 1$, $\xi_3 = \frac{5}{8}$ yield an equilibrium for the model by finding the corresponding equilibrium prices. Note that only the second activity is operated at full intensity although its rate of return is zero.   Explain.

CHAPTER FOUR

Computation.   The Simplex Method

In the preceding chapter we have developed in some detail the theory
of linear programming.   In Chap. 2 by way of background material
we were forced to investigate rather extensively a purely mathematical
topic, the theory of linear inequalities.   Most of our theorems have
been concerned with the existence of solutions, be they to programs,
equations, or inequalities, and the properties possessed by these solutions.   We have not been concerned thus far with the question of
how to obtain the solutions in practical cases.   It is time now that
we turned our attention to these matters, and accordingly this chapter
will be devoted to giving an introduction to the subject of computational methods.   We emphasize the word introduction, for the
amount of work which has been and is being done on computational
problems is already enormous and is growing constantly.   This work
is concerned, however, not so much with the theory of linear models
as with practical applications and as such lies outside our present
domain of investigation.

Our objective for this chapter is limited.   We should like to enable
the reader to solve programs with about the same degree of proficiency
with which a high-school student solves systems of simultaneous linear
equations.   We shall definitely not be concerned with problems of
large-scale computation or high-speed calculators.   In practice, of
course, actual problems are almost inevitably beyond the range of
hand computation, and often even of the fastest machines.   Compu-

tation is important, however, in a book of this sort as a means of illuminating theoretical results by providing concrete illustrations. Further, the computational procedures themselves rely heavily on the theory and hence provide additional useful applications of it.

1. Solving Simultaneous Equations and Inverting a Matrix

As a first topic we shall treat the very elementary and well-known problem of solving simultaneous linear equations. The method is the familiar one of simple elimination. However, we shall look at the problem from a point of view which is slightly different from the usual one, but more easily applicable to the problems to be treated in the sections to follow.

Problem.   Given the $m \times n$ matrix A and the n-vector b, find an m-vector x such that

$$xA = b$$

This is, of course, the linear-equation problem in matrix form. For our immediate purposes we prefer the following vector formulation.

Problem.   Given $m + 1$ vectors in R^n, $a_1, \ldots, a_m$, and b, express the vector b (if possible) as a linear combination of the vectors a_i.

We now describe our method for solving this problem. Initially, we do not know an expression for b as a linear combination of the a_i. However, we can express b as a linear combination of one set of vectors, namely, the unit vectors $v_1, \ldots, v_n$ of R^n. In fact, if $b = (\beta_1, \ldots, \beta_n)$ then

$$b = \beta_1 v_1 + \cdots + \beta_n v_n \tag{1}$$

The procedure is now to replace the vectors v_j one at a time by vectors a_i. We might, for instance, attempt to replace v_1 by a_1, thus getting an expression for b as a linear combination of $a_1, v_2, \ldots, v_n$.

$$b = \beta_1' a_1 + \beta_2' v_2 + \cdots + \beta_n' v_n \tag{2}$$

Assuming we have obtained an expression (2), we then try to replace another unit vector v_j by some vector a_i and proceed until eventually all the vectors v_j have been replaced by the vectors a_i, in which case the problem is solved. The efficiency of the method lies in the fact that the computational step from (1) to (2) above is very simple to perform and easy to describe.   In order to do so, we shall investigate a slightly more general situation.

Definition. Let $a_1, \ldots, a_m$ be a set of linearly independent vectors, and let $b_1, \ldots, b_n$ be a set of vectors each of which is a linear combination of the a_i.   The *tableau* of the vectors b_j with respect to the *basis* a_i is the matrix T expressing each of the b_j as a linear combination of the a_i.   It is written thus:

$$
\begin{array}{c|ccccc}
 & b_1 & \cdots & b_j & \cdots & b_n \\
\hline
a_1 & \tau_{11} & \cdots & \tau_{1j} & \cdots & \tau_{1n} \\
\vdots & \vdots & & \vdots & & \vdots \\
a_i & \tau_{i1} & \cdots & \tau_{ij} & \cdots & \tau_{in} \\
\vdots & \vdots & & \vdots & & \vdots \\
a_m & \tau_{m1} & \cdots & \tau_{mj} & \cdots & \tau_{mn}
\end{array} = T
$$

The coordinate τ_{ij} is the coefficient of a_i in the expression for b_j, that is,

$$
b_j = \sum_{i=1}^{m} \tau_{ij} a_i
$$

The fundamental computational step in what follows is what we have chosen to call the *replacement operation*.   Suppose in the above tableau we try to replace the vector a_r in the basis by the vector b_s. What will the new tableau look like?   This tableau is written out below:

$$
\begin{array}{c|ccccc}
 & b_1 & \cdots & b_s & \cdots & b_n \\
\hline
a_1 & \tau'_{11} & \cdots & 0 & \cdots & \tau'_{1n} \\
\vdots & \vdots & & \vdots & & \vdots \\
b_s & \tau'_{r1} & \cdots & 1 & \cdots & \tau'_{rn} \\
\vdots & \vdots & & \vdots & & \vdots \\
a_m & \tau'_{m1} & \cdots & 0 & \cdots & \tau'_{mn}
\end{array} = T'
$$

What we wish to do is describe the numbers τ'_{ij} of the new tableau in terms of the τ_{ij} of the original. The result we need is the following.

Theorem 4.1 (replacement operation). *If $\tau_{rs} \neq 0$ in the tableau T then the vectors $a_1, \ldots, a_{r-1}, b_s, a_{r+1}, \ldots, a_m$ form a basis and the entries in the new tableau T' are given by the rules*

$$\tau'_{ij} = \tau_{ij} - \frac{\tau_{is}}{\tau_{rs}}\tau_{rj} \qquad \text{for } i \neq r \tag{1}$$

$$\tau'_{rj} = \frac{\tau_{rj}}{\tau_{rs}} \tag{2}$$

Formulas (1) and (2) perhaps look more complicated than they really are. There is a very easy way to remember them. Some readers may be familiar with the notion of an *elementary row operation* on a matrix. Such an operation consists simply in adding a multiple of one row of a matrix to another. These operations are used in evaluating determinants, solving equations, and so on. It is usually desirable to perform the elementary operations so as to obtain a large number of zeros in the matrix. This is exactly what Eqs. (1) and (2) above prescribe. To see this, let t_i and t'_i denote the ith row of T and T', respectively. Formulas (1) and (2) are equivalent to the following:

Replacement Rule. *To obtain the tableau T' from the tableau T,*

$$\text{Add multiples of } t_r \text{ to each of the other rows} \atop \text{of } T \text{ so as to obtain zeros in the sth column.} \tag{1'}$$

$$\text{Divide } t_r \text{ by } \tau_{rs}. \tag{2'}$$

The reader will immediately verify that (1') and (2') are equivalent to (1) and (2).

Proof of Theorem 4.1. To show that the vectors $a_1, \ldots, a_{r-1}, b_s, a_{r+1}, \ldots, a_m$ are independent, assume that

$$\sum_{i \neq r} \lambda_i a_i + \mu_s b_s = 0 \tag{3}$$

Now from the tableau T we read

$$b_s = \sum_{i=1}^{m} \tau_{is} a_i \tag{4}$$

and combining (3) and (4) gives

$$\sum_{i \neq r} (\lambda_i + \mu_s \tau_{is}) a_i + \mu_s \tau_{rs} a_r = 0 \tag{5}$$

Since the a_i are independent, all coefficients in (5) are zero. In particular $\mu_s \tau_{rs} = 0$ and since $\tau_{rs} \neq 0$ this means $\mu_s = 0$; hence also all λ_i are zero, establishing the asserted independence.

We must now show that

$$b_j = \sum_{i \neq r} \tau'_{ij} a_i + \tau'_{rj} b_s \tag{6}$$

where the coefficients above are defined by (1) and (2). Expanding the right-hand side of (6) gives

$$\sum_{i \neq r} \tau'_{ij} a_i + \tau'_{rj} b_s = \sum_{i \neq r} \left(\tau_{ij} - \frac{\tau_{is}}{\tau_{rs}} \tau_{rj} \right) a_i + \frac{\tau_{rj}}{\tau_{rs}} b_s$$

$$= \sum_{i \neq r} \left(\tau_{ij} - \frac{\tau_{is}}{\tau_{rs}} \tau_{rj} \right) a_i + \frac{\tau_{rj}}{\tau_{rs}} \left(\sum_{i=1}^{m} \tau_{is} a_i \right) \quad \text{[from (4)]}$$

Now, collecting coefficients of a_i gives

$$\sum_{i \neq r} \tau_{ij} a_i + \tau_{rj} a_r = b_j$$

and this proves (6).

The nonzero entry τ_{rs} of the tableau T is often referred to as the *pivot* element for the given replacement.

Let us apply the replacement procedure at once to solve the following simultaneous equations:

$$2\xi_1 + 3\xi_2 - \xi_3 = 1$$
$$\xi_1 \qquad + 2\xi_3 = -2$$
$$\xi_1 + \xi_2 + \xi_3 = 2$$

In vector form we have

$$\xi_1 a_1 + \xi_2 a_2 + \xi_3 a_3 = b$$

where
$$a_1 = (2, 1, 1)$$
$$a_2 = (3, 0, 1)$$
$$a_3 = (-1, 2, 1)$$
$$b = (1, -2, 2)$$

To obtain the initial tableau T_0 we express each of the four vectors in terms of the unit vectors u_1, u_2, u_3. Thus,

$$
T_0 \quad
\begin{array}{c|ccc|c}
 & a_1 & a_2 & a_3 & b \\
\hline
u_1 & 2 & 3 & -1 & 1 \\
u_2 & ① & 0 & 2 & -2 \\
u_3 & 1 & 1 & 1 & 2 \\
\end{array}
$$

Now, in the replacement operation we may use any nonzero entry in the tableau as a pivot. For computational reasons it is desirable when possible to choose the pivot to be $+1$ or -1 since this avoids the necessity of division. For the pivot here we have chosen the element r_{21}, which is circled in the tableau. Thus we are replacing u_2 by a_1. The replacement rule leads at once to the new tableau:

$$
T_1 \quad
\begin{array}{c|ccc|c}
 & a_1 & a_2 & a_3 & b \\
\hline
u_1 & 0 & 3 & -5 & 5 \\
a_1 & 1 & 0 & 2 & -2 \\
u_3 & 0 & ① & -1 & 4 \\
\end{array}
$$

Next we replace u_3 by a_2. The pivot element r_{32} has again been circled. We get

$$
T_2 \quad
\begin{array}{c|ccc|c}
 & a_1 & a_2 & a_3 & b \\
\hline
u_1 & 0 & 0 & ⦸-2 & -7 \\
a_1 & 1 & 0 & 2 & -2 \\
a_2 & 0 & 1 & -1 & 4 \\
\end{array}
$$

The final step is to replace u_1 by a_3, giving

$$
T_3 \quad
\begin{array}{c|ccc|c}
 & a_1 & a_2 & a_3 & b \\
\hline
a_3 & 0 & 0 & 1 & 7/2 \\
a_1 & 1 & 0 & 0 & -9 \\
a_2 & 0 & 1 & 0 & 15/2 \\
\end{array}
$$

and thus the solution is $x = (\xi_1, \xi_2, \xi_3) = (-9, 15/2, 7/2)$, as the reader will immediately verify.

The reader will note that the arithmetic steps we have just gone through are precisely those which would have been involved if we had solved the equations by elimination. The tableau T_1 would have been obtained by eliminating ξ_1 from Eqs. (1) and (3), and T_2 would have been obtained by further eliminating ξ_2 from Eq. (1), and so on. Our present point of view in terms of replacement may seem rather indirect. It will prove useful, however, in what follows when we discuss problems involving inequalities.

One more question remains to be settled. What happens in the replacement scheme if the equations have no solution? The answer is simple. We shall reach a stage in the process where it is not possible to replace any more unit vectors u_i by vectors a_j because all the tableau entries τ_{ij} are zero for u_i a unit vector and a_j in the given set of vectors. Clearly if the equations have no solution this must happen eventually, for if all the vectors u_i could be replaced we would necessarily end up with a solution of the problem. Conversely, if we do "get stuck" because no more replacements are possible, then we shall either already have a solution of the equations or else no solution exists. We leave the proof of this statement to the reader (see Exercise 2).

A final elementary but important application of the replacement operation is to the problem of inverting a matrix. Recall (Chap. 2, Exercise 9) that to each square matrix A which is *regular*, there corresponds a unique matrix A^{-1} such that $AA^{-1} = A^{-1}A = I$, where I is the identity matrix (Chap. 2, Exercise 8). Let us for the moment denote the jth column of A^{-1} by $c^j = (\gamma_{1j}, \ldots, \gamma_{mj})$. Then, from the definition of matrix multiplication,

$$Ac^j = u_j$$

where, as usual, u_j is the jth unit vector.

The above equation in vector form is

$$\sum_{k=1}^{m} \gamma_{kj} a^k = u_j$$

This shows that the matrix A^{-1} is precisely the tableau of the unit vectors $u_1, \ldots, u_m$ in terms of the columns $a^1, \ldots, a^m$ of the original matrix. This way of looking upon the inverse matrix makes it readily accessible to computation via the replacement operation. Rather than discuss the matter further, let us actually use the method to invert the matrix

$$A = \begin{pmatrix} 1 & 0 & -1 \\ 1 & 2 & 0 \\ 2 & -1 & 3 \end{pmatrix}$$

Now this matrix is, in fact, nothing more than the tableau of the vectors a^1, a^2, a^3 with respect to the unit vectors. Let us write it in this form and express the unit vectors themselves in the tableau. We then have the following tableau:

		a^1	a^2	a^3	u_1	u_2	u_3
	u_1	1	0	⊝1	1	0	0
T_0	u_2	1	2	0	0	1	0
	u_3	2	−1	3	0	0	1

The procedure is now to replace the vectors u_i by the vectors a^j in the by now familiar manner. We have circled the pivot element in the tableau above. We shall simply list the remaining tableaus, circling the appropriate pivot element in each case. We have then the following sequence of tableaus:

		a^1	a^2	a^3	u_1	u_2	u_3
	a^3	−1	0	1	−1	0	0
T_1	u_2	①	2	0	0	1	0
	u_3	5	−1	0	3	0	1
	a^3	0	2	1	−1	1	0
T_2	a^1	1	2	0	0	1	0
	u_3	0	⊝11	0	3	−5	1
	a^3	0	0	1	$-\frac{5}{11}$	$\frac{1}{11}$	$\frac{2}{11}$
T_3	a^1	1	0	0	$\frac{6}{11}$	$\frac{1}{11}$	$\frac{2}{11}$
	a^2	0	1	0	$-\frac{3}{11}$	$\frac{5}{11}$	$-\frac{1}{11}$

At each stage we then get expressions for the vectors u_i and a^j in terms of the current basis. Rearranging the last tableau we obtain the tableau for the u_i in terms of the a^j:

	u_1	u_2	u_3
a_1	$\frac{6}{11}$	$\frac{1}{11}$	$\frac{2}{11}$
a_2	$-\frac{3}{11}$	$\frac{5}{11}$	$-\frac{1}{11}$
a_3	$-\frac{5}{11}$	$\frac{1}{11}$	$\frac{2}{11}$

which is the desired inverse of A, as the reader will verify by direct multiplication.

2. The Simplex Method for Linear Programming. Discussion

We come now to describe one of the most celebrated computational procedures in recent mathematical history. Although the method was intended originally to solve linear programs, it has turned out to have much wider applicability. It is, for instance, the best general method known for solving linear inequalities or finding nonnegative solutions to linear equations. So successful has the simplex method been that many discussions of linear programming concern themselves chiefly with the method, and in fact, from the literature one might be led to believe that linear programming *is* the simplex method.

The simplex method can be treated from various points of view. It can be described and justified purely algebraically, and this we shall do. It can be motivated by economic considerations, and we shall briefly consider this aspect. Finally, it can be made plausible by means of geometric considerations. This last approach will not be attempted, but we hope the algebraic and economic interpretations of the method will be sufficient to give the reader a feeling for the general technique.

Let us then consider the canonical minimum problem: to find $y \geq 0$ such that

$$yb \text{ is a minimum} \tag{1}$$

subject to

$$Ay = c \tag{2}$$

In order to carry on the economic and algebraic discussion simultaneously, let us agree to interpret this problem as a diet problem in which it is required to meet the nutritional requirements exactly. We may imagine that a physician has determined precisely the right amount of each vitamin and mineral needed in the perfect diet, and the dietitian is required to choose a diet which provides these exact quantities of each nutrient—no more, no less.

The first question which arises is how to find some diet, not necessarily the cheapest one, which satisfies the requirements, or, in general, how to find a feasible vector, i.e., a nonnegative solution of (2). This is a serious problem in itself and will be taken up in Sec. 5. For our present purposes we shall assume that this problem has been solved so that we are able to find a nonnegative solution of (2), in fact, a basic nonnegative solution. Let this initial feasible vector y_0 depend on the basis, say $a^1, \ldots, a^m$. In nutritional terms, this means that our initial diet uses only the first m foods. We now consider the tableau T_0 of the columns of A and the vector c with respect to this basis:

		a^1	a^2	$\cdots$	a^m	$\cdots$	a^s	$\cdots$	a^n	c
	a^1	1	0	$\cdots$	0	$\cdots$	τ_{1s}	$\cdots$	τ_{1n}	η_1
T_0	a^2	0	1	$\cdots$	0	$\cdots$	τ_{2s}	$\cdots$	τ_{2n}	η_2
	$\cdot$	$\cdot$	$\cdot$		$\cdot$		$\cdot$		$\cdot$	$\cdot$
	$\cdot$	$\cdot$	$\cdot$		$\cdot$		$\cdot$		$\cdot$	$\cdot$
	$\cdot$	$\cdot$	$\cdot$		$\cdot$		$\cdot$		$\cdot$	$\cdot$
	a^m	0	0	$\cdots$	1	$\cdots$	τ_{ms}	$\cdots$	τ_{mn}	η_m

The procedure of the simplex method is now to obtain by a sequence of replacement operations new feasible vectors, until eventually an optimal vector is obtained. One could proceed by successive replacements to try *all* possible bases, and we know from Theorem 3.3 that eventually one would turn up an optimal vector. This procedure would, of course, be hopelessly inefficient and time-consuming. What the simplex method does is to give a criterion for deciding which replacement to make at each stage of the calculation so as to arrive at the optimal vector in an efficient manner. In the next paragraphs we shall describe and motivate this criterion with reference to the diet problem. This somewhat informal description will then be made precise in the next section.

The dietary interpretation of the tableau T_0 is simply this: We have a feasible diet which uses the first m foods in amounts $\eta_1, \ldots, \eta_m$. Assuming this diet is not optimal, we seek to replace some food in it by a food not in it in such a way as to decrease the cost. The problem is to decide (a) which new food to bring in and (b) which old food to replace. Let us therefore examine the food F_s, which, as the tableau shows, is not in the current diet, and try to decide whether it will be economical to bring this food into the new diet. To be very concrete, let us think of F_s as carrots. Now, in the tableau T_0 we have an expression for carrots as a linear combination of the foods in the current diet, that is, we have the algebraic relation

$$a^s = \sum_{i=1}^{m} \tau_{is} a^i \tag{3}$$

The dietary meaning of this relation is quite clear. It means that one carrot has exactly the same nutritive content as τ_{1s} units of F_1 plus τ_{2s} units of F_2, and so on. We may, in fact, think of the *menu vector* $(\tau_{1s}, \ldots, \tau_{ms})$ as *synthetic carrots*, for this particular combination of other foods acts just like a carrot nutritionally (although it probably tastes quite different). Let us now ask the question: Which costs more, a real carrot or a synthetic carrot? The cost of a real carrot is β_s. The cost of a synthetic carrot is ζ_s, where ζ_s is obviously given by the expression

$$\zeta_s = \sum_{i=1}^{m} \beta_i \tau_{is}$$

Our rule is simply this: If real carrots are cheaper than synthetic carrots (that is, if $\beta_s < \zeta_s$), then real carrots should be brought into the new diet. Otherwise, forget about carrots and go on to examine spinach.

This is clearly a sensible rule, for suppose β_s is less than ζ_s. Then if we bring in one carrot we can cut back the amount of synthetic carrots by one unit and this will save money. Let us agree, then, to bring in the new food F_s provided that β_s is less than ζ_s. If it should turn out that there is no food which satisfies this inequality then, as we shall show in the next section, we have already achieved the optimal diet.

In purely algebraic terms, the first half of our replacement criterion now reads:

(a) *Let ζ_j be the scalar product of the jth column of T_0 with the cost vector $(\beta_1, \ldots, \beta_m)$. If $\beta_j < \zeta_j$ for some j then bring a^j into the new basis.*

Assuming then that we have decided to bring carrots into the diet we must now determine which food it is to replace. From Eq. (3) we see that if we bring in η_s units of carrots we must cut back the amount of F_i by $\eta_s \tau_{is}$ units for $i = 1, \ldots, m$. Since the original diet contained η_i units of F_i we are then left with η_i' units of F_i, where

$$\eta_i' = \eta_i - \eta_s \tau_{is} \qquad i = 1, \ldots, m \tag{4}$$

Now, of course, we cannot allow any of the numbers η_i' to become negative, for it is clearly meaningless to use a negative amount of some food in a diet. The rule is therefore to make η_s as large as possible subject to the condition that none of the numbers η_i' become negative. If this is done it is clear that at least one of the new numbers η_i' will be zero (otherwise a further increase in η_s would be possible). If we can find which of the η_i' is zero then we shall know which food F_i to replace. But this is algebraically also very simple. We assert that η_i' will be zero for that index i for which τ_{is} is positive and η_i/τ_{is} is a minimum. Namely, we have

$$\eta_i' = \eta_i - \eta_s \tau_{is} \geq 0 \tag{5}$$

if and only if

$$\eta_s \leq \frac{\eta_i}{\tau_{is}} \qquad \text{for } \tau_{is} > 0 \tag{6}$$

so η_s can be as large as but no larger than the smallest of the terms on the right-hand side of inequality (6).

We can now state the second part of the replacement criterion.

(b) *Having decided to bring a^s into the new basis, compute the ratios η_i/τ_{is} for $\tau_{is} > 0$, and replace the vector a^r of the old basis for which this ratio is a minimum.*

In this section we have tried to supply the economic motivation for using replacement rules (a) and (b). We now turn to the problem of proving that these rules will indeed lead us to a solution of the problem.

3. Theory of the Simplex Method

We again consider the canonical minimum problem: Find $y \geq 0$ such that

$$yb \text{ is a minimum} \tag{1}$$

subject to

$$Ay = c \tag{2}$$

The first result to be proved will justify part (a) of the replacement criterion as described in the preceding section. Assume then that we have the basis $a^1, \ldots, a^p$, the corresponding feasible vector $y = (\eta_j)$, and the tableau T. We now assert

Theorem 4.2 (optimality criterion). *Let* $\zeta_j = \sum_{i=1}^{p} \beta_i \tau_{ij}$. *Then the feasible vector* y *is optimal if*

$$\zeta_j \leq \beta_j \tag{1}$$

for all $j = 1, \ldots, n$.

Proof. Suppose (1) is satisfied for all j. Since the vectors $a^1, \ldots, a^p$ are independent there exists an m-vector x such that $xa^j = \beta_j$ for $j = 1, \ldots, p$ (Corollary of Theorem 2.3, page 37). But for $j > p$ we have $xa^j = \sum_{i=1}^{p} \tau_{ij}(xa^i) = \sum_{i=1}^{p} \tau_{ij}\beta_i = \zeta_j \leq \beta_j$. Thus the vector x satisfies the dual constraints

$$xA \leq b$$

and furthermore $xa^j = \beta_j$ if $\eta_j > 0$. Therefore, from the Equilibrium Theorem 3.2 (page 82) y is an optimal vector (and incidentally x is optimal for the dual problem).

This theorem gives the required justification for replacement rule (a), as promised in the preceding section. We now make a useful observation in connection with rule (a) of the replacement criterion. We note that this rule requires us to calculate along with each tableau the quantities

$$\zeta_j = \sum_{i=1}^{p} \beta_i \tau_{ij} \tag{2}$$

It turns out, however, that in going from tableau T to T' we can compute the new quantities ζ_j' at the same time that we perform the replacement operation on the tableau T, as we now show.

Let us define an $(n + 1)$-vector z by the rule

$$z = (\zeta_1, \ldots, \zeta_n, \zeta_0)$$

where ζ_j is given by (2) above for $j \geq 1$ and

$$\zeta_0 = \sum_{i=1}^{p} \beta_i \eta_i \tag{3}$$

Note that ζ_0 is precisely the value of the linear function yb corresponding to the feasible vector $y = (\eta_j)$.

Let us now extend the tableau T by adding in the $(p+1)$st row the vector $z - b = (\zeta_1 - \beta_1, \ldots, \zeta_n - \beta_n, \zeta_0)$. The extended tableau now looks like this:

	a^1	$\cdots$	a^p	$\cdots$	a^s	$\cdots$	a^n	c
a^1	1	$\cdots$	0	$\cdots$	τ_{1s}	$\cdots$	τ_{1n}	η_1
.	.		.		.		.	.
.	.		.		.		.	.
.	.		.		.		.	.
a^r	0	$\cdots$	0	$\cdots$	(τ_{rs})	$\cdots$	τ_{rn}	η_r
.	.		.		.		.	.
.	.		.		.		.	.
.	.		.		.		.	.
a^p	0	$\cdots$	1	$\cdots$	τ_{ps}	$\cdots$	τ_{pn}	η_p
$z - b$	0	$\cdots$	0	$\cdots$	$\zeta_s - \beta_s$	$\cdots$	$\zeta_n - \beta_n$	ζ_0

Suppose next that we have decided to replace a^r in the basis by a^s (indicated by the circling of τ_{rs} above), thus leading to a new tableau T'. Denoting as before the ith row of T by t_i, we now assert:

Lemma 4.1. *The additional row $z' - b$ in the tableau T' is given by the rule*

$$z' - b = z - b - \frac{\zeta_s - \beta_s}{\tau_{rs}} t_r$$

The lemma shows that we obtain the row $z' - b$ just as we obtained all the other rows of T', namely, we subtract from $z - b$ the proper multiple of t_r so as to give a zero in the sth column.

Proof. By definition of z' and t'_i,

$$z' = \sum_{i \neq r}^{p} \beta_i t'_i + \beta_s t'_r = \sum_{i \neq r}^{p} \beta_i \left(t_i - \frac{\tau_{is}}{\tau_{rs}} t_r \right) + \frac{\beta_s}{\tau_{rs}} t_r$$

$$= \sum_{i=1}^{p} \beta_i t_i - \beta_r t_r - \left(\frac{1}{\tau_{rs}} \sum_{i \neq r}^{p} \beta_i \tau_{is} \right) t_r + \frac{\beta_s}{\tau_{rs}} t_r = z - \left(\frac{\zeta_s - \beta_s}{\tau_{rs}} \right) t_r$$

and the result follows on subtracting b from both sides of this equation.

We now return to our study of the simplex method and examine rule (b) of the replacement criterion, which says:

(b) *Having decided to bring a^s into the new basis, compute the ratios η_i/τ_{is} for $\tau_{is} > 0$ and replace that vector a^r of the old basis for which this ratio is a minimum.*

A possible difficulty might occur here if none of the numbers τ_{is} were positive.   In this case, however, we have the following result.

Lemma 4.2.   If in trying to apply (b) above it turns out that no number τ_{is} is positive, $i = 1, \ldots , p$, then the original problem has no minimum.

Proof.   Since a^s is to be brought into the new basis, we know that $\zeta_s > \beta_s$ [by rule (a)].   Next, from the definition of the quantities in the tableau, we have

$$c = \sum_{i=1}^{p} \eta_i a^i \tag{1}$$

and

$$0 = a^s - \sum_{i=1}^{p} \tau_{is} a^i \tag{2}$$

Multiplying (2) by any positive number λ and adding to (1) gives

$$c = \lambda a^s + \sum_{i=1}^{p} (\eta_i - \lambda \tau_{is}) a^i$$

and since by assumption the numbers τ_{is} are nonpositive, this gives a new feasible solution of the original problem.   The corresponding value of the linear form being minimized is

$$\lambda \beta_s + \sum_{i=1}^{p} (\eta_i - \lambda \tau_{is}) \beta_i = \sum_{i=1}^{p} \eta_i \beta_i + \lambda (\beta_s - \zeta_s)$$

But in the last term on the right $\beta_s - \zeta_s$ is negative and λ can be made arbitrarily large; so the problem has no minimum.

To complete our discussion we must show that repeated replacements using rules (a) and (b) will eventually give a tableau satisfying the optimality criterion.   The proof turns out to be much easier if we make a certain assumption of *nondegeneracy* on the matrix A.   Letting p be the rank of A, we require the

(H) Nondegeneracy Hypothesis. It is not possible to express the vector c as a linear combination of fewer than p columns of A.

The assumption is not very restrictive. In fact, if the hypothesis should fail to be satisfied an arbitrarily small change in the vector c can be made, giving a vector c' which does satisfy (H). When (H) fails to hold, however, it is necessary to modify rule (b) of the replacement criterion in order to assure that the method will terminate. This question of "degeneracy" will be taken up in Sec. 7.

The key result needed to prove the convergence of the simplex procedure is the following:

Theorem 4.3 (improvement process). *Under hypothesis (H) if a replacement is made in accordance with rules (a) and (b), then the new basis obtained will again be feasible and the corresponding value ζ'_0 of the form being minimized will be smaller than the previous value ζ_0.*

Proof.   To establish the feasibility of the new basis we must show that the numbers η'_i of T' are nonnegative. Suppose a^s is replacing a^r. We then have

$$\eta'_i = \eta_i - \frac{\tau_{is}}{\tau_{rs}} \eta_r \qquad \text{for } i \neq r \tag{1}$$

If τ_{is} is not positive then clearly $\eta'_i \geqq 0$ (since $\tau_{rs} > 0$). If τ_{is} is positive, we have from rule (b)

$$\frac{\eta_i}{\tau_{is}} \geqq \frac{\eta_r}{\tau_{rs}}$$

so once again η'_i is nonnegative.

Next, from Lemma 4.1, we know that

$$\zeta'_0 = \zeta_0 - \frac{\zeta_s - \beta_s}{\tau_{rs}} \eta_r$$

We now use hypothesis (H) to assert that η_r is positive (otherwise we would have a feasible solution depending on fewer than p columns of A). Also $\zeta_s - \beta_s$ is positive from rule (a); hence

$$\zeta'_0 < \zeta_0$$

completing the proof.

This result shows that we shall after a finite number of replacements arrive at the desired minimum, for the value ζ_0 decreases with each replacement; hence we can never get the same basis more than once and must eventually arrive at the optimal basis.

4. Some Numerical Examples

It is now high time we illustrated the simplex method with some concrete examples. We start with a canonical minimum problem.

Example 1. Find $y = (\eta_1, \ldots, \eta_5) \geq 0$ which minimizes

$$\eta_1 + 6\eta_2 - 7\eta_3 + \eta_4 + 5\eta_5 \tag{1}$$

subject to

$$5\eta_1 - 4\eta_2 + 13\eta_3 - 2\eta_4 + \eta_5 = 20$$
$$\eta_1 - \eta_2 + 5\eta_3 - \eta_4 + \eta_5 = 8 \tag{2}$$

The example is the same as Example 1 of the previous chapter. The matrix A is

$$A = \begin{pmatrix} 5 & -4 & 13 & -2 & 1 \\ 1 & -1 & 5 & -1 & 1 \end{pmatrix}$$

Our first problem is to find a feasible solution of (2). Let us therefore use the replacement operation to solve this system. As in Sec. 1, our initial tableau with respect to the unit vectors is

		a^1	a^2	a^3	a^4	a^5	c
T_0	u_1	5	-4	13	-2	1	20
	u_2	1	-1	5	-1	①	8

and a convenient pivot element has been circled. The indicated replacement gives

T_1	u_1	④	-3	8	-1	0	12
	a^5	1	-1	5	-1	1	8

If we next use the pivot indicated above we get a nonnegative solution of the given equations, namely, $\eta_1 = 3$, $\eta_5 = 5$,

T_2	a^1	1	$-\frac{3}{4}$	2	$-\frac{1}{4}$	0	3
	a^5	0	$-\frac{1}{4}$	3	$-\frac{3}{4}$	1	5

and we are now ready to proceed with the simplex method. As a first step we must obtain the extended tableau by computing the row $z - b$, where $z = \beta_1 t_1 + \beta_5 t_2$, t_1 and t_2 being the first and second rows above. This gives

$$z = (1, -2, 17, -4, 5, 28)$$

and

$$z - b = (0, -8, 24, -5, 0, 28)$$

so the expanded tableau becomes

		a^1	a^2	a^3	a^4	a^5	c
	a^1	1	$-\tfrac{3}{4}$	②	$-\tfrac{1}{4}$	0	3
T'_2	a^5	0	$-\tfrac{1}{4}$	3	$-\tfrac{3}{4}$	1	5
	$z - b$	0	-8	24	-5	0	28

The only positive term in the last row (except for the term ζ_0) is 24 in column 3. According to replacement rule (a), therefore, we should bring a^3 into the next basis. In order to determine which basis vector to replace we compute the ratios η_i / τ_{ij} for $j = 3$. Thus

$$\frac{\eta_1}{\tau_{13}} = \frac{3}{2} \qquad \frac{\eta_5}{\tau_{53}} = \frac{5}{3}$$

Since $\tfrac{3}{2} < \tfrac{5}{3}$, we must according to rule (b) replace the vector a^1. An application of this replacement operation on T'_2 gives

		a^1	a^2	a^3	a^4	a^5	c
	a^3	$\tfrac{1}{2}$	$-\tfrac{3}{8}$	1	$-\tfrac{1}{8}$	0	$\tfrac{3}{2}$
T'_3	a^5	$-\tfrac{3}{2}$	⑦⁄₈	0	$-\tfrac{3}{8}$	1	$\tfrac{1}{2}$
	$z - b$	-12	1	0	-2	0	-8

The only positive entry in the last row is the 1 in column 2; hence a^2 must come into the next basis. The only positive entry τ_{21} is $\tfrac{7}{8}$ in the second row. Hence a^5 is replaced. The appropriate pivot, $\tfrac{7}{8}$, has been circled. The next replacement gives

		a^1	a^2	a^3	a^4	a^5	c
	a^3	$-\tfrac{1}{7}$	0	1	$-\tfrac{2}{7}$	$\tfrac{3}{7}$	$\tfrac{12}{7}$
T'_4	a^2	$-\tfrac{12}{7}$	1	0	$-\tfrac{3}{7}$	$\tfrac{8}{7}$	$\tfrac{4}{7}$
	$z - b$	$-\tfrac{72}{7}$	0	0	$-\tfrac{11}{7}$	$-\tfrac{8}{7}$	$-\tfrac{69}{7}$

and now we note with pleasure that there are no positive terms in the last row, and hence from the optimality criterion the solution is given by

$$\bar{y} = (0, \tfrac{4}{7}, 1\tfrac{2}{7}, 0, 0)$$
$$\bar{y}b = -\tfrac{60}{7}$$

Example 2. Consider the following standard maximum problem: Find nonnegative numbers ξ_1, ξ_2, ξ_3, ξ_4 such that

$$2\xi_1 + 4\xi_2 + \xi_3 + \xi_4 \qquad (1)$$

is a maximum subject to

$$
\begin{aligned}
\xi_1 + 3\xi_2 \qquad\quad + \xi_4 &\leq 4 \\
2\xi_1 + \xi_2 \qquad\qquad\quad &\leq 3 \qquad (2)\\
\xi_2 + 4\xi_3 + \xi_4 &\leq 3
\end{aligned}
$$

The given vectors are then

$$a_1 = (1, 2, 0) \qquad a_2 = (3, 1, 1) \qquad a_3 = (0, 0, 4) \qquad a_4 = (1, 0, 1)$$

and

$$b = (4, 3, 3)$$

and so (2) can be rewritten

$$\xi_1 a_1 + \xi_2 a_2 + \xi_3 a_3 + \xi_4 a_4 \leq b \qquad (3)$$

In order to convert this to a problem with equations instead of inequalities, we adjoin the unit vectors v_1, v_2, v_3 and write

$$\xi_1 a_1 + \xi_2 a_2 + \xi_3 a_3 + \xi_4 a_4 + \lambda_1 v_1 + \lambda_2 v_2 + \lambda_3 v_3 = b \qquad (4)$$

where all ξ_i and λ_j are to be nonnegative. Now it is a trivial matter to find our initial feasible solution to (4), for we simply take the unit vectors as our starting basis and get for the initial tableau

		a_1	a_2	a_3	a_4	b	v_1	v_2	v_3
	v_1	1	3	0	1	4	1	0	0
T_0	v_2	2	1	0	0	3	0	1	0
	v_3	0	1	4	①	3	0	0	1
	$z - c$	-2	-4	-1	-1	0	0	0	0

Note that the last row consists of the vector $-c$ since all the quantities ζ_j are zero because the numbers γ_i corresponding to v_1, v_2, v_3 are all zero. Since we are now maximizing instead of minimizing we look for negative rather than positive entries in the last row of the tableau. All coefficients are negative, and therefore we may bring any of the vectors a_i into the next basis. To avoid getting involved with fractions we shall bring in a_4. Since $\frac{3}{1} < \frac{4}{1}$ we must then replace v_3 and the new tableau is

		a_1	a_2	a_3	a_4	b	v_1	v_2	v_3
	v_1	①	2	-4	0	1	1	0	-1
T_1	v_2	2	1	0	0	3	0	1	0
	a_4	0	1	4	1	3	0	0	1
	$z-c$	-2	-3	3	0	3	0	0	1

We may next bring in either a_1 or a_2. In order again to avoid fractions we choose a_1, which must then replace v_1 as indicated.

		a_1	a_2	a_3	a_4	b	v_1	v_2	v_3
	a_1	1	2	-4	0	1	1	0	-1
T_2	v_2	0	-3	⑧	0	1	-2	1	2
	a_4	0	1	4	1	3	0	0	1
	$z-c$	0	1	-5	0	5	2	1	-1

We may now bring in either a_3 or v_3. We choose a_3 (an often used rule is to bring in the vector a_j for which ζ_j is most negative). We replace v_2 and get

		a_1	a_2	a_3	a_4	b	v_1	v_2	v_3
	a_1	1	$\frac{1}{2}$	0	0	$\frac{3}{2}$	0	$\frac{1}{2}$	0
T_3	a_3	0	$-\frac{3}{8}$	1	0	$\frac{1}{8}$	$-\frac{1}{4}$	$\frac{1}{8}$	$\frac{1}{4}$
	a_4	0	⑤½	0	1	$\frac{5}{2}$	1	$-\frac{1}{2}$	0
	$z-c$	0	$-\frac{7}{8}$	0	0	$4\frac{5}{8}$	$\frac{3}{4}$	$\frac{5}{8}$	$\frac{1}{4}$

At this point we have no choice. The pivot is indicated.

		a_1	a_2	a_3	a_4	b	v_1	v_2	v_3
	a_1	1	0	0	$-\frac{1}{5}$	1	$-\frac{1}{5}$	$\frac{3}{5}$	0
T_4	a_3	0	0	1	$\frac{3}{20}$	$\frac{1}{2}$	$-\frac{1}{10}$	$\frac{1}{20}$	$\frac{1}{4}$
	a_2	0	1	0	$\frac{2}{5}$	1	$\frac{2}{5}$	$-\frac{1}{5}$	0
	$z-c$	0	0	0	$\frac{7}{20}$	$13\frac{1}{2}$	$\frac{11}{10}$	$\frac{9}{20}$	$\frac{1}{4}$

Since there are now no negative entries in the last row, it follows from the optimality criterion that the solution is given by

$$\bar{x} = (1, 1, \tfrac{1}{2}, 0) \qquad \bar{x}c = 13\tfrac{1}{2}$$

This example illustrates another very important feature of the simplex method, which is the fact that the tableau T_4 contains not only the solution of the given problem but also the solution of the dual! The entries in the last row under the columns headed v_1, v_2, and v_3 provide this solution, as we easily verify, for let $y = (1\tfrac{1}{10}, \tfrac{9}{20}, \tfrac{1}{4})$. Then

$$
\begin{aligned}
1\tfrac{1}{10} + 2(\tfrac{9}{20}) &= & 2 &\geqq 2 \\
3(1\tfrac{1}{10}) + \tfrac{9}{20} + \tfrac{1}{4} &= & 4 &\geqq 4 \\
4(\tfrac{1}{4}) &= & 1 &\geqq 1 \\
1\tfrac{1}{10} \quad\quad + \tfrac{1}{4} &= 2\tfrac{7}{20} &\geqq 1
\end{aligned}
$$

so y is feasible for the dual problem, and also

$$yb = 1\tfrac{1}{10}(4) + \tfrac{9}{20}(3) + \tfrac{1}{4}(3) = 130\tfrac{}{20} = 13\tfrac{1}{2}$$

so y is also optimal.

This property of the simplex method is extremely important computationally for it provides us with a short independent method of checking our solution.

Of course, it is no accident that the solution of the dual problem drops out in this convenient way. The reason for this is most easily seen if we return to the canonical minimum problem with constraints given by

$$Ay = c \tag{1}$$

We shall assume at this point that the matrix A has rank m (this condition is easily removed, as we shall see in the last section). Let us now suppose that we have an optimal solution depending, say, on the vectors $a^1, \ldots, a^m$, so that the final tableau then looks like this:

	a^1	$\cdots$	a^m	$\cdots$	a^n	c	u_1	$\cdots$	u_m
a^1	1	$\cdots$	0	$\cdots$	τ_{1n}	η_1	λ_{11}	$\cdots$	λ_{1m}
$\cdot$	$\cdot$		$\cdot$		$\cdot$	$\cdot$	$\cdot$		$\cdot$
$\cdot$	$\cdot$		$\cdot$		$\cdot$	$\cdot$	$\cdot$		$\cdot$
$\cdot$	$\cdot$		$\cdot$		$\cdot$	$\cdot$	$\cdot$		$\cdot$
a^m	0	$\cdots$	1	$\cdots$	τ_{mn}	η_m	λ_{m1}	$\cdots$	λ_{mm}
$z - b$	0	$\cdots$	0	$\cdots$	$\zeta_n - \beta_n$	ζ_0	ξ_1	$\cdots$	ξ_m

where the unit vectors have been included as the last m column headings of the tableau. Denoting by A_m the matrix consisting of the first m columns of A, we see that the square matrix $L = (\lambda_{ij})$ is precisely the inverse of A_m (see Sec. 1). The numbers $\xi_1, \ldots, \xi_m$ in the tableau are, of course, defined by

$$\xi_j = \sum_{i=1}^{m} \beta_i \lambda_{ij} \tag{2}$$

We now assert that the vector $x = (\xi_1, \ldots, \xi_m)$ solves the dual problem. To see this, let b_m denote the vector consisting of the first m coordinates of b; thus

$$b_m = (\beta_1, \ldots, \beta_m) \qquad x = (\xi_1, \ldots, \xi_m)$$

Then from the tableau, $x = b_m L$, or since $L = A_m^{-1}$ we have $xA_m = b_m$, or

$$xa^j = \beta_j \qquad \text{for } j \leqq m \tag{3}$$

For $j > m$ we have

$$a^j = \sum_{i=1}^{m} \tau_{ij} a^i$$

Hence

$$xa^j = \sum_{i=1}^{m} \tau_{ij}(xa^i) = \sum_{i=1}^{m} \tau_{ij}\beta_i = \zeta_j \tag{4}$$

this last equality being the definition of ζ_j. Now, since we assumed $a_1, \ldots, a_m$ to be an optimal basis the optimality criterion is satisfied; hence $\zeta_j - \beta_j \leqq 0$ for all j, whence, from (4),

$$xa^j \leqq \beta_j \qquad \text{for } j > m \tag{5}$$

Together, (3) and (5) show that x is a feasible vector for the dual problem. Also, since equality (3) holds for all indices j for which a^j is in the basis, we know from the Equilibrium Theorem 3.2 that x is in fact optimal.

The proof that this same method provides the solution of the dual problem for the standard as well as canonical problem is obtained by converting the standard problem to a canonical one. Thus suppose the given problem is to find a nonnegative y which

$$\text{minimizes } yb \tag{1}$$

subject to

$$Ay \geq c \tag{2}$$

The equivalent canonical problem replaces (2) by

$$Ay - z = c \qquad z \geq 0 \tag{2'}$$

The simplex method will, as we have just seen, produce a vector x which solves the dual problem, hence satisfies the dual constraints

$$xA \leq b \qquad -xu_i \leq 0 \qquad i = 1, \ldots, m \tag{2'}*$$

but these last inequalities show that x is nonnegative, hence provides a solution of the dual of the original standard problem.

5. Nonnegative Solutions of Linear Equations

So far in describing the simplex method we have assumed that we already had an initial basic feasible vector, that is, a basic nonnegative solution of

$$xA = b \tag{1}$$

We must now show how such a vector may be found. One possible procedure would be to try to compute all basic solutions of (1) in an effort to find one which is nonnegative. If, however, m is much larger than n, i.e., if there are many more unknowns than equations, this enumeration becomes prohibitively time-consuming. An efficient method for solving the problem consists in making it into a canonical minimum problem. First, one can always arrange for the vector b to be nonnegative, by suitably changing signs of equations. Now consider the problem of finding nonnegative vectors x and y such that

$$yv \text{ is a minimum} \qquad \text{(where } v \text{ is the unit vector in } R^n) \tag{2}$$

subject to

$$xA + y = b \tag{3}$$

Clearly, (1) has a nonnegative solution if and only if the minimum value of (2) is zero, in which case the minimizing y will be zero and the minimizing x will solve (1). Let us see at once how this simple device works in a concrete instance.

Example 3.   Find $x = (\xi_1, \xi_2, \xi_3, \xi_4) \geqq 0$ such that

$$\xi_1 \qquad\quad - \xi_3 + 4\xi_4 = 3$$
$$2\xi_1 - \xi_2 \qquad\qquad = 3$$
$$3\xi_1 - 2\xi_2 \qquad - \xi_4 = 1$$

The corresponding linear program is now to find nonnegative x and $y = (\eta_1, \eta_2, \eta_3)$ such that

$$\eta_1 + \eta_2 + \eta_3 \text{ is a minimum} \tag{1}$$

subject to

$$\xi_1 \qquad\quad - \xi_3 + 4\xi_4 + \eta_1 \qquad\qquad = 3$$
$$2\xi_1 - \xi_2 \qquad\qquad\quad + \eta_2 \qquad = 3 \tag{2}$$
$$3\xi_1 - 2\xi_2 \qquad - \xi_4 \qquad\qquad + \eta_3 = 1$$

The initial tableau takes the unit vectors v_1, v_2, v_3 as a basis. The tableau sequence follows:

	a_1	a_2	a_3	a_4	b	v_1	v_2	v_3
v_1	1	0	-1	4	3	1	0	0
v_2	2	-1	0	0	3	0	1	0
v_3	③	-2	0	-1	1	0	0	1
$z - c$	6	-3	-1	3	7	0	0	0

with T_0 labelling this initial tableau.

We remark that the vector c in this case is the 7-vector $c = (0, 0, 0, 0, 1, 1, 1)$.

	a_1	a_2	a_3	a_4	b	v_1	v_2	v_3
v_1	0	ⓔ $\tfrac{2}{3}$	-1	$\tfrac{13}{3}$	$\tfrac{8}{3}$	1	0	$-\tfrac{1}{3}$
v_2	0	$\tfrac{1}{3}$	0	$\tfrac{2}{3}$	$\tfrac{7}{3}$	0	1	$-\tfrac{2}{3}$
a_1	1	$-\tfrac{2}{3}$	0	$-\tfrac{1}{3}$	$\tfrac{1}{3}$	0	0	$\tfrac{1}{3}$
$z - c$	0	1	-1	5	5	0	0	-2

	a_1	a_2	a_3	a_4	b	v_1	v_2	v_3
a_2	0	1	$-\tfrac{3}{2}$	$\tfrac{13}{2}$	4	$\tfrac{3}{2}$	0	$-\tfrac{1}{2}$
v_2	0	0	ⓔ $\tfrac{1}{2}$	$-\tfrac{3}{2}$	1	$-\tfrac{1}{2}$	1	$-\tfrac{1}{2}$
a_1	1	0	-1	4	3	1	0	0
$z - c$	0	0	$\tfrac{1}{2}$	$-\tfrac{3}{2}$	1	$-\tfrac{3}{2}$	0	$-\tfrac{3}{2}$

	a_1	a_2	a_3	a_4	b	v_1	v_2	v_3
a_2					7			
a_3					2			
a_1					5			
$z - c$	0	0	0	0	0	-1	-1	-1

In the final tableau we have calculated only the last row and the column headed by b, since the optimality criterion is now satisfied. One easily verifies that the vector $x = (5, 7, 2, 0)$ provides the desired nonnegative basic solution.

6. Solving Linear Inequalities

As a final application of the simplex method we consider the problem of solving a system of linear inequalities

$$xA \leqq b \qquad (1)$$

We solve this problem by reducing it to that of the previous section, making use of Theorem 2.7 (page 46) on solution of linear inequalities. The theorem asserts that (1) has no solution if and only if the equations

$$Ay = 0 \qquad by = -1 \qquad (2)$$

have a nonnegative solution. The answer to this question can be obtained by solving the canonical problem of

$$\text{minimizing } \eta \qquad (3)$$

subject to

$$\begin{aligned} Ay &= 0 \\ by - \eta &= -1 \end{aligned} \qquad (4)$$

where, as usual, y and η are required to be nonnegative. Now, in case the minimum value of η should be zero then the original inequalities have no solution. If, on the other hand, the minimum value of η is positive then the solution of the dual problem provides us with a vector x and number λ such that

$$\begin{aligned} xA + \lambda b &\leqq 0 \\ -\lambda &\leqq 1 \end{aligned}$$

and $-\lambda$ is positive; hence $x/(-\lambda)$ solves the original problem (1), as one immediately verifies. Thus, we attack (1) by solving the problem (3), (4), keeping an eye on the solution of the dual problem.

Example 4. Solve

$$-2\xi_1 + 2\xi_2 \leq -1$$
$$2\xi_1 - \xi_2 \leq 2$$
$$- 4\xi_2 \leq 3$$
$$-15\xi_1 - 12\xi_2 \leq -2$$
$$12\xi_1 + 20\xi_2 \leq -1$$

As shown in the previous paragraph we consider the canonical program of finding nonnegative numbers $\eta_0, \eta_1, \ldots, \eta_5$ which

$$\text{minimize } \eta_0$$

subject to

$$-2\eta_1 + 2\eta_2 \qquad - 15\eta_4 + 12\eta_5 = 0$$
$$2\eta_1 - \eta_2 - 4\eta_3 - 12\eta_4 + 20\eta_5 = 0 \qquad (5)$$
$$-\eta_0 - \eta_1 + 2\eta_2 + 3\eta_3 - 2\eta_4 - \eta_5 = -1$$

Taking the unit vectors as initial basis the initial tableau is

	a_0	a_1	a_2	a_3	a_4	a_5	c	u_1	u_2	u_3
u_1	0	-2	2	0	-15	12	0	1	0	0
u_2	0	2	⊖1	-4	-12	20	0	0	1	0
u_3	-1	-1	2	3	-2	-1	-1	0	0	1

T_0 is the label for this tableau.

Notice that $a_0 = -u_3$ so that replacing u_3 by a_0 simply changes the signs in the last row of the tableau. Next replace u_2 by a_2, and then u_1 by a_1 as indicated by the usual circles in the tableaus.

	a_0	a_1	a_2	a_3	a_4	a_5	c	u_1	u_2	u_3
u_1	0	②	0	-8	-39	52	0	1	2	0
a_2	0	-2	1	4	12	-20	0	0	-1	0
a_0	1	-3	0	5	26	-39	1	0	-2	-1

T_1 is the label for this tableau.

	a_0	a_1	a_2	a_3	a_4	a_5	c	u_1	u_2	u_3
a_1	0	1	0	-4	$-39/2$	㉖	0	$1/2$	1	0
a_2	0	0	1	-4	$- 27$	32	0	1	1	0
a_0	1	0	0	-7	$-65/2$	39	1	$3/2$	1	-1
$z - b$	0	0	0	-7	$-65/2$	39	1	$3/2$	1	-1

T_2 is the label for this tableau.

In the tableau T_2 we have added the row $z - b$ in order to start the simplex procedure. Notice that the vector b is given by $b =$

$(1, 0, 0, 0, 0, 0)$ and the vector z is exactly the same as the a_0-row of the tableau. Now the only positive entry in the last row of T_2 is the number 39 in column 5; so we must bring a_5 into the new basis. Next, according to replacement rule (b) we seek the minimum ratio η_i/τ_{ij}. In this case $0/26$ and $0/32$ are zero; so we may replace either a_1 or a_2. We have chosen to replace a_1 because as we see in the following tableau this makes all entries of the last row nonpositive and hence satisfies the optimality criterion. We have

	a_0	a_1	a_2	a_3	a_4	a_5	c	u_1	u_2	u_3
a_5							0			
a_2							0			
a_0							1			
$z - b$	0	$-\tfrac{3}{2}$	0	-1	$-1\tfrac{3}{4}$	0	1	$\tfrac{3}{4}$	$-\tfrac{1}{2}$	-1

where again we have calculated only the relevant final values.

What does this final tableau tell us? Recall that we have been looking for a solution to Eqs. (5) which minimizes η_0. We now see that the minimum value of η_0 is 1. Therefore, from the theory developed in the first part of this section we know that the original set of inequalities has a solution which is given by the solution of the dual linear program. This solution is given by

$$x = (\tfrac{3}{4}, \ -\tfrac{1}{2})$$

as one easily verifies.

Note that this solution gives equality in the second and fifth inequalities, corresponding to the fact that a_2 and a_5 occurred in the final basis of our linear program.

7. Degeneracy. The Generalized Simplex Method

In this section we shall deal exclusively with the canonical minimum problem: Find $y \geqq 0$ such that

$$yb \text{ is a minimum} \tag{1}$$

subject to

$$Ay = c \tag{2}$$

There are two types of degeneracy which will concern us: first, when the rank of A is less than m; second, when the degeneracy hypothesis (H) is not satisfied. The first of these situations can be handled quite simply. The second is considerably more involved.

If the matrix A has rank p less than m this means that the rows a_i of A are linearly dependent and that it is possible to find p rows, say $a_1, \ldots, a_p$, such that the remaining rows are linear combinations of these. Once we have found these rows we may replace (2) by the set of p equations

$$a_i y = \gamma_i \qquad i = 1, \ldots, p \qquad (3)$$

for it follows from what we have said that any vector y which satisfies Eqs. (3) must also satisfy $a_i y = \gamma_i$ for $i > p$; hence y satisfies (2). Having reduced (2) to the smaller system (3) we proceed to solve the p by n rather than the m by n problem where the new matrix A_p has rank equal to its number of rows.

The problem of finding a row basis for A is easily solved by the replacement method. Namely, write out the initial tableau of the rows a_i with respect to the unit vectors u_i. The tableau is, in fact, simply the transpose of A. Now proceed to replace the vectors u_i by vectors a_k until no further replacements are possible. We assert that the vectors a_k in the basis at this point will be a row basis for A. The proof is left to the reader (see Exercise 12).

We should remark here that the computation of the row basis for A is done almost automatically along with the construction of the initial feasible vector y by the method described in Sec. 5, so that almost no extra computation is needed when A has rank lower than m.

We shall assume from now on that A has rank m, and turn to the more difficult problem of what to do when hypothesis (H) fails to hold. In order to understand the difficulty we must look back and see precisely where (H) was used in our discussion. This happened at only one place, namely, in the proof of Theorem 4.3 on the improvement process. In this connection, recall rule (b) of the replacement criterion. Having decided to bring the vector a^s into the new basis, rule (b) tells us to look at the ratios η_i / τ_{is} with $\tau_{is} > 0$, and to replace the vector a_i for which this ratio is minimal. Now, if (H) holds, we know that all η_i are positive; hence the minimum ratio is positive and therefore we are able to show that after replacement of a^r by a^s a new feasible vector y' is obtained such that $y'b$ is less than yb, where y was the original feasible vector.   In case (H) is not satisfied the minimum of η_i/τ_{is} may be zero, in which case Theorem 4.3 is no longer true. The application of rule (b) may not yield an improved solution, and it is possible that one might continue making replacements indefinitely without getting a decrease in the form to be minimized (in this connection, however, the reader should note the remark at the end of this section).

The dilemma we have just described is solved by giving a somewhat more elaborate version of part (b) of the replacement criterion and then proving a variation of Theorem 4.3.   For this purpose we must introduce a new way of ordering the vectors of R^m.

Definition.   Given $x = (\xi_i)$ in R^m, we say x is *lexicographically positive*, written

$$x \succ 0$$

if $x \neq 0$ and the first nonvanishing coordinate of x is positive.

We can now order all vectors in R^m by the *lexicographic rule*

$$x \succ y \qquad \text{if } x - y \succ 0$$

In other terms, if i is the smallest index such that $\xi_i \neq \eta_i$ then $\xi_i > \eta_i$.

It is a simple matter to show that the relation $\succ$ is a proper ordering.   That is, if $x \succ y$ and $y \succ z$ then $x \succ z$, and so on.   These verifications will be left as exercises.

Let us now return to the canonical minimum problem and suppose we have a feasible basis, say $a^1, \ldots, a^m$.   We write out the extended tableau:

		a^1		a^n	c	u_1		u_m
	a^1	1	$\cdot\ \cdot\ \cdot$	τ_{1n}	η_1	λ_{11}	$\cdots$	λ_{1m}
	$\cdot$	$\cdot$		$\cdot$	$\cdot$	$\cdot$		$\cdot$
T	$\cdot$	$\cdot$		$\cdot$	$\cdot$	$\cdot$		$\cdot$
	$\cdot$	$\cdot$		$\cdot$	$\cdot$	$\cdot$		$\cdot$
	a^m	0	$\cdot\ \cdot\ \cdot$	τ_{mn}	η_m	λ_{m1}	$\cdots$	λ_{mm}
	$z - b$	$\zeta_1 - \beta_1$	$\cdot\ \cdot\ \cdot$	$\zeta_n - \beta_n$	ζ_0	ξ_1	$\cdots$	ξ_m

We now define the vector q_i to consist of the last $m + 1$ entries in the ith row of T.   Thus,

$$q_i = (\eta_i, \lambda_{i1}, \ldots, \lambda_{im})$$

and define q by

$$q = (\zeta_0, \xi_1, \ldots, \xi_m)$$

We shall say that the basis $a^1, \ldots, a^m$ is *strongly feasible* if each of the vectors q_i is lexicographically positive, that is,

$$q_i > 0$$

Note that if (H) holds then all the numbers η_i are positive so that every feasible basis is strongly feasible.   If for some i, η_i is zero we are requiring that the first nonzero entry λ_{ij} be positive.   We now give a new form of rule (b) of the replacement criterion as follows:

(b') *If a^s is the new vector to be brought into the basis compute the vectors q_i/τ_{is} for $\tau_{is} > 0$ and replace the vector a_i for which q_i/τ_{is} is minimal in the lexicographic ordering.*

We now give the corresponding new version of the improvement process.

Theorem 4.4.   *If a replacement is made in accordance with rules (a) and (b') the new basis obtained is again strongly feasible, and the vector q' in the new tableau T' satisfies*

$$q > q'$$

Let us observe first that this result shows that eventually the simplex algorithm will terminate, for since the vector q gets lexicographically smaller with each replacement it follows that we cannot get the same basis twice, so that eventually we must come to a basis for which the optimality criterion is satisfied.

Proof.   First note that in applying rule (b') there will be only one index i for which q_i/τ_{is} is a lexicographic minimum; for if $q_i/\tau_{is} = q_k/\tau_{ks}$ then q_i and q_k would be proportional, but this would mean that the matrix (λ_{ij}) is singular, which is impossible since it is the inverse matrix of the basis.   Therefore, if a^r is to be replaced, we have

$$\frac{q_k}{\tau_{ks}} > \frac{q_r}{\tau_{rs}} \qquad \text{for all } \tau_{ks} > 0 \tag{1}$$

Now in the replacement operation $q'_r = \dfrac{1}{\tau_{rs}} q_r$ and since $q_r > 0$ and $\tau_{rs} > 0$, it follows that $q'_r > 0$. Also

$$q'_k = q_k - \frac{\tau_{ks}}{\tau_{rs}} q_r \qquad (2)$$

and if $\tau_{ks} \leqq 0$ then clearly $q'_k > 0$, while if $\tau_{ks} > 0$, then

$$q'_k = \tau_{ks} \left(\frac{q_k}{\tau_{ks}} - \frac{q_r}{\tau_{rs}} \right)$$

and from (1) the term in parentheses is again lexicographically positive. This shows that the new basis is strongly feasible. Finally, note that

$$q' = q - \frac{\zeta_s - \beta_s}{\tau_{rs}} q_r$$

and since $\zeta_s - \beta_s > 0$ [from rule (a)] it follows that $q > q'$.

The only remaining gap in the theory is to show that we can obtain an initial strongly feasible basis. The method here is precisely like that of Sec. 5. Given the problem of finding a strongly feasible basis for the equation

$$Ay = c \qquad (3)$$

we consider first the problem of finding nonnegative y and z which

$$\text{minimize } zu \qquad (4)$$

subject to

$$Ay + z = c \qquad (5)$$

where we are assuming now that c is nonnegative (a harmless assumption since it can be achieved by simple sign changes).

For (5) we have the obvious strongly feasible initial basis consisting of the unit vectors $u_1, \ldots, u_m$. The new improvement process justified by Theorem 4.4 will eventually eliminate all the u_i from our basis and thus supply us with a strongly feasible basis for Eq. (3). We have shown now that this generalized simplex method as modified by rule (b') will solve any linear programming problem, degenerate or not.

Remarks. The situation regarding degeneracy is rather curious. In practice many realistic linear programs do turn out to be degenerate.   Despite this fact the generalized simplex method described above is, in fact, never used in actual computation.   Instead one proceeds to use the original simple form of replacement rules (a) and (b).   Now, if the problem is degenerate it may and often does happen that the "improvement process" fails to give an improvement.   Namely, if the minimum of the ratios η_i/τ_{is} is zero then replacing a^s by a^r will *not* decrease the linear function yb.   The practical rule is to make the replacement anyway.   Eventually it has always been found that after a number of these "no improvement" replacements it will again be possible either (1) to make a replacement which gives a positive improvement or (2) to satisfy the optimality criterion.

Let us ask now what could go wrong with the crude procedure just described.   It is conceivable that one could go on making replacements indefinitely without either (1) or (2) above being satisfied. This would happen if the successive replacements produced "cycling," that is, if the same sequence of bases kept recurring.   Examples of programs have been constructed for which such cycling does actually occur.   However, to date the only programs which have cycled are ones which were deliberately constructed so as to do so.   From a practical point of view, therefore, it has not been necessary to use the generalized simplex method in actual computations, and the reader is advised, in solving numerical exercises, to proceed using rules (a) and (b) with the assurance that everything will turn out all right.

Of course, our primary interest in this volume is a theoretical rather than a practical one, and for this reason it was necessary for us to treat the case of degeneracy.   It is a somewhat upsetting fact to the mathematician that quite frequently computational schemes which can be shown not to work in general will nevertheless give the desired answers in a vast majority of practical cases.   It is this feature of computational techniques which has led people to remark that computation is in some respects an art rather than a science.

Bibliographical Notes

The simplex method for solving linear programs is due to Dantzig. His fundamental paper [2] treats the nondegenerate case.   The first published treatment of degeneracy is due to Charnes [1]. The treatment of degeneracy presented here is modeled after that of Dantzig, Orden, and Wolfe [1].

Exercises

1. Consider the following tableau:

		a^1		a^m		a^j		a^n
	a^1	1	$\cdots$	0	$\cdots$	τ_{1j}		τ_{1n}
		.		.		.		.
		.		.		.		.
		.		.		.		.
T	a^i	0	$\cdots$	0	$\cdots$	τ_{ij}	$\cdots$	τ_{in}
		.		.		.		.
		.		.		.		.
		.		.		.		.
	a^m	0	$\cdots$	1	$\cdots$	τ_{mj}		τ_{mn}

Show that if $\tau_{ij} = 0$ then the vectors $a^1, \ldots a^{i-1}, a^i, a^{i+1}, \ldots a^m$ are dependent.

2. In solving the equation $xA = b$ suppose we have arrived at the following tableau:

	a_1	$\cdots$	a_k	$\cdots$	a_m	b
a_1	1	$\cdots$	τ_{1k}	$\cdots$	τ_{1m}	ξ_1
	.		.		.	.
	.		.		.	.
	.		.		.	.
a_r	0	$\cdots$	τ_{rk}	$\cdots$	τ_{rm}	ξ_r
u_1	0	$\cdots$	σ_{1k}	$\cdots$	σ_{1m}	δ_1
	.		.		.	.
	.		.		.	.
	.		.		.	.
u_s	0	$\cdots$	σ_{sk}	$\cdots$	σ_{sm}	δ_s

Prove that if no further replacements of the u_i are possible then either the numbers $\xi_1, \ldots, \xi_r$ solve the given equation or else there is no solution.

3. Consider the canonical problem

$$\text{maximize } xu_1 \tag{1}$$

subject to

$$xA = b \qquad (2)$$

where

$$A = \begin{pmatrix} 1 & 0 \\ 1 & 1 \\ 0 & 1 \end{pmatrix} \qquad b = (1, 0)$$

a. Construct the tableau for this problem with respect to the basis a_1, a_2.

b. Show that the corresponding solution of (2) is optimal although the optimality criterion of Theorem 4.2 is *not* satisfied.

c. Find a new basis for which the optimality criterion is satisfied.

4. Show that for a linear program satisfying the nondegeneracy hypothesis any optimal basis satisfies the optimality criterion of Theorem 4.2.

5. Rewrite the final tableau for Example 1 of the text including two additional columns for the unit vectors and thus find the solution of the dual problem.

6. Solve by the simplex method:

$$\xi_1, \xi_2, \xi_3 \geq 0$$
$$3\xi_1 + 4\xi_2 + \xi_3 \leq 25$$
$$\xi_1 + 3\xi_2 + 3\xi_3 \leq 50$$
and
$$8\xi_1 + 19\xi_2 + 7\xi_3 = \text{maximum}$$

Check by means of the dual.

7. Maximize

$$\xi_1 + 750\xi_2 + 10\xi_3 \qquad (1)$$

subject to

$$0.15\xi_1 + 75\xi_2 + 1.3\xi_3 \leq 2$$
$$0.10\xi_1 + 170\xi_2 + 1.1\xi_3 \leq \tfrac{5}{3} \qquad (2)$$
$$\xi_1, \xi_2, \xi_3 \geq 0$$

8. Maximize

$$\xi_1 + 3\xi_2 + \xi_3 \qquad (1)$$

subject to

$$5\xi_1 + 3\xi_2 \qquad \leq 3$$
$$\xi_1 + 2\xi_2 + 4\xi_3 \leq 4 \qquad (2)$$

9. Find a nonnegative solution to the equations

$$5\xi_1 + \xi_2 + 6\xi_3 \qquad - 5\xi_5 = 2$$
$$-7\xi_1 - \xi_2 - 2\xi_3 + \xi_4 + 2\xi_5 = -5$$

10. Use the method of Sec. 5 to find a feasible solution for Example 1 of Sec. 4.

11. Solve the inequalities

$$
\begin{aligned}
5\xi_1 + 4\xi_2 - 7\xi_3 &\leqq \ \ 1 \\
-\xi_1 + 2\xi_2 - \ \ \xi_3 &\leqq -4 \\
-3\xi_1 - 2\xi_2 + 4\xi_3 &\leqq \ \ 3 \\
3\xi_1 - 2\xi_2 - 2\xi_3 &\leqq -7
\end{aligned}
$$

12. Prove that a row basis for A is obtained if we start with the tableau

	a_1		a_m
u_1	τ_{11}	$\cdots$	τ_{1m}
.	.		.
.	.		.
.	.		.
u_m	τ_{m1}	$\cdots$	τ_{mm}

and replace vectors u_i in any manner until no further replacements are possible.

13. Find a row basis for the following matrix:

$$
\begin{pmatrix}
1 & 0 & 3 & -2 \\
2 & 1 & 2 & 0 \\
0 & 1 & -4 & 4 \\
1 & 1 & 1 & -2 \\
1 & 0 & 1 & 2
\end{pmatrix}
$$

14. Show that the lexicographic ordering satisfies the following conditions:

a. For any two distinct vectors x and y either $x > y$ or $y > x$.

b. If $x > y$ and $y > z$ then $x > z$.

c. If $x > y$ and $z > w$ then $x + z > y + w$.

d. If $x > y$ and $\lambda > 0$ then $\lambda x > \lambda y$.

CHAPTER FIVE

Integral Linear Programming

In this chapter we shall consider a special but important class of linear programs in which the optimal vectors are required to have integral coordinates. Such problems are of obvious practical significance. For example, solutions of a production problem in which the output is some indivisible good, such as an automobile or a radio, would clearly have to satisfy the requirement that solutions be integral. There is at the present time no general theory which covers all such integral problems, although some highly ingenious computational devices have been invented for obtaining numerical solutions.[1] This topic, however, is beyond the range of our present study. On the other hand, for a restricted but highly important class of integral problems a very complete and elegant theory does exist and it is this theory which will be developed here. The theory is essentially independent of the general theory of linear programming treated in Chap. 3, so that mathematically the present chapter is nearly self-contained. As usual, we introduce the subject by a set of examples.

1. Examples

Example 1. Transportation Problem with Indivisible Commodity. This is simply the transportation problem as described in Example 2 of Chap. 1 except that the commodity to be shipped, instead of being "continuously divisible" such as steel, comes in dis-

[1] See especially R. E. Gomory: Outline of an Algorithm for Integer Solutions to Linear Programs, *Bull. Amer. Math. Soc.*, vol. 64, no. 5, 1958.

crete amounts as, for instance, automobiles. The constraints and function to be minimized are just as before, but only integral values of the variables ξ_{ij} are admissible. We shall give a detailed treatment of this problem in Sec. 7.

Example 2. The Optimal-assignment Problem. Suppose a certain factory has n different jobs to fill, denoted by $J_1, \ldots, J_n$, and suppose m different applicants $I_1, \ldots, I_m$ are possible candidates for each of the jobs. Suppose further that each applicant is given an aptitude test which provides quantitative information as to his fitness for each of the n jobs. Specifically, let α_{ij} be a nonnegative number giving the *rating* of I_i for the job J_j. It is then desired to assign individuals to jobs in such a way as to maximize effectiveness as measured by the sum of the ratings (see Chap. 1, Exercise 17).

At first glance this does not appear to be a linear programming problem at all. Since there are but a finite number of possible assignments of individuals to jobs it is only necessary to examine all possible assignments, choosing the one for which the sum of the ratings is a maximum. Of course the number of possible assignments is very large when m and n are large (if $m = n$ the number is $n!$), so that this enumeration becomes computationally infeasible. Instead, therefore, let us consider the integral linear program of finding nonnegative *integers* ξ_{ij} which

$$\text{maximize} \sum_{i,j} \alpha_{ij}\xi_{ij} \qquad (1)$$

subject to

$$\sum_{i=1}^{m} \xi_{ij} \leqq 1 \qquad j = 1, \ldots, n$$

$$\sum_{j=1}^{n} \xi_{ij} \leqq 1 \qquad i = 1, \ldots, m \qquad (2)$$

Suppose now we have a solution to this problem. Since the numbers ξ_{ij} are integers they must from (2) be either 0 or 1. From the solution of the program we immediately obtain an optimal assignment by assigning I_i to J_j if and only if $\xi_{ij} = 1$. Conditions (2) assure that this will indeed give an assignment, for the first inequality shows that at most one individual is assigned to a job and the second shows that no one is assigned to more than one job.

We shall see in the course of the chapter that the above formulation of the assignment problem brings moderate-sized examples within easy range of hand computation.

Example 3.   The Loading Problem.   An airplane is able to carry M lb.   There is a given collection of n objects; the ith object weighs α_i and its value is β_i.   How should the plane be loaded so as to maximize the value of its cargo without exceeding the weight limit?

Here again is a question which could be settled by direct enumeration.   One simply examines in turn each of the 2^n possible sets of objects, and among those which do not exceed the weight limit one selects the most valuable.   The difficulty again is, of course, the magnitude of the quantity 2^n.   The equivalent linear program is easily seen to be: Find nonnegative integers ξ_i such that

$$\Sigma \xi_i \beta_i \text{ is a maximum} \tag{1}$$

subject to

$$\xi_i \leq 1$$
$$\Sigma \xi_i \alpha_i \leq M \tag{2}$$

The theory to be developed in this chapter unfortunately does *not* apply to this problem, and indeed at the time of this writing no significant theory for this problem exists.   We mention it here to indicate what seems an interesting direction for future research.

2. *Flows in Networks*

The transportation problem is the prototype for all the problems considered in this chapter.   However, for the applications we have in mind it will be necessary to generalize the notion in several directions.   Let us recall the simple graphical picture corresponding to the problem and illustrated for a particular case in Fig. 1.1.   We associated with each plant P_i and market M_j a *node* or *vertex* of a *graph* and with each pair of nodes (P_i, M_j) we associated an *edge* directed from P_i to M_j with a cost γ_{ij}.   The situation is illustrated in Fig. 5.1.

Now in practice it may often happen that it is not possible to ship directly from every plant to every market. This suggests that in general not all the edges (P_i, M_j) will belong to the graph. A graph with three plants and three markets might, for instance, look like the one shown in Fig. 5.2.

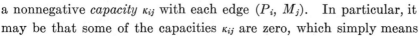

Let us now further suppose that there is an upper bound to the amount that can be shipped along a given edge. This is certainly in accordance with reality since an actual transportation system can accommodate only a limited amount of cargo during a fixed time period. We therefore associate

FIG. 5.1

a nonnegative *capacity* κ_{ij} with each edge (P_i, M_j). In particular, it may be that some of the capacities κ_{ij} are zero, which simply means that it is not possible to ship from P_i to M_j.

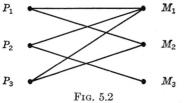

FIG. 5.2

As a final generalization let us remove the requirements that every node of the transportation graph be either a plant or market. If we think of actual rail networks it is clear that frequently in shipping from one city to another one may have to ship through a number of intermediate cities. A general *capacitated* transportation graph might look like the one in Fig. 5.3, where the numbers on the edges now represent capacities rather than costs.

We are now prepared to give an abstract definition of a network.

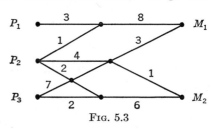

FIG. 5.3

In the definition all nodes will be treated alike; that is, we do not specify whether a given node is a plant, market, or intermediate point.

Definition. A *capacitated network* (N, k) consists of a finite set N of *nodes* which will be denoted by the letters x, y, etc. An ordered pair of nodes (x, y) is called an *edge* of the network. The *capacity function k* attaches to each edge (x, y) a nonnegative integer $k(x, y)$.

Remark. In Fig. 5.3 we attached numbers to "nonoriented" edges, the implication being that the capacity is the same regardless of the direction in which the edge is traversed. In the definition above no such requirement of symmetry is imposed. Some of the edges might, for instance, be "one-way streets."

We next formalize the idea of a shipping schedule, or a *flow* as we shall call it.

Definition. A *flow* in the network (N, k) is a function f which attaches an integer $f(x, y)$ to each *edge* (x, y) of the network and satisfies

$$f(x, y) = -f(y, x) \qquad \text{(skew symmetry)} \qquad (1)$$
$$f(x, y) \leqq k(x, y) \qquad \text{(feasibility)} \qquad (2)$$

The meaning of condition (2) is obvious: The flow along an edge must not exceed the capacity of that edge. Condition (1) is simply a useful convention. To illustrate its purpose, suppose under a given shipping schedule an amount α was sent from x to y and at the same time an amount β was sent from y to x. Since we are interested here only in *net* flows, the significant fact is that under this schedule the net flow from x to y is $\alpha - \beta$ and from y to x is $\beta - \alpha$. The skew-symmetry convention allows us to replace the two parameters α and β by the single parameter $\alpha - \beta$.

At this point we shall introduce a notational device which will save us writing many summation signs in the arguments that follow.

Notation. If A is a subset of N and g is a function on N, we define

$$g(A) = \sum_{x \varepsilon A} g(x)$$

If h is a function on edges (x, y) and A and B are subsets of N, we define

$$h(A, B) = \sum_{x \varepsilon A, y \varepsilon B} h(x, y)$$

We shall make frequent use of the following properties which follow at once from the definition of the above notations:

If $A, B, C \subset N$ and $A \cap B$ is empty, then (g and h being as above)[1]

[1] The set-theoretic symbols are those introduced in Sec. 5 of Chap. 2.

$$g(A \cup B) = g(A) + g(B)$$
$$h(A \cup B, C) = h(A, C) + h(B, C) \tag{i}$$
and
$$h(C, A \cup B) = h(C, A) + h(C, B) \tag{ii}$$

In the notation just defined, conditions (1) and (2) on flows are equivalent to

$$f(A, A) = 0 \qquad \text{for all } A \subset N \tag{1'}$$
$$f(A, B) \leqq k(A, B) \qquad \text{for all } A, B \subset N \tag{2'}$$

This set notation is a very natural one for flow problems, for note that $f(A, B)$ represents the net flow from A to B, and $k(A, B)$ is the total capacity of edges starting in A and ending in B.

Let us now consider the problem of shipping from a specified node s called a *source* to another specified node s' called a *sink*, where the nodes s and s' may be connected by an arbitrarily complicated intermediate network. The *maximum-flow problem* is that of determining how much can be shipped from s to s'. We formalize this as follows:

Definition. A node s in N is called a *source for the flow f* if $f(s, N) > 0$. A node s' is called a *sink for the flow f* if $f(s', N) < 0$. A flow with a single source s and sink s' is called a *flow from s to s'*.

We remark that, if f is a flow from s to s', then $f(x, N) = 0$ for all x other than s or s'. Also $f(s, N) = f(N, s')$ (i.e., whatever flows out of the source flows into the sink). This follows by a simple algebraic argument using condition (1') above (see Exercise 1). The *value* of the flow f is the number $f(s, N) = f(N, s')$, and a flow whose value is as large as possible is called a *maximal flow*.

One more notion is needed in order to treat the maximum-flow problem.

Definition. A *cut in the network N with respect to s and s'* is a partition of the nodes N into two sets S and S' (i.e., $S \cup S' = N$, $S \cap S'$ is empty) such that

$$s \varepsilon S \qquad \text{and} \qquad s' \varepsilon S'$$

The *capacity of the cut* (S, S') is simply $k(S, S')$. A cut whose capacity is as small as possible is called a *minimal cut*.

The connection between cuts and flows is given by the following rather obvious

Lemma 5.1.   If f is a flow in N from s to s' and S, S' is a cut in N, then the value of f is at most k(S, S').

Proof.   For the flow f we have

$$f(s, N) = f(s, N) + f(S - s, N) \qquad [\text{since } f(S - s, N) = 0]$$
$$= f(S, N) = f(S, S) + f(S, S') \qquad [\text{from (ii) above}]$$
$$= f(S, S') \leqq k(S, S') \qquad [\text{from (1') and (2')}] \qquad (3)$$

which is the asserted inequality.

Note that, if equality should hold in (3) above, we would know at once that f was a maximal flow and (S, S') a minimal cut.   The following important theorem states that there always exist a flow and cut for which (3) becomes an equality.   The result plays the key role in this chapter.

Theorem 5.1 (max flow min cut).   *The value of a maximal flow in (N, k) is equal to the capacity of a minimal cut.*

Proof.   Let $\bar{f}$ be a maximal flow.   Such a flow certainly exists since there are in fact only finitely many flows in (N, k) because of the feasibility restriction and the requirement that flows be integral valued.

Let us say that the edge (x, y) is *saturated* by the flow $\bar{f}$ if $\bar{f}(x, y) = k(x, y)$.   We now define a certain cut (S, S') as follows: The node x belongs to S if x = s or if there is an *unsaturated path* from s to x, by which we mean a sequence of edges $(s, x_1), (x_1, x_2), \ldots, (x_k, x)$, none of which is saturated.   The set S' is then the complement of S. To show that (S, S') is a cut we need only show that s' is in S'.   If on the contrary s' were in S, then there would be an unsaturated path P from s to s'; that is, for all edges (x, y) in P, $\bar{f}(x, y) < k(x, y)$.   But then if $\delta = \min_{(x,y)\varepsilon P} [k(x, y) - \bar{f}(x, y)]$, we could define a new flow f' where

$$f'(x, y) = \bar{f}(x, y) + \delta \qquad \text{for } (x, y) \text{ in } P$$
$$f'(x, y) = \bar{f}(x, y) \qquad \text{otherwise}$$

and clearly the value of f' would be greater by δ than the value of $\bar{f}$, contradicting maximality.

We can now show that equality holds in (3) of the preceding lemma, for if

$$\bar{f}(S, S') < k(S, S') \qquad (4)$$

then it follows that $\bar{f}(x, y) < k(x, y)$ for some x in S and y in S'.   On the other hand, we know from the definition of S that there is an unsaturated path from s to x, but since the edge (x, y) is also unsaturated this would mean that the path could be extended to an unsaturated path from s to y, contradicting the fact that y is in S'.   This shows that inequality (4) is impossible and completes the proof.

We call attention to the fact that the above proof goes through verbatim when the capacities and flows take on any real values, not necessarily integers, except for the proof that maximal flows exist. This, however, follows from the results of Chap. 3.

Like the duality theorem of linear programming, the max flow min cut theorem is important because it provides a means of verifying that a given flow is optimal.   Namely, one looks for a cut whose capacity is equal to the given flow.   Actually the theorem does more than this, for the proof gives a constructive method for finding maximal flows in the following way: Starting from a given flow f_1 (possibly the zero flow), we construct the set S_1 of all nodes which can be reached from s by an unsaturated path.   If s' is in S_1, then there is an unsaturated path from s to s' on which we can superimpose an additional flow f_1', obtaining a new flow $f_2 = f_1 + f_1'$ with a larger value.   If s' is not in S_1, then f_1 is already maximal and (S_1, S_1') is a minimal cut.

We now illustrate the technique by the numerical example illustrated by Fig. 5.4.

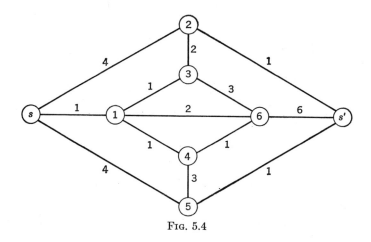

FIG. 5.4

The circled numbers are simply labels for the nodes.   The numbers on the edges represent capacities which are assumed to be the same in both directions.   The whole network is easily represented by its *capacity matrix,*

	s	1	2	3	4	5	6	s'
s	0	1	4	0	0	4	0	0
1	1	0	0	1	1	0	2	0
2	4	0	0	2	0	0	0	1
3	0	1	2	0	0	0	3	0
4	0	1	0	0	0	3	1	0
5	4	0	0	0	3	0	0	1
6	0	2	0	3	1	0	0	6
s'	0	0	1	0	0	1	6	0

where the ijth coordinate of this matrix is the capacity of the edge (i, j).

In order to get started, let us use an initial flow f_1 in which one unit is shipped along the "upper" path of the network, one unit along the "lower" path, and one unit through the middle.   This flow, which one easily finds by inspection, will shorten the computation and permit us to get on to the interesting part of the method.   The *flow matrix* for f_1 is

	s	1	2	3	4	5	6	s'
s		1	1			1		
1	-1						1	
2	-1							1
3								
4								
5	-1							1
6		-1						1
s'			-1			-1	-1	

where, from here on, we agree that all empty places in the matrix correspond to zeros.

We must now look for paths which are not saturated by the flow f_1. A convenient way of doing this is to subtract the flow f_1 from the capacity k, giving a new capacity function $k_1 = k - f_1$ defined on the original network. The problem is then to find paths of positive capacity relative to k_1. In the example under consideration the new capacity matrix is given by

	s	1	2	3	4	5	6	s'
s		0	(3)			3		
1	2			1	1		1	
2	[5]			(2)				0
3		1	[2]				(3)	
4		1				3	1	
5	5				3			0
6		3		[3]	1			(5)
s'			2			2	[7]	

We now look first for all nodes which can be reached from s by an unsaturated edge. These correspond to the positive entries in the first row of the k_1 matrix and are nodes ② and ⑤. Next we look at all nodes which are reachable from ② or ⑤. These turn out to be nodes ③ and ④. From nodes ③ and ④ we can reach node ⑥ and from ⑥ we can reach ⑤'. Thus we have the unsaturated path $(s, 2)$, $(2, 3)$, $(3, 6)$, and $(6, s')$. The corresponding entries have been circled in the k_1 matrix, and we have put squares around the entries corresponding to edges in the opposite direction. Now the minimum value of the capacities of the circled edges is 2; so we can send a flow of 2 along the chosen path. We need not write down the new flow matrix f_2 since we can obtain the new capacity matrix k_2 directly by simply subtracting 2 from each of the circled entries and adding 2 to each of the "squared" entries, giving

	s	1	2	3	4	5	6	s'
s		0	1			(3)		
1	2			1	1		1	
2	7			0				0
3		1	4				1	
4		1				[3]	(1)	
5	[5]				(3)			0
6		3		5	[1]			(3)
s'			2			2	[9]	

This time there is a path from ⑤ to ⑤ to ④ to ⑥ to ⑤, and the appropriate entries have been circled and squared accordingly. Since the capacity of edge (4, 6) is 1, we can ship only 1 additional unit this time. The new capacity matrix k_3 is obtained as before and is

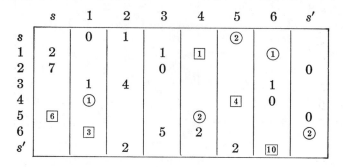

	s	1	2	3	4	5	6	s'
s		0	1			②		
1	2			1	[1]		①	
2	7			0				0
3		1	4				1	
4	①				[4]	0		
5	[6]				②			0
6		[3]		5	2			②
s'			2			2	[10]	

The path is as indicated: ⑤→ ⑤ → ④ → ① → ⑥ → ⑤, and the next capacity matrix k_4 is

	s	1	2	3	4	5	6	s'
s		0	①			①		
1	2			1	2		0	
2	7			0				0
3		1	4				1	
4		0				5	0	
5	7				①			0
6		4		5	2			1
s'			2			2	11	

Now in this matrix we have circled all nodes which can be reached from s. These do not include s', and therefore the computation is finished. The only nodes which can be reached from s are ⑤, ②, ④, and ⑤, and these therefore form the set S of the minimal cut. From the original capacity matrix we see that

$$k(S, S') = k(s, 1) + k(2, 3) + k(2, s') + k(4, 1) + k(4, 6) + k(5, s')$$
$$= 1 + 2 + 1 + 1 + 1 + 1 = 7$$

Finally we must determine the maximal flow matrix $\hat{f}$, but this is clearly equal to $k - k_4$. Subtracting the k_4 matrix from the k matrix gives

s	1	2	3	4	5	6	s'
	1	3			3		
1	−1				−1		2	
2	−3			2				1
3			−2				2	
4		1				−2	1	
5	−3				2			1
6		−2		−2	−1			5
s'			−1			−1	−5	

The total flow out of s is the sum of the numbers in row one and is, of course, equal to the total flow into s' which is the sum of the numbers in the last column. The value of this flow is 7, which is equal to the capacity of the minimal cut, and we thus have a check on our calculations. Note also that the sums of the entries in all rows and columns except the first and last are zero, as they must be (why?).

Returning to the graphical representation, the flow diagram in Fig. 5.5 should be self-explanatory. The numbers on the edges give the

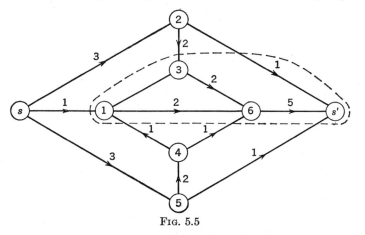

Fig. 5.5

values of the flow in the direction of the arrows. The nodes surrounded by the dashed line form the set S' of the minimum cut.

3. The Simple-assignment Problem

The problem to be considered in this section is a special case of the optimal-assignment problem described in Example 2 of Sec. 1. As there, we consider m individuals $I_1, \ldots, I_m$ and n jobs $J_1, \ldots, J_n$. Each individual I_i is qualified for certain of the jobs J_j and unqualified for others. The problem is then to determine whether it is possible to assign all individuals to jobs for which they are qualified in such a way that exactly one job is assigned to each individual.[1] We may formalize the problem in the following way: Consider the *qualification matrix* $Q = (\alpha_{ij})$ in which $\alpha_{ij} = 1$ if I_i is qualified for J_j, and $\alpha_{ij} = 0$ otherwise. The problem is then to choose m distinct ones from the matrix Q no two of which are in the same row or column. In this form it is clear that the simple-assignment problem is the special case of the optimal-assignment problem in which each α_{ij} is either 1 or 0.

Now, an obvious necessary condition for the problem to have a solution is this: If we are given any subset of k individuals they must among them qualify for at least k distinct jobs, for if not, then clearly not all the k individuals can be assigned. An important and classical result states that the converse of this proposition is also true. In precise terms, if S is any set of individuals let $J(S)$ be all jobs J_j for which at least one member of S is qualified. Then we state

Theorem 5.2. *It is possible to assign all individuals I_i to jobs J_j if and only if for any set S of individuals $J(S)$ contains at least as many elements as S.*

We shall give a proof of this theorem from the max flow min cut theorem. To do this we must first describe the appropriate network. It is convenient here to introduce the number *infinity* represented by the symbol ∞. This number is simply an abstract element which we adjoin to the set of nonnegative integers and which has the following two defining properties:

$$\text{For any integer } n, \; n + \infty = \infty \qquad \text{(i)}$$
$$\text{For any integer } n, \; n < \infty \qquad \text{(ii)}$$

We now define the *assignment* network. There are $n + m + 2$ nodes consisting of a source s, a sink s', the m individuals I_i, and the n jobs J_j. The capacity function is defined by the rules

[1] A more picturesque version of the same problem is the so-called "marriage problem" in which one asks if it is possible to marry off a certain set of boys to a set of girls in such a way that each boy marries someone he likes.

$$k(s, I_i) = 1 \qquad \text{for all } i \tag{1}$$
$$k(J_j, s') = 1 \qquad \text{for all } j \tag{2}$$
$$k(I_i, J_j) = \infty \qquad \text{if } I_i \text{ is qualified for } J_j \tag{3}$$

All other capacities are zero.

Figure 5.6 gives a schematic picture of such a network.

Note that the maximal flow in this network is at most m since the cut $(s, N - s)$ has capacity m. It is easy to see that if there is a flow $\bar{f}$ of value m then the assignment problem can be solved. Namely, since $\bar{f}(s, N) = m$, there must be one unit flowing into each node I_i, hence

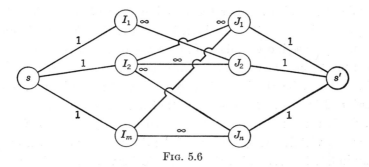

FIG. 5.6

also one unit flowing out of I_i. Let us assign I_i to J_j if $\bar{f}(I_i, J_j) = 1$. It is clear that only one person will be assigned to a job J_j under this scheme for the flow out of each J_j is at most 1; hence this is also true of the flow in.

Proof of Theorem 5.2. We have already seen that the given condition is necessary. To prove sufficiency, suppose it is not possible to assign all individuals. Then the maximal flows and minimal cuts in the assignment network have values less than m. Let (S, S') be a minimal cut and, say, S is given by

$$S = \{s, I_1, \ldots, I_p, J_1, \ldots, J_q\}$$

Then for $i \le p$ and $j > q$, I_i is not qualified for J_j, for if I_i were qualified for J_j we would have $k(I_i, J_j) = \infty$ and $k(S, S') = \infty$. We then get

$$m > k(S, S') = \sum_{i>p} k(s, I_i) + \sum_{j \le q} k(J_j, s') = m - p + q$$

and hence $p > q$, and the p individuals $I_1, \ldots, I_p$ are qualified for at most q jobs $J_1, \ldots, J_q$, as asserted.

Because of the importance of this theorem we present a second proof of it which is entirely independent of any notions connected with networks.

Second Proof. We proceed by induction on m. The proof for $m = 1$ being immediate, assume the theorem true for all positive integers less than m.

Case 1. Every set of k individuals, $k < m$, is qualified for at least $k + 1$ jobs. Then assign the first individual to any one of the jobs for which he qualifies. For the remaining set of $m - 1$ individuals the hypothesis of the theorem is satisfied, and therefore, by induction hypothesis, these individuals can all be assigned as required.

Case 2. There is a set of k individuals, $k < m$, qualified for exactly k jobs. Then, by the induction hypothesis, these k individuals can be assigned to jobs. Now suppose that among the remaining $m - k$ individuals there are r who are qualified for only s jobs with $s < r$. This would violate the hypothesis of the theorem, for then the original k individuals together with these r would between them be qualified for only $k + s$ jobs. Thus the hypothesis is satisfied also for the remaining $m - k$ individuals, and so once again, by induction hypothesis, they can be assigned.

While this second proof is much shorter than the first, it has the serious drawback of being nonconstructive. For this reason the reasoning via network flows will be more useful to us in solving actual problems, which we are about to do.

Consider the qualification matrix shown on page 147.

Here the rows correspond to individuals, the columns to jobs, and an x in the ith row and jth column indicates that I_i is qualified for J_j. Now, one could translate this problem at once into the corresponding maximal-flow problem and solve by the procedure of the previous section. This would, however, involve working with a square matrix with $m + n + 2$ rows and columns. It turns out that for the case at hand one can work directly with the qualification matrix. We shall describe this procedure using the terminology of flows rather than assignments. In these terms one would consider the matrix below as a capacity matrix where $k(I_i, J_j) = \infty$ if there is an x in the ith row and jth column and $k(I_i, J_j) = 0$ otherwise.

I \ J	J_1	J_2	J_3	J_4	J_5	J_6	J_7	J_8	J_9	J_{10}
I_1				(x)	x				x	
I_2								(x)	x	x
I_3	(x)	x	x			x	x			
I_4									(x)	x
I_5				x	(x)			x	x	
I_6	x	(x)	x				x			
I_7			(x)			x	x			
I_8	x	x				(x)				x
I_9				x	x			x		
I_{10}				x	x				x	

In the above tableau we have chosen an initial flow f_1 by assigning I_1 to the job for which he was qualified having the lowest subscript, in this case J_4. Having assigned the first k individuals, we assign the $(k + 1)$st to the job for which he qualifies, which has not been previously assigned, having the lowest subscript. In this way we see that we have assigned all individuals except 9 and 10, and all jobs but 7 and 10, the circles in the tableau indicating the assignments.

The next step is to write out the new capacity matrix $k_1 = k - f_1$. It is fortunately not necessary to rewrite the matrix at this point, as one can obtain the matrix of k_1 by suitably interpreting the original matrix. Namely, we say that $k_1(I_i, J_j) = \infty$ if there is an *uncircled* x in the ith row and jth column [thus $k_1(I_3, J_3) = \infty$] and $k_1(J_j, I_i) = 1$ if the i, jth entry in the matrix is a *circled* x [thus $k_1(J_6, I_8) = 1$]. All other capacities are zero. We now try to increase the flow by finding a "path" from an unassigned individual to an unassigned job. Such a path is seen to be from I_9 to J_8, from J_8 to I_2, and from I_2 to J_{10}.

If we now superimpose a flow of 1 along this path we must circle the entries (I_9, J_8) and (I_2, J_{10}) but remove the circle from (J_8, I_2) since the new flow along this edge cancels out the previous flow from I_2 to J_8. The new matrix becomes

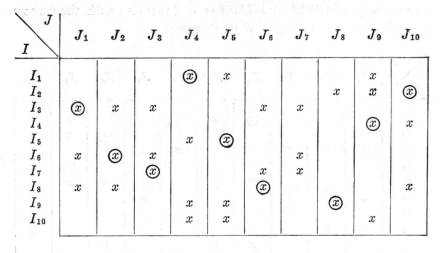

I \ J	J_1	J_2	J_3	J_4	J_5	J_6	J_7	J_8	J_9	J_{10}
I_1				⊗	x				x	
I_2							x	x	⊗
I_3	⊗	x	x			x	x			
I_4									⊗	x
I_5				x	⊗					
I_6	x	⊗	x				x			
I_7			⊗			x	x			
I_8	x	x				⊗				x
I_9				x	x			⊗		
I_{10}				x	x				x	

In this new tableau all but I_{10} and J_7 have been assigned and it remains to determine whether there exists a path from I_{10} to J_7. If we now start from I_{10} we find there are paths to I_1, I_2, I_4, I_5, I_9, J_4, J_5, J_8, J_9, J_{10}, but no others. Thus the 6 individuals I_1, I_2, I_4, I_5, I_9, I_{10} qualify for only the 5 jobs J_4, J_5, J_8, J_9, J_{10}. It follows that at most 9 assignments are possible and these have already been achieved; so the problem is solved. (Of course the solution is far from unique.)

We shall use the solution of the simple-assignment problem again when we treat the optimal-assignment problem in Sec. 5.

4. The Transshipment Problem

We return now to more general transportation networks in which as in our earlier examples some of the nodes are to be thought of as *plants* and others as *markets*. We denote the set of plants by P and the set of markets by M. The *supply* at the plant x in P is denoted by $\sigma(x)$ and the *demand* at the node x in M is denoted by $\delta(x)$. Assuming that we have a capacitated network (N, k), it is natural to ask whether it is possible to satisfy the given demands from the given supplies. There will in general be neutral nodes x in N at which there is neither a supply nor a demand. It will be convenient to include these nodes in the set P. A problem of this sort will be referred to as a *transshipment problem*.

Definition. A transshipment problem is called *feasible* if there is a flow f such that

$$f(N, x) \geq \delta(x) \qquad \text{for } x \,\varepsilon\, M \tag{1}$$
$$f(x, N) \leq \sigma(x) \qquad \text{for } x \,\varepsilon\, P \tag{2}$$

A flow f satisfying (1) and (2) will be called a *feasible flow*.

The following result will enable us to determine when a transshipment problem is feasible and to construct feasible flows when they exist.

Theorem 5.3 (feasibility theorem). *A transshipment problem is feasible if and only if for every set of nodes S*

$$\delta(S' \cap M) - \sigma(S' \cap P) \leq k(S, S') \tag{3}$$

Proof. The necessity of the condition is intuitively clear for it expresses the requirement that the *net demand* (i.e., demand minus supply) of any set be no greater than the total capacity leading into that set. Formally, suppose we have a feasible flow f and let S be any subset of N. Then

$$\delta(S' \cap M) = \sum_{x \varepsilon S' \cap M} \delta(x) \leq \sum_{x \varepsilon S' \cap M} f(N, x) = f(N, S' \cap M), \tag{4}$$

and
$$\sigma(S' \cap P) = \sum_{x \varepsilon S' \cap P} \sigma(x) \geq \sum_{x \varepsilon S' \cap P} f(x, N) = f(S' \cap P, N) \tag{5}$$
$$= -f(N, S' \cap P)$$

Subtracting (5) from (4) gives

$$\delta(S' \cap M) - \sigma(S' \cap P) \leq f(N, S' \cap P) + f(N, S' \cap M)$$
$$= f(N, S') = f(S, S') + f(S', S') = f(S, S') \leq k(S, S')$$

as asserted.

To prove sufficiency we adjoin to N a source s and sink s' and define a capacity $\bar{k}$ on this extended network $\bar{N}$ by the rule

$$\bar{k}(x, y) = k(x, y) \qquad \text{for } x, y \text{ in } N$$
$$\bar{k}(s, x) = \sigma(x) \qquad \text{for } x \text{ in } P$$
$$\bar{k}(x, s') = \delta(x) \qquad \text{for } x \text{ in } M$$
$$\bar{k}(x, y) = 0 \qquad \text{in all other cases}$$

We next assert that a minimal cut of $\bar{N}$ with respect to s and s' is $(N \cup s, s')$. To see this, let S be any subset of N and $(S \cup s, S' \cup s')$ the corresponding cut of $\bar{N}$. Then

$$\bar{k}(S \cup s, S' \cup s') = \bar{k}(s, S') + \bar{k}(S, S') + \bar{k}(S, s')$$

$$= \sigma(S' \cap P) + k(S, S') + \delta(S \cap M) \quad (6)$$

But $\qquad \bar{k}(N \cup s, s') = \delta(M) = \delta(S \cap M) + \delta(S' \cap M) \quad (7)$

and subtracting (7) from (6) gives

$$\bar{k}(S \cup s, S' \cup s') - \bar{k}(N \cup s, s') = k(S, S') + \sigma(S' \cap P) - \delta(S \cap M)$$

and this expression is nonnegative by the hypothesis of the theorem.

We now apply the max flow min cut theorem to the network $(\bar{N}, \bar{k})$ which shows that there exists a flow $\bar{f}$ whose value is $\bar{k}(N \cup s, s') = \delta(M)$. This means

$$\sum_{x \varepsilon N} \bar{f}(x, s') = \sum_{x \varepsilon M} \delta(x)$$

hence $\qquad \bar{f}(x, s') = \delta(x) \qquad$ for all $x \varepsilon M \qquad (8)$

Now letting f be $\bar{f}$ restricted to edges of N, it is clear that f is a flow on (N, k) and it remains to verify that f is feasible [i.e., satisfies (1) and (2)]. Since $\bar{f}$ is a flow from s to s', we know that for x in N

$$0 = \bar{f}(\bar{N}, x) = f(N, x) + \bar{f}(s, x) + \bar{f}(s', x) \quad (9)$$

For $x \varepsilon M$, $\bar{f}(s, x) = 0$ and we have, from (8) and (9),

$$f(N, x) = -\bar{f}(s', x) = \bar{f}(x, s') = \delta(x)$$

so condition (1) is satisfied. For $x \varepsilon P$, $\bar{f}(s', x) = 0$ and we have from (9)

$$f(x, N) = \bar{f}(s, x) \leq \bar{k}(s, x) = \sigma(x)$$

so condition (2) is also satisfied.

The proof of the feasibility theorem shows that we can solve a transshipment problem by setting up the equivalent maximal-flow problem. Let us illustrate the procedure by an example.

Suppose we are given four plants $P_1, \ldots, P_4$ with supplies 15, 6, 13, and 8, respectively, and four markets $M_1, \ldots, M_4$ with demands

14, 9, 7, and 12.   For this special case we shall assume that the only nonzero capacities are from plants to markets; i.e., capacities between plants, between markets, and from markets to plants are zero.   Letting κ_{ij} be the capacity of (P_i, M_j), we may represent the situation by the following table:

Demands Supplies		M_1 14	M_2 9	M_3 7	M_4 12
P_1	15	4	5	4	2
P_2	6	4	1	2	2
P_3	13	2	5	4	3
P_4	8	4	1	3	5

Note that the simple-assignment problem of the previous section is a special case of the feasibility problem in which all supplies and demands are 1, and all capacities are 0 or ∞.

Again one might turn this problem into a maximum-flow problem as in the proof of Theorem 5.3.   However, because of the special nature of the network involved, a less cumbersome method is convenient.   We first make an enlarged table in which we list the capacities from market to plant as well as those from plant to market. Initially, of course, all of these back capacities are zero.   However, recall that if at some stage of the computation we have imposed a flow ξ_{ij} from P_i to M_j, then at the next iteration we must assume a capacity $k(M_j, P_i) = 0 - \xi_{ji} = \xi_{ij}$.   The   expanded   table   looks like this:

		M_1	14	M_2	9	M_3	7	M_4	12
P_1	15	4	0	5	0	4	0	2	0
P_2	6	4	0	1	0	2	0	2	0
P_3	13	2	0	5	0	4	0	3	0
P_4	8	4	0	1	0	3	0	5	0

To obtain an initial flow we start by shipping as much as possible from the first plant P_1 without exceeding the capacities or demands. We thus ship 4 to M_1, 5 to M_2, 4 to M_3, and 2 to M_4.   The supplies, demands, and capacities after these first shipments have been made are shown below.

		M_1	10	M_2	4	M_3	3	M_4	10
P_1	0	0	4	0	5	0	4	0	2

Note that the supply at P_1 and all capacities out of P_1 have been reduced to zero, but we now have positive capacities from the markets into P_1. Next, distributing the supply at P_2 in the same way, the second row becomes

		M_1	6	M_2	3	M_3	2	M_4	10
P_2	0	0	4	0	1	1	1	2	0

Next shipping from P_3 we send 2 units to M_1, 3 to M_2 (although the capacity would permit sending 5, this would exceed the demand), 2 to M_3, and 3 to M_4. The third row is

		M_1	4	M_2	0	M_3	0	M_4	7
P_3	3	0	2	2	3	2	2	0	3

Finally, from P_4 we ship 4 units to M_1 and 4 units to M_4. The full tableau is now

		M_1	0	M_2	0	M_3	0	M_4	3
P_1	0	0	4	0	5	0	4	0	2
P_2	0	0	4	0	①	1	1	②	0
P_3	3	0	2	②	3	2	2	0	3
P_4	0	0	4	1	0	3	0	1	4

The figures in the right-hand column under each market M_j give the flows along the corresponding edges as well as the "back capacities" of these edges from market to plant, while the figures in the left-hand columns give the new forward capacities. The problem is now to get the remaining three units from P_3 to M_4. To do this we seek "paths" connecting these two nodes. One such is from P_3 to M_2 (capacity 2), from M_2 to P_2 (capacity 1), and from P_2 to M_4 (capacity 2). Upon adding an additional unit flow along this path, one finds a second such path from P_3 to M_3 to P_2 to M_4. Here the smallest capacity is that from M_3 to P_2, which is 1; so again we may increase the flow. In the table we have circled and "squared" the entries corresponding to the edges involved in the first and second of these paths, respectively. Having added the flows in the usual manner, we get as the new capacity matrix

		M_1	0	M_2	0	M_3	0	M_4	1
P_1	0	0	4	0	5	0	4	0	2
P_2	0	0	4	1	0	2	0	0	2
P_3	1	0	2	1	4	1	3	0	3
P_4	0	0	4	1	0	3	0	1	4

It now turns out that there are no further paths from P_3 to M_4. In fact, the only nodes which can be reached from P_3 are P_1, M_2, and M_3. This shows that there is an oversupply of one unit among these four nodes, and this one readily verifies from the original table. Namely, the net supply of this set is $15 + 13 - 9 - 7 = 12$, whereas the capacity leading out of this set is $k(P_1, M_1) + k(P_1, M_4) + k(P_3, M_1) + k(P_3, M_4) = 4 + 2 + 2 + 3 = 11$, so that plants P_1 and P_3 are "stuck" with one unit which they can never get rid of; hence the problem is not feasible.

There is an important final observation to be made concerning the transshipment problem.   We remark again that we have nowhere used in the proof of Theorems 5.1 and 5.3 the fact that the capacities and demands are integers, and hence the theorems remain valid when these are replaced by any nonnegative real numbers.   On the other hand, the proof of the feasibility theorem shows that if a transshipment problem with integral constraints is feasible in real numbers then it has a feasible flow which is integral.   Of course, among the set of all feasible flows there will, in general, be an infinite number which are not integral.   The following theorem will describe exactly what the situation is.   We consider a slightly more general form of the transshipment problem.

Let (N, k) be a network, and let a and b be two integer-valued functions on N, with $a(x) \leq b(x)$ for all $x \, \varepsilon \, N$.   A *feasible flow* on (N, k) is a flow f such that $a(x) \leq f(x, N) \leq b(x)$.

Although the functions k, a, and b are integer-valued, we allow the flow f to be any real-valued function satisfying the feasibility conditions.   Supposing the set N to contain n elements, a flow f is in an obvious way a vector in a space of dimension n^2, the n^2 coordinates of f being the values of f on the n^2 edges (x, y). Letting F be the set of all feasible flows, one at once verifies that F is a convex set. The main result on integral-valued flows is

Theorem 5.4. *The set F of all real-valued feasible flows is a convex polytope whose extreme points are integral flows.*[1]

Proof. The set F consists of all flows satisfying the inequalities

$$f(x, y) \leq k(x, y) \qquad \text{for all } x \text{ and } y \qquad (1)$$

$$\sum_y f(x, y) \leq b(x) \qquad \text{for all } x \qquad (2)$$

$$-\sum_y f(x, y) \leq -a(x) \qquad \text{for all } x \qquad (3)$$

This set is clearly bounded in view of the inequalities (1). It follows from Exercise 38 of Chap. 2 that F is a convex polytope.

Now let f be a feasible flow which is not integral; i.e., $f(x, y)$ is non-integral for at least one edge (x, y). We shall call such an edge a *fractional edge*. By a *fractional path* P is meant a sequence of nodes $(x_1, x_2, \ldots, x_k)$ such that (x_i, x_{i+1}) is a fractional edge for $i = 1, \ldots,$ $k - 1$. Such a path is called a *fractional cycle* if $x_k = x_1$.

Case 1. There exists a fractional cycle $P = (x_1, \ldots, x_k)$. Then for all x_i in P we have $k(x_i, x_{i+1}) > f(x_i, x_{i+1}) > -k(x_{i+1}, x_i)$ (using skew symmetry of f), because the function k is integral-valued. It follows that we can choose a small but positive number ϵ and define new feasible flows f_1 and f_2 by the rules

$$f_1(x_i, x_{i+1}) = f(x_i, x_{i+1}) + \epsilon \text{ on } P$$
$$f_2(x_i, x_{i+1}) = f(x_i, x_{i+1}) - \epsilon \text{ on } P$$

and $\quad f_1(x, y) = f_2(x, y) = f(x, y) \qquad$ for edges (x, y) not in P

But then

$$f(x, y) = \tfrac{1}{2}f_1(x, y) + \tfrac{1}{2}f_2(x, y) \qquad \text{for all } x, y \text{ in } N$$

so f is not an extreme point.

Case 2. There are no fractional cycles. Then let $P = (x_1, \ldots, x_k)$ be the longest fractional path in N. Then all the nodes x_i in P are distinct, for otherwise P would contain a fractional cycle. Now the

---

[1] For this theorem we need the definition and results of Chap. 2, Sec. 7.

edge (x_1, x_2) is fractional by definition, but all other edges (x_1, y), $y \neq x_2$, are integral, for if not we could extend the path P to include y, contrary to the assumption that P was longest.   It follows that

$$f(x_1, N) = f(x_1, x_2) + f(x_1, N - x_2)$$

is a fraction and hence

$$a(x_1) < f(x_1, N) < b(x_1) \tag{1}$$

since $a(x_1)$ and $b(x_1)$ are integers.   Similarly,

$$a(x_k) < f(x_k, N) < b(x_k) \tag{2}$$

Once again we may choose a small positive ϵ and construct flows f_1 and f_2 exactly as before so that the flows f_1 and f_2 also satisfy (1) and (2) above and are therefore again feasible.   But then $f = \frac{1}{2}f_1 + \frac{1}{2}f_2$ so that f is again not extreme.   This completes the proof.

The above property of the transshipment problem is characteristic of all problems treated in this chapter.   Namely, all extreme feasible vectors turn out to be integral.   This property seems to be closely associated with the existence of simple combinatorial procedures for solving the problems.

5. The Optimal-assignment Problem

We turn now to the optimal-assignment problem described in Sec. 1. We shall not repeat the "story" behind this problem (the reader should refresh himself on this if necessary) but simply recall that we were given a nonnegative *rating matrix* $A = (\alpha_{ij})$ and we sought nonnegative integers ξ_{ij} which

$$\text{maximize} \sum_{i,j} \xi_{ij}\alpha_{ij} \tag{1}$$

subject to

$$\sum_{i=1}^{m} \xi_{ij} \leqq 1 \qquad \text{for all } j$$

$$\sum_{j=1}^{n} \xi_{ij} \leqq 1 \qquad \text{for all } i \tag{2}$$

As a preliminary simplification of the problem we shall show that it suffices to consider the special case $m = n$, for if there are, say, more individuals than jobs, we introduce $m - n$ "dummy" jobs, for which all individuals have the same rating, say zero. It is clear that any solution of this modified problem yields a solution of the original. Namely, if an individual is assigned to a dummy job in the modified problem, he is not assigned at all in the original, and optimality is preserved. Now, in the case $m = n$ we may assume that every individual is assigned to some job since, as the α_{ij} are nonnegative, there is no advantage to leaving an individual unassigned. Thus the inequalities (2) become equations,

$$
\begin{aligned}
\sum_{i=1}^{n} \xi_{ij} &= 1 \qquad \text{for all } j \\
\sum_{j=1}^{n} \xi_{ij} &= 1 \qquad \text{for all } i
\end{aligned}
\tag{2$'$}
$$

Forgetting for the moment the requirement that the ξ_{ij} be integers, we have nothing more than a canonical maximum problem whose dual is easily seen to be that of finding numbers $\xi_1, \ldots, \xi_n$ and $\eta_1, \ldots, \eta_n$ such that

$$
\sum_{i=1}^{n} \xi_i + \sum_{j=1}^{n} \eta_j \qquad \text{is a minimum} \tag{1}^*
$$

subject to

$$
\xi_i + \eta_j \geqq \alpha_{ij} \qquad \text{for all } i \text{ and } j \tag{2}^*
$$

In order to solve the assignment problem we shall prove the duality theorem for this problem with the restriction that the numbers ξ_i, η_j, and ξ_{ij} be integers. The proof is entirely independent of the general duality theory of Chap. 3 and, like the other proofs of this chapter, is constructive and leads at once to an efficient method of computation.

Theorem 5.5. *Assuming all variables ξ_i, η_j, and ξ_{ij} are integers, the maximum of (1) subject to (2$'$) is equal to the minimum of (1)* subject to (2)*.*

Proof. As usual, it is clear that

$$
\max \left(\sum_{i,j} \xi_{ij} \alpha_{ij} \right) \leqq \min \left(\sum_{i=1}^{n} \xi_i + \sum_{j=1}^{n} \eta_j \right)
$$

since
$$\sum_{i,j} \xi_{ij}\alpha_{ij} \leqq \sum_{i,j} \xi_{ij}(\xi_i + \eta_j)$$

$$= \sum_i \xi_i \left(\sum_j \xi_{ij}\right) + \sum_j \eta_j \left(\sum_i \xi_{ij}\right)$$

$$= \sum_i \xi_i + \sum_j \eta_j \tag{3}$$

Conversely, suppose $\xi_1, \ldots, \xi_n$ and $\eta_1, \ldots, \eta_n$ minimize (1)* subject to (2)*. Then, let P be the set of all pairs of indices (i, j) such that $\xi_i + \eta_j = \alpha_{ij}$ [i.e., equality holds in (2)*], and consider the simple-assignment problem with n individuals and n jobs in which I_i is qualified for J_j if and only if $(i, j) \, \varepsilon \, P$.

Case 1. In the above simple-assignment problem all n individuals can be assigned. In this case, perform a complete set of assignments (we already know how to carry out this computation) and let $\xi_{ij} = 1$ if and only if I_i is assigned to J_j. If we now substitute these values of ξ_{ij} into (3) we see that the inequality becomes an equation, since, by the construction of the set P, $\xi_{ij} = 1$ only if $\alpha_{ij} = \xi_i + \eta_j$, and $\xi_{ij} = 0$ otherwise. It follows that the assignment given by these ξ_{ij} is optimal.

Case 2. It is not possible to assign all n of the individuals. Then by Theorem 5.2, there exists a set of k individuals, denoted by K, such that the set Q of jobs for which they are qualified contains q members where $q < k$. We then define new dual variables ξ_i' and η_j' by

$$\xi_i' = \begin{cases} \xi_i - 1 & \text{for } I_i \, \varepsilon \, K \\ \xi_i & \text{for } I_i \, \notin \, K \end{cases}$$

$$\eta_j' = \begin{cases} \eta_j + 1 & \text{for } J_j \, \varepsilon \, Q \\ \eta_j & \text{for } J_j \, \notin \, Q \end{cases}$$

and we assert that the numbers ξ_i' and η_j' still satisfy (2)*. Namely,

if $I_i \notin K$ then $\xi_i' + \eta_j' \geqq \xi_i + \eta_j \geqq \alpha_{ij}$

if $I_i \, \varepsilon \, K, J_j \, \varepsilon \, Q$ then $\xi_i' + \eta_j' = \xi_i - 1 + \eta_j + 1 = \xi_i + \eta_j \geqq \alpha_{ij}$

if $I_i \, \varepsilon \, K, J_j \notin Q$ then $(i, j) \notin P$ (i.e., I_i is not qualified for J_j)

hence by definition, $\xi_i + \eta_j > \alpha_{ij}$, or, since all numbers involved are integers,

$$\xi_i + \eta_j \geqq \alpha_{ij} + 1 \quad \text{or} \quad (\xi_i - 1) + \eta_j \geqq \alpha_{ij}$$

hence
$$\xi_i' + \eta_j' \geqq \alpha_{ij}$$

so the variables ξ_i', η_j' are feasible.

On the other hand,

$$\sum_i \xi_i' + \sum_j \eta_j' = \sum_i \xi_i - k + \sum_j \eta_j + q = \sum_i \xi_i + \sum_j \eta_j + (q - k)$$

and since $q < k$ we have obtained a smaller value of $(1)^*$ contrary to the assumption that the ξ_i and η_j were minimizing. This completes the proof.

We immediately apply the theorem to solve the assignment problem whose rating matrix is

		J_1	J_2	J_3	J_4	J_5
	η_j / ξ_i	0↑	0	0	0	0*
I_1	12↓	⑫′	9	10	3	8
I_2	9↓	6	6	2	2	⑨′
I_3	11	6	8	10	⑪′	9
I_4	6↓	⑥	3	4	1	1
I_5	12↓	11	1	10	9	⑫

We have also picked an initial set of dual variables ξ_i and η_j satisfying $(2)^*$ by letting all η_j be zero and letting $\xi_i = \max_j \alpha_{ij}$. We have circled the entries α_{ij} for which $\alpha_{ij} = \xi_i + \eta_j$, and now consider these circled entries as the x's in a qualification matrix. By the method of Sec. 3 we easily find that the maximum possible number of assignments for this problem is 3. In the example we have put a prime above those circled entries for which assignments have been made. According to Theorem 5.2 there must now be a set of $k + 2$ individuals who qualify for only k jobs. These are easily found, for we look for those I_i's and J_j's which can be "reached" from the unassigned individuals I_4 and I_5. These are seen to be I_1, I_2, I_4, I_5, J_1, and J_5. It is therefore possible to decrease ξ_1, ξ_2, ξ_4, and ξ_5 by at least 1, while increasing η_1 and η_5 correspondingly, and still not violate condition $(2)^*$. In fact, in this case we see that it is possible to change these ξ_i and η_j by 2 units without violating the condition. In the previous tableau we have placed downward arrows next to the ξ_i which are to be decreased, and upward arrows next to the η_j which are to be increased. If we make these changes we get the new tableau

		J_1	J_2	J_3	J_4	J_5
		2↑	0	0↑	0	2↑
I_1	10↓	⑫′	9	⑩	3	8
I_2	7↓	6	6	2	2	⑨′
I_3	11	6	8	10	⑪′	9
I_4	4↓	⑥	3	④′	1	1
I_5	10↓	11	1	⑩	9	⑫

This time it is possible to assign 4 individuals, but no more, for we see that I_1, I_2, I_4, and I_5 qualify only for J_1, J_3, and J_5. The arrows at the head of the rows and columns have the same meaning as before. Accordingly, we decrease the marked ξ_i and increase the marked η_j by 1, obtaining the new tableau

		J_1	J_2	J_3	J_4	J_5
		3	0	1	0	3
I_1	9	⑫′	⑨	⑩	3	8
I_2	6	6	6	2	2	⑨′
I_3	11	6	8	10	⑪′	9
I_4	3	⑥	③′	④	1	1
I_5	9	11	1	⑩′	⑨	⑫

The primed entries show that it is now possible to assign all the individuals and accordingly we now have an optimal assignment whose value is

$$12 + 9 + 11 + 3 + 10 = 45$$

As an independent check that this is correct we see that the sum of the ξ_i and η_j is

$$(9 + 6 + 11 + 3 + 9) + (3 + 0 + 1 + 0 + 3) = 38 + 7 = 45$$

and thus we have obtained equal values for the two dual problems and therefore have found the solution of each.

6. A Problem Related to Optimal Assignment.   Price Equilibrium

There are a number of interesting results which can be obtained as simple consequences of the Duality Theorem 5.5 for the optimal-assignment problem.   We shall take up one of these in this section.

Let us imagine that n individuals $I_1, \ldots , I_n$ are all interested in purchasing, say, houses and suppose that n such houses $H_1, \ldots , H_n$ are available for sale.   The sale prices, however, have not yet been set but are to be determined by some sort of negotiation with the buyers. Let us also assume that house H_j is worth α_{ij} dollars to I_i.   The matrix $A = (\alpha_{ij})$ will be called the *value* matrix.

Let us next imagine that sale prices $\pi_1, \ldots , \pi_n$ for the n houses have been announced.   How will the ith individual behave?   First of all, he will offer to buy a house H_j only if $\alpha_{ij} \geqq \pi_j$; that is, he must feel he is getting his money's worth.   If there are houses which he is willing to buy, he will clearly offer to buy that house H_j for which $\alpha_{ij} - \pi_j$ is a maximum, for this number measures the increase in value to I_i from the purchase of H_j.   We impose the condition that each person may buy at most one house.   If at the given prices no two people offer to buy the same house, then there is no difficulty in selling the houses to the people who want to buy them.   Prices at which no two buyers select the same house will be called *equilibrium prices*. In general an arbitrary set of prices will not have this equilibrium property; that is, there will be some houses which several people want and others which no one wants.   Thus, for some houses the demand will exceed the supply; for others the supply will exceed the demand. Equilibrium prices are therefore prices which balance supply and demand in the classical economic sense.   The question is now whether we can always be sure that such prices will exist.   In order to settle this question we must first translate it into algebraic language.

Let p be a *price vector*, $p = (\pi_1, \ldots , \pi_n) \geqq 0$, and let $\mu_i = \max_j (\alpha_{ij} - \pi_j)$.   We call the entry α_{ij} *admissible* with respect to p if $\alpha_{ij} = \mu_i + \pi_j$.   The vector p is called an *equilibrium price vector* if

The numbers μ_i are nonnegative   (1)

There exists a set of admissible entries α_{ij} with exactly one entry
in each row and column of A $\qquad$ (2)

The reader should verify that the formal requirements (1) and (2)
correspond exactly to our economic description of equilibrium prices
in the paragraph which preceded.

Theorem 5.6. *For any value matrix A there exists an equilibrium
price vector.*

Proof. From Theorem 5.5 we can find integers μ_i, π_j such that

$$\mu_i + \pi_j \geqq \alpha_{ij} \qquad \text{for all } i, j \qquad (3)$$

There exists a set S of entries α_{ij}, one in each row and column, such
that

$$\sum_i \mu_i + \sum_j \pi_j = \sum_{\alpha_{ij} \varepsilon S} \alpha_{ij} \qquad (4)$$

Further, we may assume that the numbers μ_i and π_j are nonnegative,
for if this is not the case, let $\delta = \min [\mu_i, \pi_j]$, say $\delta = \mu_1 < 0$. Then
define

$$\mu_i' = \mu_i - \mu_1$$
$$\pi_j' = \pi_j + \mu_1$$

Clearly μ_i' and π_j' still satisfy (3) and (4). Also by the choice of μ_1
all the numbers μ_i' are nonnegative. But the numbers π_j' are also nonnegative, since $\pi_j' = \pi_j + \mu_1 \geqq \alpha_{1j} \geqq 0$.

We now simply note that $\mu_i \geqq \alpha_{ij} - \pi_j$ for all i and j from (3),
and since there is some entry α_{ij} of S in row i, it follows that $\mu_i = \max_j (\alpha_{ij} - \pi_j)$. The set S forms the desired set of admissible entries
and thus $p = (\pi_1, \ldots, \pi_n)$ satisfies conditions (1) and (2) for
equilibrium.

We call attention to the following important fact in connection with
the result we have just proved. Let $p = (\pi_1, \ldots, \pi_n)$ be an equilibrium price vector and suppose we relabel the house H_j, if necessary,
in such a way that each I_i buys house H_i at these prices. We can
now measure the total increase in value to the community of these
n transactions. The "profit" to I_i is, of course, $\alpha_{ii} - \pi_i$. The profit
to the seller of H_i is simply the money he receives, π_i. The sum of all
these profits is then

$$\Sigma(\alpha_{ii} - \pi_i) + \Sigma\pi_i = \Sigma\alpha_{ii} \qquad (5)$$

Now, no other assignment of houses to buyers will have a greater increase in total value to the community, for we have already seen in Theorem 5.5 that the numbers α_{ii} correspond to an optimal assignment. We can see this once again very simply, for we know

$$\alpha_{ii} - \pi_i \geqq \alpha_{ij} - \pi_j \qquad \text{for all } i, j \tag{6}$$

Now, take any collection S of entries α_{ij} with exactly one entry in each row and column. Summing all inequalities (6) for which α_{ij} is in S, we get

$$\sum_i \alpha_{ii} \geqq \sum_S \alpha_{ij}$$

for the price terms $\Sigma \pi_i$ and $\Sigma \pi_j$ clearly cancel out.

We have thus shown that for the case treated the classical notion of price equilibrium always leads to a distribution which yields "the greatest good for the greatest number." As the reader has probably noticed, the result of this section is quite similar to that of the resource allocation problem of Chap. 3, Sec. 5. The main difference is the fact that the equilibrium distribution here is required to be integral.

7. *The Transportation Problem*

Perhaps the most important instance of a problem solvable by the methods of this chapter is the transportation problem with "indivisible" commodities described in Sec. 1, in which all supplies, demands, flows, and prices are to be integral. As in Chap. 1, Example 2, we have the supply σ_i at the ith plant, the demand δ_j at the jth market, and the cost γ_{ij} of shipping one unit from the ith plant to the jth market. Letting ξ_{ij} be the amount shipped from i to j, we wish

$$\text{to minimize} \sum_{i,j} \gamma_{ij}\xi_{ij} \tag{1}$$

subject to

$$\xi_{ij} \geqq 0 \qquad \sum_j \xi_{ij} \leqq \sigma_i \qquad \sum_i \xi_{ij} \geqq \delta_j \qquad \text{for all } i, j \tag{2}$$

and, of course, the ξ_{ij} must be integers.

We make the obvious preliminary observation that in order for the constraints (2) to be feasible it is necessary that $\sum_i \sigma_i \geqq \sum_j \delta_j$; i.e., total supply must be at least equal to total demand. Now, as with the assignment problem, we may restrict ourselves to the special case in which the above inequality is an equation. Suppose, in fact, that $\sum_i \sigma_i > \sum_j \delta_j$. Then let the *surplus*, δ, be defined by $\delta = \sum_i \sigma_i - \sum_j \delta_j$ and introduce an $(n + 1)$st market called a *dump* at which the demand is δ. Let the cost $\gamma_{i,n+1}$ of shipping from any plant to the dump be zero. In this new problem total supply and demand are equal and, on the other hand, any minimizing solution for the new problem also gives a minimum cost for the old, since shipping to the dump is free. Now, if total supply and demand are equal, then the constraints (2) become equations

$$\xi_{ij} \geqq 0 \qquad \sum_j \xi_{ij} = \sigma_i \qquad \sum_i \xi_{ij} = \delta_j \qquad \text{for all } i \text{ and } j \qquad (2')$$

The dual of the canonical linear program given by (1) and (2′) is: To find "prices" $\pi_1, \ldots, \pi_m$ and $\pi'_1, \ldots, \pi'_n$ which

$$\text{maximize} \sum_j \pi'_j \delta_j - \sum_i \pi_i \sigma_i \qquad (1)*$$

subject to

$$\pi'_j - \pi_i \leqq \gamma_{ij} \qquad \text{for all } i \text{ and } j \qquad (2)*$$

As in the previous examples, we shall give a proof of the duality theorem for this model which is independent of the general duality theorem, which stays within the domain of integers, and which leads immediately to a computational procedure for solving the problem.

Theorem 5.7.   *If the integers ξ_{ij} satisfy (1) and (2′) and the integers π_i and π'_j satisfy (1)* and (2)* then*

$$\sum_{i,j} \gamma_{ij} \xi_{ij} = \sum_j \pi'_j \delta_j - \sum_i \pi_i \sigma_i$$

Proof.   From (2′) and (2)* we have

$$\sum_j \pi'_j \delta_j - \sum_i \pi_i \sigma_i = \sum_j \pi'_j \left(\sum_i \xi_{ij} \right) - \sum_i \pi_i \left(\sum_j \xi_{ij} \right)$$
$$= \sum_{i,j} \xi_{ij} (\pi'_j - \pi_i) \leqq \sum_{i,j} \xi_{ij} \gamma_{ij} \qquad (3)$$

We must show that this inequality is in fact an equation. To do this we consider a network with $m + n$ nodes consisting of the m plants and n markets and a capacity κ_{ij} from the ith plant to jth market where

$$
\begin{aligned}
\kappa_{ij} &= \infty && \text{if } \pi'_j - \pi_i = \gamma_{ij} \\
&= 0 && \text{if } \pi'_j - \pi_i < \gamma_{ij}
\end{aligned}
$$

where the π'_j and π_i are solutions of (1)* and (2)*.

We now consider the transshipment problem with supplies σ_i, demands δ_j, and capacities κ_{ij}. Suppose first that this problem is feasible. Then the integers ξ'_{ij} which solve the problem satisfy the constraints (2′) by definition. Also substituting the ξ'_{ij} for ξ_{ij} in inequality (3) we must obtain an equation since by definition of the κ_{ij}, the numbers ξ'_{ij} are nonzero only when $\pi'_j - \pi_i = \gamma_{ij}$. In this case, therefore, the assertion is proved.

Suppose next that this transshipment problem is not feasible. Then by Theorem 5.3, there is a set of nodes S such that the net demand of S exceeds the capacity from S' into S. This can happen in our case only if the capacity from S' to S is zero (for otherwise it would be infinite). Let U be the nodes of S which are plants and let V be the nodes of S which are markets. Then Theorem 5.3 becomes

$$
\delta(S) - \sigma(S) = \sum_{M_j \varepsilon V} \delta_j - \sum_{P_i \varepsilon U} \sigma_i > k(S', S) = 0 \tag{4}
$$

We now obtain a contradiction by showing that the numbers π_i and π'_j do not maximize (1)*, for we may define

$$
\begin{aligned}
\bar{\pi}_i &= \pi_i + 1 && \text{for } P_i \varepsilon U & \bar{\pi}_i &= \pi_i && \text{for } P_i \varepsilon U' \\
\bar{\pi}'_j &= \pi'_j + 1 && \text{for } M_j \varepsilon V & \bar{\pi}'_j &= \pi'_j && \text{for } M_j \varepsilon V'
\end{aligned}
$$

Using (4) we have

$$
\sum_j \bar{\pi}'_j \delta_j - \sum_i \bar{\pi}_i \sigma_i = \sum_j \pi'_j \delta_j - \sum_i \pi_i \sigma_i + \left(\sum_{M_j \varepsilon V} \delta_j - \sum_{P_i \varepsilon U} \sigma_i \right) > \sum_j \pi'_j \delta_j - \sum_i \pi_i \sigma_i
$$

It only remains to show that π_i and π_j' satisfy (2)*, that is,

$$\pi_j' - \pi_i \leq \gamma_{ij} \tag{5}$$

The only case in which (5) might not hold is when $M_j \, \varepsilon \, V$ and $P_i \, \varepsilon \, U'$, but if $P_i \, \varepsilon \, U'$ then $P_i \, \varepsilon \, S'$; hence $\kappa_{ij} = 0$ and hence by definition of the capacities $\pi_j' - \pi_i < \gamma_{ij}$ or $\pi_j' - \pi_i \leq \gamma_{ij} - 1$, and therefore $\pi_j' - \pi_i = \pi_j' + 1 - \pi_i \leq \gamma_{ij}$, so that also for this case condition (2)* is satisfied and we have the desired contradiction which proves the theorem.

We proceed at once to the solution of an example, given by the following tableau:

			M_1	M_2	M_3	M_4	M_5	M_6
		π_j'	2	3	3	3	7	2
π_i	σ_i	δ_j	3	3	6	2	1	2
P_1	0	3	5	③	7	③	8	5
P_2	0	4	5	6	12	5	⑦	11
P_3	0	2	②	8	③	4	8	②
P_4	0	8	9	6	10	5	10	9

This is a problem with 4 plants and 6 markets. The numbers in the column headed σ_i are the supplies and those in the row labeled δ_j are the demands. The (i, j)th entry in the table is, of course, the cost γ_{ij}.

In order to start the computation we must choose some "prices" π_i and π_j'. A simple method for doing this is to let all π_i be zero and let $\pi_j' = \min_i \gamma_{ij}$. This has been done in the above table, and we have also circled those entries γ_{ij} for which $\gamma_{ij} = \pi_j' - \pi_i$. We note that there is no circled entry in the last row so that we can actually "improve" our initial set of prices by letting $\pi_4 = -2$ (prices need not be positive). The procedure we shall follow, as in the assignment problem, consists of two routines which are used alternately. The first is to try to solve a transshipment problem as in Sec. 4, and the second is to choose improved prices for the dual problem. The following tableau indicates the first of these routines:

	π_i	σ_i		M_1		M_2		M_3		M_4		M_5		M_6	
π'_j				2		3		3		↓ 3		↓ 7		2	
δ_j				3	1	3	0	6	6	2	0	1	0	2	2
P_1	0	3	0	5		③	3	7		③		8		5	
P_2	↓ 0	4	3	5		6		12		5		⑦	1	11	
P_3	0	2	0	②	2	8		③		4		8		②	
P_4	↓ −2	8	6	9		6		10		⑤	2	10		9	

We explain this tableau. The column headed π_i and row labeled π'_j contain the initial prices as already determined. In this iteration we begin to ship from plants to markets. In the double column headed σ_i the left-hand entries give the initial supplies at the markets and the right-hand entries give the supplies after the first set of shipments has been made. These will in turn be the initial supplies for the next iteration. Similarly, the left-hand entries in the row headed δ_j represent the initial demand, while the right-hand entries represent the unfulfilled demand after the first set of shipments has been made. In the cost matrix itself we have again circled the entries for which $\pi'_j - \pi_i = \gamma_{ij}$. These always appear in the left-hand box of the double column.

We now proceed to solve the transshipment problem, that is, to satisfy as much of the demand as possible using only edges (i, j) for which the corresponding cost has been circled. The procedure here is precisely the routine described in Sec. 4. The right-hand side of the double box (i, j) in the matrix is used to record the amount shipped from P_i to M_j. Thus on our first iteration we ship 3 units from plant P_1 to market M_2, 1 unit from P_2 to M_5, 2 units from P_3 to M_1, and 2 units from P_4 to M_4, as the table shows. We are now left with 3 units at

P_2 and 6 units at P_4, as is seen from the right-hand column under σ_i. Furthermore, no further shipments can be made at this time, for the only markets which can be reached from P_2 and P_4 are M_4 and M_5, and at these markets the demand has already been satisfied. We see now that there is an excess supply of 9 units among the nodes P_2, P_4, M_4, and M_5. If we now reduce all prices at these nodes we shall obtain a feasible solution of the dual which has increased by at least 9 units. The downward-pointing arrows in the diagram indicate which prices are to be reduced. (We remark that in the proof of Theorem 5.7 we found a set with an excess demand rather than supply, and increased rather than decreased prices. The situation, however, is clearly symmetric, and in this case it is more convenient to decrease prices.) Lowering all indicated prices by one unit the new tableau is this:

				M_1	M_2		M_3	M_4		M_5		M_6
		π'_j		2	↓	3	3	↓ 2	↓	6		2
	π_i	δ_j		1 ¦ 1	0 ¦ 0		6 ¦ 6	0 ¦ 0	0 ¦ 0		2 ¦ 2
		σ_i									
P_1	↓ 0	0 ¦ 0		5 ¦	③ ¦ 3		7 ¦	3 ¦	8 ¦		5 ¦
P_2	↓ −1	3 ¦ 3		5 ¦	6 ¦		12 ¦	5 ¦	⑦ ¦ 1	11 ¦
P_3	0	0 ¦ 0		② ¦ 2	8 ¦		③ ¦	4 ¦	8 ¦		② ¦
P_4	↓ −3	6 ¦ 6		9 ¦	⑥ ¦		10 ¦	⑤ ¦ 2	10 ¦		9 ¦

Here we see that the only new circled entry is the 6 in the last row under M_2. On the other hand, the 3 in the first row under M_4 which was circled on the first iteration is no longer so, for π'_4 was decreased while π_1 remained fixed. One sees after applying the algorithm for solving the transshipment problem that no further shipments are possible at this stage, and that the nodes P_1, P_2, P_4, M_2, M_4, and M_5 carry a surplus supply of 9 units. Accordingly we may again decrease the corresponding prices. This time a decrease of 2 units is possible without violating the constraints on the prices.

	π_i	σ_i	δ_j	M_1		M_2		M_3		M_4		M_5		M_6	
π'_j				2		1		↑ 3		0		4		↑ 2	
				1	0	0	0	6	6	0	0	0	0	2	0
P_1	−2	0	0	5		③	3	7		3		8		5	
P_2	−3	3	0	⑤	3	6		12		5		⑦	1	11	
P_3	↑ 0	0	0	②		8		③		4		8		②	2
P_4	−5	6	6	9		⑥		10		⑤	2	10		9	

We now circle the entry 5 in row 2, under M_1. We then ship 1 unit from P_2 to M_1 and 2 units first from P_2 to M_1, then from M_1 back to P_3, for notice that in the previous tableau we have 2 units of back capacity from M_1 to P_3. Then we ship these 2 units forward again from P_3 to M_6. We are left with 6 units at P_4 and a demand for 6 units at M_3. Now there is an excess demand of 6 units among the nodes P_3, M_3, and M_6, and the capacity into this set is zero. The next tableau is obtained by increasing π_3, π'_3, and π'_6 by 1 unit.

	π_i	σ_i	δ_j	M_1		M_2		M_3		M_4		M_5		M_6	
π'_j				2		1		↑ 4		0		4		↑ 3	
				0	0	0	0	6	4	0	0	0	0	0	0
P_1	−2	0	0	5		③	1	7		3		8		⑤	2
P_2	−3	0	0	⑤	3	6		12		5		⑦	1	11	
P_3	↑ 1	0	0	2		8		③	2	4		8		②	
P_4	−5	6	4	9		⑥	2	10		⑤	2	10		9	

The new circled entry is the 5 in row 1 under M_6. This permits us to ship 2 units from P_4 to M_2 to P_1 to M_6 to P_3 to M_3. The appropriate changes have been made in the tableau. We now have a surplus demand of 4 units on P_3 and M_3 and a capacity of zero into these nodes so that we may again increase π_3 and π'_3, giving

	π_i	σ_i	M_1		M_2		M_3		M_4		M_5		M_6	
π'_j			2		1		5		0		4		3	
δ_j			0	0	0	0	4	0	0	0	0	0	0	0
P_1	-2	0	5		③	1	⑦		3		8		⑤	2
P_2	-3	0	⑤	3	6		12		5		7	1	11	
P_3	2	0	2		8		③	2	4		8		2	
P_4	-5	4	9	0	⑥	2	⑩	4	⑤	2	10		9	

New circles have appeared under M_3 in rows 1 and 4. Because of the circle in row 4, we can ship the remaining 4 units directly from P_4 to M_3; so this last transshipment problem is feasible and we have therefore a solution to the original problem. The solution is immediately read from the last tableau, for the nonzero flows ξ_{ij} are precisely the nonzero entries in the right-hand parts of the double columns of the matrix. The solution is

$$\xi_{12} = 1 \qquad \xi_{16} = 2 \qquad \xi_{21} = 3 \qquad \xi_{25} = 1$$
$$\xi_{33} = 2 \qquad \xi_{42} = 2 \qquad \xi_{43} = 4 \qquad \xi_{44} = 2$$

and the minimum cost is simply the sum of the products of each pair of right- and left-hand entries in the tableau; thus cost $= 3 \times 1 + 5 \times 2 + 5 \times 3 + 7 \times 1 + 3 \times 2 + 6 \times 2 + 10 \times 4 + 5 \times 2 = 103$.

We also get the solution of the dual problem,

$$(\pi_1, \pi_2, \pi_3, \pi_4) = (-2, -3, 2, -5)$$
and
$$(\pi'_1, \pi'_2, \pi'_3, \pi'_4, \pi'_5, \pi'_6) = (2, 1, 5, 0, 4, 3)$$

and, of course, we have the important independent check on our computations by computing the value of the dual:

$$\sum_j \pi'_j \delta_j - \sum_i \pi_i \sigma_i = 2 \times 3 + 1 \times 3 + 5 \times 6 + 0 \times 2$$
$$+ 4 \times 1 + 3 \times 2 + 2 \times 3 + 4 \times 3 - 2 \times 2 + 5 \times 8 = 103$$

While this algorithm has taken some time to describe, it can actually be performed very rapidly, particularly on a blackboard where one easily erases and replaces entries in the tableau without having to rewrite all the numbers at each iteration. Observe that we have solved here a problem in 24 unknowns and 10 constraints in a much shorter time than would be required by the simplex method.

8. Other Examples: Shortest Route; The Caterer

One of the simplest and most elegant applications of the methods of this chapter is in connection with the problem of finding the shortest path through a network. We are again given a network N with a source s and a sink s'. Corresponding to each edge (x, y) is a non-negative number $\tau(x, y)$ called the *transit time* of the edge which gives the time required to go from x to y. In case there is no way of getting from x to y directly we set $\tau(x, y)$ equal to infinity. The problem is now to find a path $P = (x_0, x_1, \ldots, x_n)$ where $x_0 = s$, $x_n = s'$ which has the shortest *length* where the length $l(P)$ is defined by

$$l(P) = \sum_{i=1}^{n} \tau(x_{i-1}, x_i) \tag{1}$$

To solve the problem we may reinterpret it as a shipping problem in which we wish to send one unit from s to s'. The function $\tau(x, y)$ is now to be thought of as the cost of shipping one unit from x to y, and we seek the cheapest route. As the dual problem, we try to find "prices" $\pi(x)$ at the nodes such that

$$\pi(s') \text{ is a maximum} \tag{1*}$$

subject to

$$\pi(y) - \pi(x) \leqq \tau(x, y) \qquad \text{for all } x, y \tag{2*}$$

and

$$\pi(s) = 0$$

Theorem 5.8. *The maximum value of* (1)* *is the length of the shortest path from* s *to* s'.

Proof. If π satisfies (2)* and $(x_0, x_1, \ldots, x_n) = P$ is any path from s to s' then

$$l(P) = \sum_{i=1}^{n} \tau(x_{i-1}, x_i) \geqq \sum_{i=1}^{n} [\pi(x_i) - \pi(x_{i-1})]$$

$$= \pi(x_n) - \pi(x_0) = \pi(s') - \pi(s) = \pi(s') \tag{3}$$

Suppose that π is the maximizing price function. If there is a path $P = (x_0, x_1, \ldots, x_n)$ from s to s' such that

$$\pi(x_i) - \pi(x_{i-1}) = \tau(x_{i-1}, x_i) \qquad \text{for all } i$$

then equality will hold in (3), so P will be minimizing. If no such path exists, let $S \subset N$ be all nodes which can be reached from s by a path consisting of edges (x, y) where $\pi(y) - \pi(x) = \tau(x, y)$. By assumption s' is not in s. We now define $\bar{\pi}(x)$ by the rules

$$\bar{\pi}(x) = \pi(x) \qquad \text{for } x \, \varepsilon \, S$$
$$\bar{\pi}(x) = \pi(x) + 1 \qquad \text{for } x \, \varepsilon \, S'$$

Now $\bar{\pi}$ also satisfies (2)*, for the only place where it could fail is for $x \, \varepsilon \, S$, $y \, \varepsilon \, S'$, but if $x \, \varepsilon \, S$ there is an "admissible" path from s to x; hence $\pi(y) - \pi(x) < \tau(x, y)$; otherwise this path could be extended to a path from s to y. Thus $\pi(y) - \pi(x) \leqq \tau(x, y) - 1$, so $\tau(x, y) \geqq \pi(y) + 1 - \pi(x) = \bar{\pi}(y) - \bar{\pi}(x)$, proving the assertion. On the other hand, $\bar{\pi}(s') = \pi(s') + 1 > \pi(s')$, contradicting maximality of π and completing the proof.

This theorem is also immediately translatable into a computational algorithm. The procedure is quite analogous to that used for the assignment and transportation problems, though somewhat simpler. A numerical example for solution is given in the exercises and provides an opportunity for the reader to test his understanding of the methods of this chapter (Exercise 15).

There are a number of other problems whose subject matter has nothing to do with network flows but which can be solved by translating them into equivalent network problems. An example of this is the *caterer's problem*, which we now describe.

A caterer is to supply napkins for banquets on m successive days, the number δ_i of napkins being required on the ith day. Napkins can (1) be bought at the store for α cents each, (2) be sent to a laundry and laundered by the quick q-day service at β cents each, or (3) be laundered by the regular r-day service at γ cents each. If $q < r$ and $\gamma < \beta < \alpha$, how many napkins should be bought and laundered by each of the services so as to supply all the banquets at minimum cost?

The equivalent transportation problem is the following: There are m markets corresponding to the banquets, the demand at the ith market being δ_i. There are $m + 1$ plants; the first, P_0, is the store which has a supply of $\sum_{i=1}^{m} \delta_i$. The ith plant corresponds to the ith hamper of used napkins and accordingly has a supply of δ_i napkins. Finally, the costs γ_{ij} are as follows:

$$\gamma_{0j} = \alpha \qquad \text{for } j = 1, \ldots, m$$

since a napkin can be shipped from the store to any banquet at cost α.

$$\gamma_{ij} = \infty \qquad \text{for } i \neq 0 \qquad \text{and} \qquad j < i + q$$
$$\gamma_{ij} = \beta \qquad \text{for } i \neq 0 \qquad i + q \leq j < i + r$$
$$\gamma_{ij} = \gamma \qquad \text{for } i \neq 0 \qquad i + r \leq j$$

The three relations express the fact that napkins cannot be laundered in less than q days and can be laundered at the higher cost if needed in less than r days. It is clear that this transportation problem is equivalent to the original problem, and hence the methods of the previous section are applicable. Exercise 16 at the end of the chapter will give the reader an opportunity to solve a numerical example.

9. Concluding Remarks and Open Questions

We have considered in this chapter only a few of the simplest integral problems which can be solved by the methods described. An obvious and important case which has not been treated is a combination of the transportation and transshipment problems in which it is desired to find among all feasible flows in the sense of Sec. 4 one which minimizes shipping costs. The required duality theorem is stated in the exercises and can be used to give an effective computational algorithm for finding the optimal flow. Since this problem involves both capacities and costs the calculations are somewhat more lengthy than those treated in this chapter, but they are no more difficult in principle.

Another interesting problem is the so-called dynamic maximum-flow problem in which we are given a network with source and sink and transit times as well as capacities associated with each edge.   The problem is then to maximize the flow from s to s' in a given fixed period of time.   It is not very difficult to extend the methods of this chapter to handle this dynamic problem.

On the other hand, there are problems which appear to be very similar to those we have discussed and yet cannot be handled by the present methods.   A striking illustration of this is a transshipment problem involving more than one commodity.

The following simple example illustrates the type of difficulty which may arise.   This is a transshipment problem involving 6 plants and 4 markets.   Plants P_1 and P_2 produce "circles," plants P_3 and P_4 produce "squares," and plants P_5 and P_6 produce both.   Circles and squares are each assumed to occupy one unit of volume.   At each market there is a demand for one circle and one square, and the plants are connected to the markets by edges of capacity 1 unit, as shown in the figure.

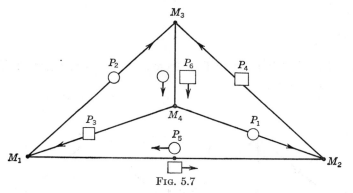

FIG. 5.7

The question is now whether or not the demands are feasible.   One sees at once that the demands can be satisfied by shipping half a circle and half a square from each plant to the adjacent markets.   On the other hand, there is no solution to this problem in integers, for we may assume by symmetry that the circle at P_5 is sent to M_1.   Then the circle at P_2 must go to M_3, and the circle at P_6 must go to M_4.   Also the square at P_5 goes to M_2, the square at P_4 goes to M_3, but this means the square at P_6 goes to M_4, and this overloads the route from P_6 to M_4.

Problems of the above type provide an important subject for future investigation.

Bibliographical Notes

The max flow min cut theorem which was the starting point for the analysis of this chapter was first proved by Ford and Fulkerson [1]. The feasibility theorem for the simple-assignment problem is due to P. Hall [1].   The second proof of this result is that given by Halmos and Vaughan [1].   The feasibility theorem for the transshipment problem is due to Gale [1].   In the treatment of the optimal-assignment problem we have followed the work of Kuhn [3].   The price equilibrium model is presented here for the first time.   The transportation problem is solved in Sec. 7 by the methods of Ford and Fulkerson [2], who are also responsible for the numerical example treated there.   The shortest-route problem is described by Ford [1] and the caterer problem was originally proposed by Jacobs [1] and treated as a transportation problem by Prager [1].

Exercises

1. Prove that if f is any flow from s to s' in the network N then $f(s, N) = f(N, s')$.

2. Find a maximum flow in the network shown below.

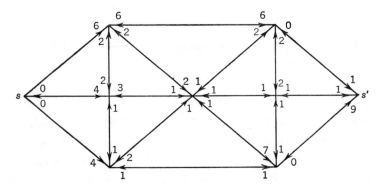

The numbers next to each edge represent the capacities in the directions indicated by the arrows.

3. In the network below, nodes ① and ⑥ are sources with supplies $\sigma(1) = 3$, $\sigma(6) = 5$. Nodes ④ and ⑧ are sinks with demands $\delta(4) = 4$, $\delta(8) = 4$. The numbers on the edges are capacities which are assumed to be the same in both directions. Determine whether this transshipment problem is feasible.

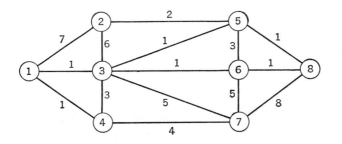

4. Let (S, S') and (R, R') be two minimal cuts in the network N. Show that $(S \cap R, S' \cup R')$ is also a minimal cut. (We remark that this theorem can be stated without defining the notion of a flow, but its proof apparently requires the max flow min cut theorem.)

5. Let Q be the qualification matrix for a simple-assignment problem. A *cover* of Q consists of a set R of rows and C of columns of Q so that every nonzero entry of Q lies in either a row of R or column of C. Prove that the maximum number of people that can be assigned is the minimum number of rows plus columns which will cover Q.

6. Find a minimal cover for the qualification matrix of Sec. 3.

7. Find a solution of the optimal-assignment problem whose rating matrix is the following:

0	15	9	1	3	4	19
2	0	19	11	9	3	14
12	5	17	12	24	15	16
19	11	14	23	16	17	29
20	15	23	22	19	21	24
23	12	16	17	24	25	26
25	16	8	26	21	20	23

8. Let $A = (\alpha_{ij})$ be an $n \times n$ rating matrix, and let $A' = (\alpha_{ij} + \alpha_i)$, where $\alpha_1, \ldots, \alpha_n$ are any n numbers. Show that an assignment is optimal for A' if and only if it is optimal for A.

9. Let $A = (\alpha_{ij})$ be an $n \times n$ rating matrix. Show that there exist numbers α_i such that for the matrix $A' = (\alpha'_{ij}) = (\alpha_{ij} + \alpha_i)$, the value of an optimal assignment is given by the formula

$$\mu = \sum_{j=1}^{n} \max_{i} (\alpha'_{ij})$$

10. Show that in any optimal assignment at least one person is assigned to the job at which he is best. Show how to construct an $n \times n$ rating matrix, for any n, in which only one person is assigned to his best job in the optimal assignment.

11. An $n \times n$ matrix is called *doubly stochastic* if all the entries are nonnegative and all its row and column sums are unity. Show that these matrices form a convex polytope whose extreme points are precisely the *permutation* matrices, i.e., the matrices all of whose row and column vectors are unit vectors. (Hint: Define an equivalent-flow problem and use Theorem 5.4.)

12. For any nonnegative $n \times n$ matrix $A = (\alpha_{ij})$ show that the solutions of the canonical linear program

$$\sum_{i=1}^{n} \lambda_{ij} = 1 \qquad \sum_{j=1}^{n} \lambda_{ij} = 1$$
$$\sum \lambda_{ij}\alpha_{ij} = \text{maximum}$$

form a convex polytope whose extreme points are precisely the optimal assignments.

13. In the problem of equilibrium prices show that the sets of *admissible entries* [satisfying (2) of Sec. 6] correspond to all possible optimal assignments.

14. Solve the 3 by 4 transportation problem whose cost matrix is

4	4	9	3
3	5	8	8
2	6	5	7

and the supplies are

$$\sigma_1 = 3 \qquad \sigma_2 = 5 \qquad \sigma_3 = 7$$

and the demands are

$$\delta_1 = 2 \qquad \delta_2 = 5 \qquad \delta_3 = 4 \qquad \delta_4 = 4$$

15. Find the shortest path through the following network:

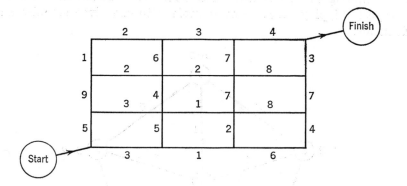

The numbers next to the edges give the mileages.

16. The caterer must supply 60 napkins on Monday, 50 on Tuesday, 80 on Wednesday, 40 on Thursday, 50 on Friday. Napkins cost 5 cents, can be laundered in 1 day for 2 cents and in 2 days for 1 cent. What is the most economical plan for the caterer?

17. The following is a generalization of the transportation problem. In a network N the cost of shipping one unit from x to y is $c(x, y)$. The demand at node x is $d(x)$, and a negative demand is interpreted as a supply. Assuming $d(N) = 0$, show that the problem of satisfying the demand at minimum cost is correctly given as follows: Find a nonnegative function g on edges of N such that

$$\sum_{x,y} g(x, y)c(x, y) \text{ is a minimum} \tag{1}$$

subject to

$$g(N, x) - g(x, N) \geqq d(x) \qquad \text{for all } x \tag{2}$$

Show that the following is the correct dual problem by proving the duality theorem: Find a function π on N such that

$$\sum_{x} \pi(x)d(x) \text{ is a maximum} \tag{1*}$$

subject to

$$\pi(y) - \pi(x) \leqq c(x, y) \qquad \text{for all } x, y \tag{2*}$$

18. In the network below, nodes ① and ③ are sources with supplies $s(1) = 5$, $s(3) = 3$. Nodes ②, ④, and ⑤ are sinks with demands

$d(2) = 2$, $d(4) = 4$, $d(5) = 2$.   The numbers next to the edges are unit shipping costs, assumed the same in either direction.   Find the cheapest shipping schedule compatible with the given supplies and demands.

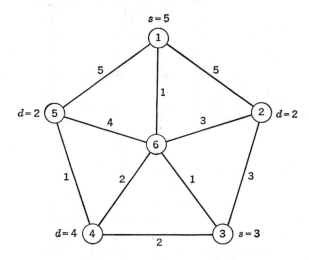

19. Consider a transportation problem in which there is a capacity κ_{ij} as well as a cost γ_{ij} from the plant P_i to the market M_j.   Show that a feasible shipping schedule ξ_{ij} is optimal if and only if there exist prices $\pi_1, \ldots, \pi_m, \pi'_1, \ldots, \pi'_n$ such that

$$\text{if } \pi'_j - \pi_i > \gamma_{ij} \qquad \text{then } \xi_{ij} = \kappa_{ij} \qquad (1)$$
$$\text{if } \pi'_j - \pi_i < \gamma_{ij} \qquad \text{then } \xi_{ij} = 0 \qquad (2)$$

(Hint: See Exercise 16 of Chap. 3.)

20. In a network N with source s and sink s' let x_1 and x_2 be any nodes of N.   Suppose

If capacity $k(s, x_1)$ is increased by δ_1 then the value μ of the maximum flow is increased by Δ_1 (1)

If $k(s, x_2)$ is increased by δ_2 then μ is increased by Δ_2 (2)

If $k(s, x_1)$ and $k(s, x_2)$ are increased simultaneously by δ_1 and δ_2 then μ is increased by Δ_{12} (3)

Prove that $\Delta_{12} \leqq \Delta_1 + \Delta_2$.

21. As in Exercise 20 suppose

If $k(s, x_1)$ is increased by δ_1 then μ is increased by Δ_1	(1)
If $k(x_2, s')$ is increased by δ_2 then μ is increased by Δ_2	(2)
If both capacities are increased simultaneously by δ_1 and δ_2 then μ is increased by Δ_{12}	(3)

Prove that $\Delta_{12} \geqq \Delta_1 + \Delta_2$.

22. An airline must make n flights, $F_1, \ldots, F_n$, in a certain year. We say that F_i *precedes* F_j, written $F_i > F_j$, if it is possible for a plane to make the flight F_i and subsequently the flight F_j. From the meaning of the problem it is clear that the relation $>$ satisfies

$$\text{if } F_i > F_j \text{ and } F_j > F_k, \text{ then } F_i > F_k \qquad (1)$$
$$\text{if } F_i > F_j, \text{ then } F_j \not> F_i \qquad (2)$$

Two flights are called *noncomparable* if neither precedes the other. Prove: *the minimum number of planes needed to meet a given schedule is equal to the maximum number of mutually noncomparable flights.*

Hint: Consider the $n \times n$ simple-assignment problem with qualification matrix $A = (\alpha_{ij})$, where $\alpha_{ij} = 1$ if and only if $F_i > F_j$. Suppose the maximum number of assignments and therefore the minimum cover of A is k (see Exercise 5).

a. Using the k assignments, show that all flights can be made by $n - k$ planes.

b. Show that if a cover of A includes both the ith row and the ith column of A it is not minimal. Hence show that the flights F_i for which neither the ith row nor column lies in the minimal cover form a set of $n - k$ noncomparable flights.

CHAPTER SIX

Two-person Games: Examples, Definitions, and Elementary Theory

The economic models which we have studied in the foregoing chapters have been of a single type often referred to as *optimization models*.[1] The problem in such models is to find a procedure for achieving some well-defined goal, as, for instance, the maximization of profits or minimization of costs. In economics such models apply typically to situations involving a single firm or possibly a single country with a planned economy. Optimization theory is undoubtedly the most extensively developed branch of theoretical economics. However, optimization problems constitute only a small and rather special kind of economic problem. They do not include most problems about the economy as a whole, the so-called "market problems." In fact, they do not include any situations in which there are groups or individuals with opposing interests, for an optimal situation for one such group may be far from optimal for another.

The remaining chapters of this book will be concerned mainly with models which are not of the simple optimization type, and the reader must at this point prepare himself for a definite change in the nature of our discussions. In the treatment of linear programming we pre-

---

[1] Exceptions are the price-equilibrium problems of Chap. 3, Sec. 5, and Chap 5, Sec. 6.

sented a fairly definitive theory. The problems discussed made obvious sense. The theory of the problems was quite thoroughly developed, one even had efficient methods for finding solutions, and most important of all, it was clear from the outset exactly what questions had to be answered. In nonoptimization situations, on the other hand, the first and usually the most difficult problem is to decide what questions to ask. Much of the remainder of this book will be concerned with some of the answers which have been given to this problem in various sorts of situations. These answers will necessarily be more tentative than those given for simple maximum and minimum problems, and the reader must not expect to be presented with polished and complete theories. The subject of "multi-objective" models is still very young, and the best we can do at this point is to present the reader with some of the more promising attacks which have been made on it in some special cases.

We have already mentioned as the characteristic property of nonoptimization models the idea of individuals or groups with conflicting interests. The theory of games attempts to study economic behavior by isolating this particular aspect, which occurs in its simplest form in games of strategy. The program of von Neumann and Morgenstern can be described very roughly as an attempt to learn about economic models by first analyzing these simpler and therefore more tractable game models. At the time of this writing it is still not clear whether this program will succeed as regards its applicability to economics. It is generally agreed, however, that the theory of the so-called two-person zero-sum game has already achieved a rather spectacular success, not as a tool for studying economic phenomena directly, but as an example par excellence of model formulation and analysis. In the two chapters which follow, the reader will have an opportunity to study in some detail this example of a significant self-contained mathematical theory which successfully describes and analyzes a certain kind of "economic-like" behavior. For anyone interested in the formulation and study of models of behavior, an understanding of this prototype is therefore indispensable.

Let us in accordance with our usual procedure begin by illustrating the game concept with a set of concrete examples.

1. First Examples and Definitions

All games discussed in this chapter will involve two players, player 1 and player 2, to be denoted by P_1 and P_2, respectively. We shall proceed to describe a number of games, first by a set of "rules" given verbally, and later in formal mathematical notation.

Example 1. Odds and Evens (Matching Pennies). *Rules.* Each player chooses either the number 1 or 2 without knowing his opponent's choice. Upon revealing their choices, P_1 pays or receives one dollar from P_2 according to whether the sum of the chosen numbers is odd or even.

This is, of course, a familiar game usually played by "throwing" one or two fingers. It is clear that the mechanism by which choices are made is irrelevant as far as the outcome of the game is concerned. It will be useful to have a formalism which retains the essential features of the game but eliminates these irrelevancies. What is essential in the above game is the fact that each player has two courses of action or *strategies* open to him; he may "play" either the number 1 or 2. If we denote these strategies for P_1 by s_1 and s_2, respectively, and for P_2 by t_1 and t_2, then the game can be concisely represented in the following tabular form:

$$
\begin{array}{c|cc}
 & t_1 & t_2 \\
\hline
s_1 & 1 & -1 \\
s_2 & -1 & 1
\end{array}
\tag{1}
$$

where the number appearing in the ith row and jth column of the table represents the amount which P_1 wins from P_2 when P_1 plays s_i and P_2 plays t_j. This table is called the *payoff matrix* of the game described.

Let us now consider a second game, that of *matching pennies*.

Rules. Each player places a penny on a table. If both pennies show heads or tails P_1 takes them, while if one shows heads and the other tails, P_2 takes them.

It is clear at once that this game is in essence identical with the previous one. Let the strategies consisting of choosing heads or tails be denoted by s_H, s_T, and t_H, t_T for the two players. The payoff matrix is then

$$
\begin{array}{c}
\quad\quad t_H \quad\; t_T \\
\begin{array}{c} s_H \\ s_T \end{array}
\left|\begin{array}{rr} 1 & -1 \\ -1 & 1 \end{array}\right|
\end{array}
\tag{2}
$$

The only differences between tables (1) and (2) are the different names given to the strategies and the change of monetary unit, neither of which should have any effect on the way the game is played. For theoretical purposes one can therefore identify a game with its payoff matrix. Thus *all games having the same payoff matrix will henceforth be considered as the same game.*

Before introducing further terminology, we consider another example which is an elaboration of the previous game.

Example 2. Morra. Rules. The players simultaneously show either one or two fingers, and at the same time, each player announces a number. If the number announced by one of the players is the same as the total number of fingers shown by both players, then he wins that number from his opponent (hence, if both players guess right, then the net payment to each is zero).

Here we see that each player has four possible strategies open to him. He may show one finger and guess the total to be either two or three, or he may show two fingers and guess a total of three or four. (There are, of course, other possibilities, like showing one and guessing four, but this strategy can obviously never win; so one may as well eliminate it from consideration.) If we denote by s_{ij} and t_{ij} the strategy "show i fingers and guess the number j" for the respective players then we get the following payoff matrix:

$$
\begin{array}{c}
\quad\quad t_{12} \quad\; t_{13} \quad\; t_{23} \quad\; t_{24} \\
\begin{array}{c} s_{12} \\ s_{13} \\ s_{23} \\ s_{24} \end{array}
\left|\begin{array}{rrrr}
0 & 2 & -3 & 0 \\
-2 & 0 & 0 & 3 \\
3 & 0 & 0 & -4 \\
0 & -3 & 4 & 0
\end{array}\right|
\end{array}
\tag{3}
$$

Thus, for example, if P_1 plays s_{13} and P_2 plays t_{24} then P_1 has shown one finger, P_2 has shown two fingers, giving a total of three, which was the number announced by P_1 (but not P_2); so that P_1 wins three from P_2 as shown in the matrix.

With the preceding examples as illustrations, we are now prepared to begin formalizing some of the above ideas.

Definition.   A *two-person zero-sum* game Γ consists of a pair of sets S and T and a real-valued function ϕ defined on pairs (s, t), where s is in S and t is in T.

Terminology.   The elements s and t of the sets S and T are called *strategies* for player P_1 and P_2, respectively.   The function ϕ is called the *payoff function*, or simply the *payoff*.

Interpretation.   The number $\phi(s, t)$ is the amount which P_2 pays P_1 in case P_1 plays strategy s and P_2 plays strategy t.

The term two-person is self-explanatory.   The term zero-sum means that corresponding to any pair of strategies s and t the sum of payments from P_1 to P_2 plus those from P_2 to P_1 is zero, or more simply, what one player wins the other loses.   From now until further notice, the word "game" will be used as an abbreviation for the cumbersome phrase "two-person zero-sum game."

Notation.   We shall denote the game Γ with strategy sets S and T and payoff function ϕ by the symbols $(S, T; \phi)$.

If the sets S and T are finite then, as we have seen, the payoff ϕ can be represented by a matrix.   Such games will be called *matrix games*.

It is natural to ask whether these formal definitions really include what we normally think of as games, for instance, chess, bridge, poker. If this book were intended as a treatise on game theory, a thorough investigation of these questions would be obligatory.   Suffice it to say here that these games can be subsumed under the general class of matrix games, although the actual writing down of the sets S and T and the payoff matrix ϕ would be a practical impossibility because of the enormous number of strategies involved.   The examples which we treat in the next section should give the reader some idea of how one could show that the games mentioned can be put into the general framework we have just defined.

2. Further Examples of Matrix Games

Example 3.   Goofspiel.   Rules.   Each player is provided with a hand of n cards numbered 1 to n.   On the first "move," each player chooses a card from his hand, and the player holding the higher card wins a score of a_1, or if the cards are equal, then each player wins $a_1/2$. On the next move, each player chooses one of the cards remaining in his hand, and this time high man receives a score of a_2, and in case of a tie, each gets $a_2/2$. Play continues in this way until all n cards have been played, after which the player with the higher score wins an amount equal to the difference in scores from his opponent. (The numbers $a_1, \ldots, a_n$ are known to both players in advance.)

We wish to show that goofspiel may be considered as a matrix game. To do this we must describe the sets of strategies S and T. Now, the defining property of a pair of strategies is the fact that once they have been chosen the outcome or payoff is determined. Thus the decision to play card i on the first move is *not* a strategy. On the other hand, the decision to play card i_1 on the first move, i_2 on the second, $\ldots$, i_n on the nth is a strategy. However, this is a very special (and not very good) type of strategy, since all decisions are made in advance and no use is made of the information which a player gains in the course of play as to which cards his opponent still holds. The most general strategy might read something like this: on the first move play card i; on the second move play card i_1, i_2, $\ldots$, or i_n according as the opponent played card $1, 2, \ldots$, or n on his first move. On the third move play card $i_{(j,k)}$ if the opponent played card j on the first move and k on the second, etc.

Let us actually compute the number of strategies for 3-card goofspiel. Using the notation of the previous paragraph a strategy may be written in the form $(i; i_1, i_2, i_3)$. The number i, the card played on the first move, may be chosen in 3 ways, and each of the numbers i_1, i_2, and i_3 may be chosen in 2 ways from the remaining cards. Thus the total number of strategies for each player is 24.

A strategy for this game and for games generally may be described in words as "a set of instructions which tells a player what to do in all possible situations which may arise at each stage." (This notion can, of course, be made precise, but this would require introducing a great amount of formalism, which we do not wish to do here.)

We remark that familiar games like chess, checkers, and ticktacktoe may be formulated as matrix games, at least in theory. For ticktacktoe one might even attempt to write out a strategy. For chess, of course, the task would be a practical impossibility. However, for theoretical purposes we need only know that such a formulation exists.

Example 4. Bluffing. Rules. Two cards marked Hi and Lo are placed in a hat. P_1 draws a card and inspects it. He may then "fold," in which case he pays P_2 the amount $a > 0$ ($a = $ ante); or he may "bet," in which case P_2 may either "fold," paying amount a to P_1, or "call." If P_2 calls he receives from or pays to P_1 the amount b ($b = $ bet) according as P_1 holds Lo or Hi. We assume $b > a$.

Before writing down the payoff matrix, let us observe that if P_1 draws Hi it is certainly pointless for him to fold and lose a, when by betting he can win at least a. If we agree to eliminate this obviously "bad" strategy, then P_1 has two strategies corresponding to betting or folding when he draws Lo. We denote these by s_B and s_F. P_2 also has two strategies t_C (call) and t_F (fold).

This game contains a new element which we have not previously encountered because of the initial "chance move" of P_1 in drawing a card. This means that we must consider *expectations* in computing the payoff function. Thus, if P_1 plays s_B and P_2 plays t_C, then since P_1 holds Hi and Lo with probability $\frac{1}{2}$ his expected payoff is zero. If P_1 plays s_B and P_2 plays t_F then P_1 wins the amount a no matter which card he draws. If P_1 plays s_F and P_2 plays t_C, then P_1 wins b when he holds Hi, that is, half the time, and loses a the other half; so his expectation is $(b - a)/2$. Finally if both players fold, then again the expected payoff is 0. Thus we have

$$
\begin{array}{c|cc}
 & t_C & t_F \\
\hline
s_B & 0 & a \\
s_F & \dfrac{b-a}{2} & 0 \\
\end{array}
\qquad (4)
$$

The game is called bluffing because of P_1's first strategy, in which he bets even though he holds the low card. Note that if P_1 never bluffs then by always playing t_F, P_2 can assure himself an expectation of zero. On the other hand, if P_1 always bluffs P_2 can again break even by always calling. Experience and common sense suggest that an intermediate course of bluffing part of the time is desirable. The theory which we shall shortly develop confirms this feeling and makes it precise by showing just how much P_1 should bluff and what he may expect to gain by so doing.

Example 5. *A, B, C.* *Rules.* A deck containing three cards marked A, B, and C is shuffled and each player is dealt one card. After inspecting his card, P_1 announces his guess as to which card P_2 holds. After inspecting his card and hearing P_1's guess, P_2 also announces his guess as to which card P_1 holds. If either player guesses correctly the other pays him one dollar.

This game combines both the multimove feature of goofspiel and the chance element of the bluffing game. It is, in fact, a 3-move game, the first being the deal which introduces the chance element, the second being P_1's guess, and the third being P_2's guess.

Let us now determine the strategy sets S and T. Recalling that a strategy is a "complete set of instructions," we see that P_1 must know what to guess in case his card is A, B, or C. As an example, his strategy might be to guess C if he is dealt A, guess A if he is dealt either B or C. This strategy can be represented by the symbols (C, A, A). In general, a strategy for P_1 may be written in the form (X, Y, Z), where X, Y, and Z may take on any of the three values A, B, or C, and the symbols are read, "if dealt A guess X; if dealt B guess Y; if dealt C guess Z." Since each of the three variables X, Y, and Z may assume any of the values A, B, or C, there are in all 27 strategies for P_1.

A strategy for P_2 is even more complicated, as he has two pieces of information on which to base his decision, the knowledge of the card he holds and his opponent's guess. A strategy for P_2 could be represented by the following table:

$$P_2 \text{ holds}$$

$$P_1 \text{ guesses} \begin{cases} A \\ B \\ C \end{cases} \begin{array}{c|ccc} & A & B & C \\ \hline A & X_{AA} & X_{AB} & X_{AC} \\ B & X_{BA} & X_{BB} & X_{BC} \\ C & X_{CA} & X_{CB} & X_{CC} \end{array} \qquad (5)$$

The elements X_{AA}, X_{AB}, etc., take on the value A, B, or C. If P_2 holds card A and P_1 guesses card C, then P_2 shall guess card X_{CA}, and so forth. Since each of the nine entries can assume any of three values, the total number of possibilities for P_2 is $3^9 = 19,683$. Some of these strategies, however, can be immediately eliminated. It is clearly senseless for P_2 to guess the card he holds. (This is not the case for P_1, however, as we shall shortly see.) In other words, the entries in the table can be assumed to take on only two values and the number of strategies becomes $2^9 = 512$, which is nevertheless too large for convenient computation.

Fortunately, some simple common-sense arguments will reduce the above game to manageable dimensions. Note first that there are essentially only two possible courses of action for P_1. He may either guess the card he holds in his hand, or he may call one of the other cards. Let us denote these strategies, respectively, by s_S (S = same) and s_D (D = different). For P_2 there are also two possibilities. If P_1 names the card which P_2 is holding then P_2 will guess one of the other cards, it makes no difference which. The only case in which P_2 has a true choice of strategy is that in which his card is not the one named by P_1. In this case, he has two alternatives: (a) to name the same card as that named by P_1, (b) to name the third card. These strategies will be denoted by t_S and t_D, respectively. We have essentially now reduced the above game to a game in which each player has but two strategies. We proceed to evaluate the payoff matrix.

Case 1. P_1 plays s_S; P_2 plays t_S. In this case, the payoff (from P_1 to P_2) is -1 since P_2 has correctly guessed P_1's card.

Case 2. P_1 plays s_S; P_2 plays t_D. In this case, neither player guesses correctly and the payoff is zero.

Case 3. P_1 plays s_D; P_2 plays t_S. Half the time P_1 will not guess the card held by P_2 and then P_2 will also guess wrong, giving a payoff of zero. When P_1 guesses correctly, there is a $\frac{1}{2}$ probability that P_2 will also be correct. The expected payoff in this case is therefore $\frac{1}{4}$.

Case 4. P_1 plays s_D; P_2 plays t_D. In this case, if P_1 does not guess correctly, then P_2 is certain to do so. This will happen half the time. If P_1 guesses correctly, the analysis is the same as in case 3. The payoff is $-\frac{1}{4}$. The matrix is

$$
\begin{array}{c c}
& \begin{array}{c c} t_S & \quad t_D \end{array} \\
\begin{array}{c} s_S \\ s_D \end{array} &
\begin{array}{|c c|}
\hline
-1 & 0 \\
\tfrac{1}{4} & -\tfrac{1}{4} \\
\hline
\end{array}
\end{array}
\qquad (6)
$$

The verbal argument which led to this drastic reduction of the payoff matrix can, of course, be formalized. The interested reader is referred to the bibliography at the end of this chapter for further details.

From the simplified matrix above, certain properties become immediately evident. The strategy s_S is a bluffing strategy as in the previous example. Obviously s_S can never win for P_1. On the other hand, if P_2 feels sure that P_1 will never bluff, then he can assure himself an expected payoff of $-\tfrac{1}{4}$ by playing t_D. Once again, one might expect that the answer for P_1 is some sort of mixture or combination of the two policies.

3. Solutions of Games.   Mixed Strategies

We have given five examples of matrix games of varying degrees of complexity. We shall now proceed to "solve" these examples, or rather to define a notion of solution for them and exhibit solutions for Examples 1, 2, and 4 (the game of goofspiel is to date "unsolved").

Consider first a player P_1 about to play a game of odds and evens. He knows nothing about his opponent's psychological leanings; in particular, he has no information as to whether P_2 is more likely to choose one strategy than the other. Under these circumstances, it is clear that P_1 cannot hope to win the game or even have a positive expectation of winning. The best he can hope for, in fact, is to break even, that is, obtain an expectation of zero. We see now that there is a simple way in which P_1 can be assured of an expectation of zero, no matter how astute P_2 may be. All he has to do is toss a "true" coin, playing s_1 if the coin falls heads, s_2 if it falls tails. Neglecting the possibility of clairvoyance on the part of P_2, P_1 in this way guarantees himself an expectation of zero. Note, however, that it is important that the coin tossed by P_1 be true, for suppose, say, it had more than an even chance of falling heads. Then P_1 would play s_1 with probability greater than $\tfrac{1}{2}$, and P_2 would obtain a positive expectation by playing t_2.

In summary, we say that a *solution* for the game of odds and evens is for P_1 (and by symmetry, P_2 as well) to choose one of the two strategies at random, but with equal probability. This procedure has the property of guaranteeing each player an expectation of zero. Since no higher expected payoff for either player can be guaranteed, it seems reasonable to regard this program as, in some sense, optimal.

The game of odds and evens is so simple that the solution just obtained may seem obvious and almost trivial. We turn, therefore, to the more complicated game of morra, where the same ideas lead to a solution which is by no means obvious in advance. For this game, the payoff matrix was

	t_1	t_2	t_3	t_4
s_1	0	2	-3	0
s_2	-2	0	0	3
s_3	3	0	0	-4
s_4	0	-3	4	0

Because the game is "symmetrical" (we shall shortly make this notion precise), it is clearly not possible for either player to adopt a strategy ensuring him a positive expectation (indeed, any procedure adopted by P_1 could be "copied" by P_2, making the expected payoff zero). At best, therefore, we may hope for a procedure which assures a player's not losing. We assert that such a procedure for P_1 is to choose one of the strategies s_2 or s_3 by some random device which selects s_2 with probability $\frac{3}{5}$ and s_3 with probability $\frac{2}{5}$ (put 5 cards in a hat, three labeled s_2, two labeled s_3, mix well and draw—for instance). We easily compute the expected payoff from this program against all possible action by P_2. Suppose by some means or other, P_2 has arrived at the decision to play t_1. Against this strategy, P_1 will lose 2 with probability $\frac{3}{5}$ and win 3 with probability $\frac{2}{5}$. The expected payoff is therefore

$$\tfrac{3}{5}(-2) + \tfrac{2}{5}(3) = 0$$

If P_2 chooses to play either t_2 or t_3, then clearly neither player will win. Finally, if P_2 plays t_4, then P_1 wins 3 with probability $\frac{3}{5}$ and loses 4 with probability $\frac{2}{5}$; so the expected payoff is

$$\tfrac{3}{5}(3) + \tfrac{2}{5}(-4) = \tfrac{1}{5}$$

Thus, as asserted, P_1 is assured of an expectation of at least zero, regardless of what P_2 does. We refer therefore to this procedure as *optimal*. One may ask if there are any other optimal procedures, and for this game, it turns out there are. We can, in fact, exhibit an infinite set of such optimal procedures, namely: Let P_1 choose either s_2 or s_3 and let the probability of choosing s_2 be any number ρ between $\tfrac{4}{7}$ and $\tfrac{3}{5}$ (the probability of choosing s_3 being, of course, $1 - \rho$). Any such procedure achieves a payoff of zero against t_2 or t_3; against t_1 we have

$$\rho(-2) + (1 - \rho)(3) = -5\rho + 3 \geq 0 \qquad \text{since } \rho \leq \tfrac{3}{5}$$

and against t_4 we have

$$\rho(3) + (1 - \rho)(-4) = 7\rho - 4 \geq 0 \qquad \text{since } \rho \geq \tfrac{4}{7}$$

It is not hard to see that the set of procedures described above includes *all* optimal randomizing procedures. Before showing this, let us formalize this concept of randomized procedures, which is indeed the key idea in the theory to follow.

Definition. Let Γ be the game $(S, T; \phi)$. A *mixed strategy* σ for P_1 is a real-valued function on S such that

$$\sigma(s) \geq 0 \tag{1}$$

$$\sigma(s) = 0 \qquad \text{for all but a finite number of strategies } s \text{ of } S \tag{2}$$

$$\sum_{s \in S} \sigma(s) = 1 \tag{3}$$

A mixed strategy τ for P_2 is defined in a precisely analogous fashion. The set of all mixed strategies for P_1 and P_2 are denoted by $<S>$ and $<T>$, respectively.

Interpretation. The number $\sigma(s)$ represents the probability with which P_1 plays strategy s.

In order to distinguish between the original strategies s and t and the mixed strategies σ and τ we shall occasionally refer to s and t as *pure strategies*. Note, however, that the pure strategy s is, in fact, a special mixed strategy σ, where $\sigma(s) = 1$, $\sigma(s') = 0$ for $s' \neq s$. The payoff function ϕ now extends in an obvious manner to mixed strategies, namely,

$$\phi(\sigma, \tau) = \sum_{s,t} \sigma(s)\tau(t)\phi(s, t)$$

this expression being simply the expected value of the payoff when P_1 plays σ, P_2 plays τ.

We refer to the game in which the strategies and payoff have been extended in the above manner as the *extended game* and denote it by $<\Gamma> = (<S>, <T>; \phi)$.

For the case of matrix games, a special notation for mixed strategies is convenient. If S and T contain m and n strategies, respectively, we denote them in some order by $s_1, \ldots, s_m$, and $t_1, \ldots, t_n$ and denote the payoff $\phi(s_i, t_j)$ by α_{ij}. A mixed strategy for P_1 is then given by an *m-vector* $x = (\xi_1, \ldots, \xi_m)$, where ξ_i is the probability that P_1 plays s_i (thus, $\xi_i \geq 0$ and $\Sigma\xi_i = 1$). Similarly, a mixed strategy for P_2 is an *n-vector* $y = (\eta_1, \ldots, \eta_n)$ with the corresponding interpretation. The formula for the expected payoff is now

$$\phi(x, y) = \sum_{i,j} \xi_i \alpha_{ij} \eta_j = xAy$$

where A is the payoff matrix of the game.

Using the concepts just introduced, we shall say that a "solution" (this term has not yet been formally defined) to the game of morra consists of a mixed strategy

$$\bar{x} = (0, \rho, 1 - \rho, 0) \qquad \text{where } \tfrac{4}{7} \leq \rho \leq \tfrac{3}{5}$$

We now show that these are the only mixed strategies giving an expectation of at least zero against all strategies of P_2. To see this, let

$$x = (\xi_1, \xi_2, \xi_3, \xi_4)$$

be any mixed strategy for P_1 which guarantees a nonnegative expected payoff. We first see that $\xi_1 = 0$, for if ξ_1 is positive, then let P_2 play the mixed strategy $y = (0, \tfrac{4}{7}, \tfrac{3}{7}, 0)$. The payoff is

$$\phi(x, y) = \tfrac{4}{7}(2\xi_1 - 3\xi_4) + \tfrac{3}{7}(-3\xi_1 + 4\xi_4) = -\tfrac{1}{7}\xi_1 < 0$$

Likewise $\xi_4 = 0$, for if not let $y = (0, \tfrac{3}{5}, \tfrac{2}{5}, 0)$. The payoff is

$$\phi(x, y) = \tfrac{3}{5}(2\xi_1 - 3\xi_4) + \tfrac{2}{5}(-3\xi_1 + 4\xi_4) = -\tfrac{1}{5}\xi_4 < 0$$

Next, if $\xi_2 > \frac{3}{5}$, let P_2 play t_1, giving

$$\phi(x, t_1) = -2\xi_2 + 3(1 - \xi_2) = -5\xi_2 + 3 < 0$$

and, finally, if $\xi_2 < \frac{4}{7}$, let P_2 play t_4, giving

$$\phi(x, t_4) = 3\xi_2 - 4(1 - \xi_2) = 7\xi_2 - 4 < 0$$

which shows the only optimal strategies to be those specified. The reader will note the rather complicated structure of the solution of this game despite the simplicity of its rules.

4. Value of a Game and Optimal Strategies

We next reexamine the bluffing game of Example 4, whose matrix is

	t_1	t_2
s_1	0	a
s_2	$\dfrac{b-a}{2}$	0

Since this game is not symmetrical, it is not clear in advance what expected payoff P_1 should aim to achieve. Suppose, however, P_1 plays the mixed strategy $\bar{x} = \left(\dfrac{b-a}{b+a}, \dfrac{2a}{b+a}\right)$. One immediately verifies that his expectation is $\omega = a(b-a)/(b+a)$ against any strategy mixed or otherwise of P_2. In other words, P_1 can assure himself of at least ω, which is positive since $b > a$, but note that he can do so only by bluffing, that is, playing s_1, which means betting when he holds the low card. Indeed, honesty is a poor policy for P_1, for if he does not bluff and P_2 is aware of this, then playing t_2 makes it impossible for P_1 to win. Of course, bluffing all the time is equally bad, for then P_2 plays t_1 and again P_1 wins nothing.

Next, we note that P_1 cannot guarantee an expected payoff greater than ω, for if P_2 plays the mixed strategy $\bar{y} = \left(\dfrac{2a}{b+a}, \dfrac{b-a}{b+a}\right)$, then P_1 will win exactly ω no matter what he does, as one verifies at once. This means that ω is the largest payoff which P_1 can guarantee himself. We see that ω plays the role played by zero in the previous examples. It is called the *value* of the game.

We summarize. *By playing appropriately P_1 can assure himself of at least ω, and by playing appropriately, P_2 can be sure that P_1 will not get more than ω.* The mixed strategies $\bar{x}$ and $\bar{y}$ are called *optimal;* the number ω is called the *value* of the game.

We can now state a general

Definition. The game $\Gamma = (S, T; \phi)$ has the *solution* $(\bar{s}, \bar{t}; \omega)$ if

$$\phi(\bar{s}, t) \geqq \omega \qquad \text{for all } t \, \varepsilon \, T$$
$$\phi(s, \bar{t}) \leqq \omega \qquad \text{for all } s \, \varepsilon \, S$$

The pure strategies $\bar{s}$ and $\bar{t}$ are called *optimal;* the number ω is called the *value* of the game. Note that $\omega = \phi(\bar{s}, \bar{t})$ (why?).

The game Γ is said to have a *solution in mixed strategies* if the extended game $<\Gamma>$ has a solution.

We have just seen that the game of bluffing has a solution in mixed strategies. The reader should show that the strategies given are the only optimal strategies; thus, in order to be sure of attaining ω it is not only necessary for P_1 to bluff, but he must bluff in a very particular manner, that is, with probability $(1 - a/b)/(1 + a/b)$. This shows that the larger the ratio of bet to ante, the greater the probability of bluffing. The amount P_1 wins is always less than a but approaches a as a/b tends to zero.

The above analysis bears out one's "common-sense" feeling that it is desirable to bluff part of the time in games of this sort. However, the analysis goes far beyond common sense by making the intuitive feelings precise and quantitative, telling not only that one should bluff but exactly how much bluffing one should do and what one stands to gain by doing it. In theory at least, a similar analysis might be carried out for "real" games of this type, such as the various forms of poker. In practice, of course, the enormous number of strategies involved in such games makes the computational problem prohibitive.

As the reader has probably suspected by this time, the behavior of the examples we have been discussing is characteristic of matrix games in general. We have been observing specific instances of what has rightfully been called

The Fundamental Theorem of Game Theory.   *Every matrix game has a solution in mixed strategies.*

The proof of this theorem will be given in Sec. 8.   One fact, however, can be deduced immediately from the definition.

Theorem 6.1.   *A game Γ has at most one value.*

Proof.   Let $(\bar{\sigma}_1, \bar{\tau}_1; \omega_1)$ and $(\bar{\sigma}_2, \bar{\tau}_2; \omega_2)$ be solutions of Γ.   Then

$$\omega_1 = \phi(\bar{\sigma}_1, \bar{\tau}_1) \geqq \phi(\bar{\sigma}_2, \bar{\tau}_1) \geqq \phi(\bar{\sigma}_2, \bar{\tau}_2) = \omega_2 \geqq \phi(\bar{\sigma}_1, \bar{\tau}_2) \geqq \phi(\bar{\sigma}_1, \bar{\tau}_1) = \omega_1$$

so $\omega_1 = \omega_2$.

A verbal argument is perhaps more transparent.   If, say, $\omega_1 \leqq \omega_2$, then P_1 can assure himself of ω_2.   However, P_2 can keep P_1 from winning more than ω_1.   This must mean that $\omega_1 = \omega_2$.

Remark.   We call the reader's attention to the following useful fact. In order to show that $(\bar{\sigma}, \bar{\tau}; \omega)$ is a solution to a game Γ it suffices to show that

$$\phi(\bar{\sigma}, t) \geqq \omega \geqq \phi(s, \bar{\tau})$$

for all *pure* strategies s and t, for if $\phi(\bar{\sigma}, t) \geqq \omega$ for all t in T, then

$$\phi(\bar{\sigma}, \tau) = \sum_t \tau(t)\phi(\bar{\sigma}, t) \geqq \omega \sum_t \tau(t) = \omega, \text{for all } \tau, \text{and similarly } \phi(s, \tau) \leqq \omega$$

for all σ.

Henceforth, in view of the above, we shall verify that a given mixed strategy is optimal by showing that it achieves the value of the game against all pure strategies of the opponent.

Let us look now at the game A, B, C of Example 5, whose matrix is

	t_S	t_D
s_S	-1	0
s_D	$\frac{1}{4}$	$-\frac{1}{4}$

We leave it to the reader to check that a solution of the game is $\bar{x} = (\frac{1}{3}, \frac{2}{3})$, $\bar{y} = (\frac{1}{6}, \frac{5}{6})$, $\omega = -\frac{1}{6}$, and that the optimal strategies are unique.   This is a rather extraordinary result, for it states that P_1 should bluff, that is, guess his own card, with probability $\frac{1}{3}$.   This is precisely what would happen if P_1 paid no attention to the card in his hand and simply guessed a card at random.   In fact, one optimal action for P_1 is always to guess, say A, without even looking at his own card, for this will clearly cause him to bluff with the correct probability.   This situation may be interpreted as follows: The information which P_1 gains by inspecting his own card is of no use to him, because if he chooses any method of play which makes use of this information, he reveals information to his opponent.

We have given this rather lengthy discussion of the last two examples because they illustrate in a striking manner the concise way in which game theory settles rather subtle strategic questions.

5. Some Infinite Games

As a first example of a game which is not a matrix game, we consider the following infinite variation on the bluffing game of Example 4.

Example 6.   Continuous Bluffing.   Rules. P_1 draws one of the cards Hi or Lo from a hat.   He may now bet an amount x where $a \leq x \leq b$, a and b being given positive numbers, whereupon P_2 may fold and lose the amount a, or call, winning or losing x according as P_1 holds Lo or Hi.

Let us determine the strategies and payoff for this game.   A strategy for P_1 consists of a pair of numbers (x, y) between a and b, where the above symbols are to be read: "If Hi is drawn, bet x; if Lo is drawn, bet y."   The set S consists of all such pairs (x, y).   A strategy for P_2 consists in choosing a set of numbers C on the interval $[a, b]$ ($[a, b]$ denotes the set of numbers x where $a \leq x \leq b$).   He then calls if P_1's bet is in the set C and folds otherwise.

The strategy set T for P_2 thus corresponds to all subsets C of the interval $[a, b]$, and the payoff ϕ is now defined as follows:

$$\phi[(x, y), C] = \frac{x - y}{2} \qquad \text{if } x, y \text{ are in } C$$

$$= \frac{x + a}{2} \qquad \text{if only } x \text{ is in } C$$

$$= \frac{a - y}{2} \qquad \text{if only } y \text{ is in } C$$

$$= a \qquad \text{if neither } x \text{ nor } y \text{ is in } C$$

We shall now solve this game, though the form of the solution will be somewhat different from that of the previous examples.

First, suppose P_1 ignores the possibility of making intermediate bets x between a and b and decides to play as though the only possibilities were a or b as follows: When he draws Hi, he always bets b.   When he draws Lo, he bets b with probability $(b - a)/(b + a)$ and he bets a with the complementary probability $2a/(b + a)$.   Now clearly P_2 should never fold on a bet of a (why?), so the only thing that P_2 must decide is whether to call or fold on a bet of b.   We leave it to the reader to show that in either case the expectation of P_1 is $a(b - a)/(b + a)$. It remains now to decide whether it is possible for P_1 to obtain a greater payoff by taking advantage of the opportunity of making intermediate bets.   We will show that this is not possible by describing an optimal counter-strategy for P_2.   Let P_2 then behave as follows: If his opponent makes a bet of x, P_2 will call with probability $2a(x + a)$ and fold with the complementary probability $(x - a)/(x + a)$.   Supposing now that P_1 plays the pure strategy (x, y), we compute his expectation against the procedure just described for P_2.

With probability $\frac{1}{2}$ player 1 draws Hi and bets x, in which case he wins x with probability $2a/(x + a)$ and wins a with probability $(x - a)/(x + a)$.   The expectation for this case is therefore

$$\frac{2ax}{x + a} + \frac{(x - a)a}{x + a} = \frac{3ax - a^2}{x + a} \qquad (1)$$

If P_1 draws Lo he bets y, losing y with probability $2ay/(y + a)$ and winning a with probability $(y - a)a/(y + a)$.   The expectation is

$$\frac{-2ay}{y + a} + \frac{(y - a)a}{y + a} = -a \qquad (2)$$

and averaging (1) and (2) above gives the net expectation

$$\frac{1}{2}\left(\frac{3ax - a^2}{x + a} - a\right) = \frac{2ax - 2a^2}{2(x + a)} = \frac{a(x - a)}{x + a} \leqq \frac{a(b - a)}{b + a} \qquad (3)$$

since $x \leqq b$.   Therefore, P_2 can assure that P_1 will not win more than $a(b - a)/(b + a)$ and we have found the value of the game and optimal strategies.

Note that the optimal procedure for P_2 is not a mixed strategy in the strict sense of the definition, for a mixed strategy involved "randomizing" among the given pure strategies.   The procedure described, on the other hand, instructs P_2 to randomize only after P_1 has made his first "move."   Such a procedure is called a *behavior strategy*. There is an interesting relationship between behavior strategies and mixed strategies, but to investigate this question would take us too far from our main subject.

Example 7.   Duels.   Rules.   Two duelists face each other at a distance d apart.   Each is equipped with a pistol containing a single bullet.   The duelists advance toward each other and at any instant either one may fire.   The probability of P_1 or P_2 killing his opponent from a distance x is given by the *accuracy functions* $p_1(x)$ and $p_2(x)$, respectively.   It is generally assumed that the functions p_i are strictly decreasing and $p_i(0) = 1$.   One player wins if he kills his opponent and survives himself.   Otherwise, the game is a draw.

We shall not be able to exhibit a solution of this game as this would involve introducing ideas which would be outside the scope of this book.   We content ourselves with describing the payoff.   For this purpose, however, we must distinguish two cases, according to whether or not the duelists' guns are equipped with silencers.   This will obviously make a great difference in the way the game will be played, for in the "noisy" case, if one of the players hears his opponent fire (this is possible only in case his opponent misses, as bullets travel faster than sound), then he will clearly wait until he has reached his opponent before firing, and thereupon dispatch him with probability one.   In the silent case, on the other hand, he will not know at any time whether his opponent has fired or not.

Let us compute the payoff for the silent case (the computation for the noisy case is left as an exercise).   A strategy for either duelist consists in choosing a number between 0 and d, giving the distance from his opponent at which he will fire.   Let x and y be the numbers chosen by P_1 and P_2 respectively.   The payoff ϕ is easily seen to be given by

$$\phi(x, y) = \begin{cases} -p_2(y) + [1 - p_2(y)]p_1(x) & \text{for } x < y \\ p_1(x) - [1 - p_1(x)]p_2(y) & \text{for } y < x \\ p_1(x) - p_2(x) & \text{for } x = y \end{cases}$$

This function can be expressed in the neater form

$$\phi(x, y) = p_1(x) - p_2(y) + sgn(x - y)p_1(x)p_2(y)$$

where *sgn* stands for the *sign* function defined by the rules

$$sgn\ x = 1 \qquad \text{for } x > 0$$
$$= 0 \qquad \text{for } x = 0$$
$$= -1 \qquad \text{for } x < 0$$

There are many variations of the duel-type problem, some of which will be treated in the exercises.

Example 8. The Oil Prospector (a Game against Nature). You own some land in Texas on which you believe there is oil. You know that the average depth of oil is d ft below the ground, and you have sufficient funds to dig a total of f ft either in a single spot or in several spots. If you strike oil before running out of money, you become a millionaire and win. If not, you have nothing to show for your troubles but a number of dry holes, you are bankrupt—and you lose. What to do?

This sort of situation is familiar even to people who have done their digging on a more modest scale, say for clams. After digging for some time without success, one is inclined to move on to a new spot, but at the same time, one wonders if perhaps just one more shovelful at the old one would have uncovered the prize. The game we are about to describe is intended to capture some of the spirit of this situation. In order to be able to give a proper analysis, we shall have to specialize the game rather drastically.

Rules. P_1, the driller, has a choice of two sites S_1 and S_2 at which to drill for oil. The depth of oil below the surface has been set by P_2, "nature," and is y_1 at S_1, y_2 at S_2. These depths are not known to P_1, but the average depth is known to be $d/2$, that is, $y_1 + y_2 = d$. P_1 may drill x_1 ft at S_1 and x_2 ft at S_2, where x_1 and x_2 are any non-negative numbers such that $x_1 + x_2 = f$, where f is also known to both players. P_1 wins if he strikes oil, loses otherwise.

We hasten to admit that our game is artificial in many respects. Especially unnatural is the notion that nature is a skilled gamester (gamestress?), whose sole aim is to frustrate the driller. If taken with a sizable grain of salt, a study of this game will nevertheless be instructive.[1]

---

[1] The analysis of this game is somewhat involved, and the reader may wish to omit it on first reading.

For convenience, we assume that $f = 1$. We first dispose of some trivial cases. If $d \leqq 1$, then the game is clearly a win for the driller, who simply picks one of the sites and drills a distance 1. If, on the other hand, $d > 2$, then nature wins by setting $y_1 = y_2 = d/2$. The interesting case is therefore $d = 1 + \Delta$, where $0 < \Delta \leqq 1$; letting x be the distance P_1 digs at S_1, and letting y be the depth at S_1, the payoff is seen to be

$$\phi(x, y) = -1 \quad \text{if } x < y < x + \Delta$$
$$= 1 \quad \text{otherwise}$$

To see this, note that, in the first case above, $x < y$ so that the driller fails to strike oil in the first spot, but also, $1 - x < d - y$, and he also fails in the second spot.

We shall now give a complete solution of this game, which depends in a very curious manner on the value of Δ.

First we write

$$1 = q\Delta + r \tag{1}$$

where the quotient q is a positive integer, and the remainder r is a nonnegative fraction less than Δ. We assert that the value of the game is

$$\omega = \frac{q - 1}{q + 1}$$

Before proving this, let us observe what the result means. It states that, if d is between 2 and $\frac{3}{2}$, then $\omega = 0$, but for d equal to $\frac{3}{2}$, ω suddenly jumps to the value $\frac{1}{3}$, then jumps again to $\frac{1}{2}$, as d decreases beyond $\frac{4}{3}$, and so forth. Thus the value changes in a "discontinuous" manner with continuous changes in d. To put it more graphically, if $d = 1.5001$ then the driller stands only a fifty-fifty chance of hitting oil, but if $d = 1.5$ then the driller will hit pay dirt two-thirds of the time.

We now exhibit the optimal strategies for the game. Let us denote by x_k the strategy for P_1, which consists in drilling a distance k/q at the first site (and hence, $1 - k/q$ at the second), and let P_1 play the strategies $x_0, \ldots, x_q$ with equal probabilities, $1/(q + 1)$. Now, if P_2 plays strategy y, he will win against x_k only if $x_k < y < x_k + \Delta$, but from (1), it follows that $\Delta \leqq 1/q$, and hence P_2 wins only if $x_k < y < x_{k+1}$, but this occurs with probability at most $1/(q + 1)$. The rest of the time, the game is won by P_1; so the expected payoff to P_1 is at least $q/(q + 1) - 1/(q + 1) = (q - 1)/(q + 1)$.

On the other hand, let $\bar{y}$ be any number such that $1/(q + 1) < \bar{y} < \Delta$ and let P_2 play the strategies $\bar{y}, 2\bar{y}, \ldots, (q + 1)\bar{y}$, with equal probability. Now, for any strategy x of P_1, consider the smallest number k such that $x < k\bar{y}$. If $k = 1$, then we have $0 \leqq x < \bar{y} < \Delta \leqq x + \Delta$; so P_2 wins. If $k > 1$, then, since k was the smallest number for which $x < k\bar{y}$, we have $x \geqq (k - 1)\bar{y}$, or $x + \Delta \geqq k\bar{y} + (\Delta - \bar{y}) > k\bar{y}$, and again P_2 wins. Since P_2 plays strategy $k\bar{y}$ with probability $1/(q + 1)$, he will win with at least this probability; hence P_1 cannot expect more than the amount $(q - 1)/(q + 1)$, which is thus shown to be the value of the game, as asserted.

It frequently occurs in game theory that two games which seem quite different as to rules turn out to have the same or equivalent payoffs. We have already seen a trivial example of this in the games of odds and evens, and matching pennies. We next present a game which is essentially equivalent to the one just discussed, although this may not be apparent at first glance.

Example 8a.   The Bomber and the Submarine. Rules. A submarine is able to remain submerged for an interval of 5 hr during a certain 12-hr day. An enemy bomber is to pass overhead during the day, and if the submarine is on the surface at that instant, it will be destroyed. Assuming that no advance warning is available to the submarine, his problem is to choose the 5-hr period during which to be submerged, so as to maximize his chance of survival.

We leave to the reader the problem of solving this game by showing its equivalence to the oil-drilling game above.

Two final examples will conclude this section.

Example 9.   High Number. Rules. Each player chooses a positive integer, the player choosing the higher winning.

The reader undoubtedly feels that this game is somehow absurd, that there is no sensible way of playing it. He is right. The example is included as a simple illustration of the fact that the fundamental theorem does not extend in general beyond finite games. In fact, the problem as to whether or not the fundamental theorem holds for a given infinite game is often a very delicate matter. For certain large and important classes of games, the question has been settled, but nothing like general necessary and sufficient conditions for existence of solutions is known.

Example 10. Low Number. *Rules.* Each player chooses a positive integer. The player choosing the lower integer wins 1, unless his choice was exactly 1 less than his opponent's, in which case he loses 2.

Unlike its predecessor, this game has a solution, the details of which are given in the exercises.

6. Saddle Points and Minimax

We turn now from consideration of specific examples in order to look at some general questions of a preliminary nature. We first note that the mathematical notions involved in the statement of the fundamental theorem are quite independent of any concept of a game. For theoretical purposes, it is appropriate to deal with the abstract formulation.

Definition. Let S and T be arbitrary sets. A function (real-valued) of the two variables s in S and t in T is said to have a *saddle point* at $(\bar{s}, \bar{t})$ if

$$\phi(\bar{s}, t) \geq \phi(s, \bar{t}) \qquad \text{for all } s \text{ in } S, t \text{ in } T$$

The number $\omega = \phi(\bar{s}, \bar{t})$ is then called a *saddle value*.

This definition is essentially the same as that of a solution of a game. More precisely, to say that a game has a solution in the sense of Sec. 4 is exactly the statement that its payoff has a saddle point. The word "saddle point" refers to the familiar shape of a riding saddle. If one moves backward or forward from the center of the saddle, the surface rises (this corresponds to changing t while keeping s fixed at $\bar{s}$), while if one moves sideways (varies s, holding t at $\bar{t}$), the saddle surface drops off.

We now introduce another notion closely related to that of saddle point.

Definition.   Let ϕ be a function of s and t.   Define

$$\phi_M(t) = \max_{s \varepsilon S} \phi(s, t)$$

$$\phi_m(s) = \min_{t \varepsilon T} \phi(s, t)$$

Then we define

$$minimax \; \phi = \min_{t \varepsilon T} \phi_M(t)$$

and

$$maximin \; \phi = \max_{s \varepsilon S} \phi_m(s)$$

It is assumed above that all maxima and minima involved in the definition are actually assumed by the function ϕ.   The notions of minimax, maximin, and saddle point are related by the following.

Theorem 6.2.   *If ϕ is a function for which both minimax and maximin exist, then*

$$maximin \; \phi \leqq minimax \; \phi \tag{1}$$

and equality holds if and only if ϕ has a saddle point.

Proof.   Let ϕ_M and ϕ_m be as in the above definition.   Then

$$\begin{aligned} \phi_m(s) &\leqq \phi(s, t) \\ \phi_M(t) &\geqq \phi(s, t) \end{aligned} \quad \text{for all } s, t \tag{2}$$

Letting maximin $\phi = \phi_m(\bar{s})$ and minimax $\phi = \phi_M(\bar{t})$, we have, from (2), $\phi_m(\bar{s}) \leqq \phi_M(\bar{t})$, which is (1) above.

If $\phi_m(\bar{s}) = \phi_M(\bar{t})$, then again, from (2),

$$\phi(\bar{s}, t) \geqq \phi_m(\bar{s}) = \phi_M(\bar{t}) \geqq \phi(s, \bar{t})$$

so that $(\bar{s}, \bar{t})$ is a saddle point.

Finally, if $(\bar{s}, \bar{t})$ is a saddle point, then since

$$\phi(\bar{s}, t) \geqq \phi(s, \bar{t}) \qquad \text{for all } s, t$$

it follows that

$$\phi_m(\bar{s}) \geqq \phi_M(\bar{t})$$

On the other hand, from (2),

$$\phi_m(s) \leqq \phi_M(t) \qquad \text{for all } s \text{ and } t$$

so that $\phi_m(\bar{s}) = \phi_M(\bar{t}) = \max \phi_m(s) = \min \phi_M(t)$, and thus

$$\text{maximin } \phi = \text{minimax } \phi$$

The result just proved has a natural game theoretic interpretation. Recall that, in introducing the notion of solution and optimal strategy, we assumed that each player considered his opponent just as clever as himself. Specifically, this means that, whatever course of action a player adopts, he assumes his opponent will find out about it. Thus, if I, as player 1, decide to use the mixed strategy σ, I shall assume that you, as player 2, will choose that strategy τ which makes my payoff a minimum, that is, I shall expect to get the amount $\min_{\tau} \phi(\sigma, \tau) = \phi_m(\sigma)$. I therefore choose a strategy σ for which $\phi_m(\sigma)$ is a maximum, and thus I guarantee myself an expectation of $\max \phi_m(\sigma) = \text{maximin } \phi$. If you, as second player, reason in a similar fashion, you will be playing so as to be sure I do not receive more than $\text{minimax } \phi$. For games in which the fundamental theorem holds, these two amounts will be equal, as is seen from the result just proved. Because of the interpretation just given, the fundamental theorem is frequently referred to as the *minimax theorem*.

Generally speaking, functions will not have saddle points. As a simple example, let S and T consist of two points each, s_1, s_2, and t_1, t_2, respectively, and let $\phi(s_1, t_1) = \phi(s_2, t_2) = 1$, $\phi(s_1, t_2) = \phi(s_2, t_1) = -1$; then maximin $\phi = -1$, but minimax $\phi = 1$.

As a simple consequence of Theorem 6.2, we are able to show that the value of a game (if it has one) depends "continuously" on the payoff. The precise statement is

Theorem 6.3. *If ϕ and ϕ' are two functions of s and t with saddle values ω and ω' and for some $\epsilon > 0$, and all (s, t), $|\phi(s, t) - \phi'(s, t)| \leq \epsilon$, then $|\omega - \omega'| \leq \epsilon$.*

This follows at once from Theorem 6.2 and the fact that, if two functions differ by at most ϵ, so also do their maxima and minima. The proof is left as an exercise.

7. Symmetric Games

Definition. A game $\Gamma = (S, T; \phi)$ is called *symmetric* if $S = T$ and $\phi(s, t) = -\phi(t, s)$ for all (s, t). It follows that $\phi(s, s) = 0$ for all s.

The games of morra and goofspiel are typical examples of symmetric games in which both players have the same set of strategies. This is reflected formally in the fact that the payoff is a *skew-symmetric func-tion*. Notice that the game of odds and evens is *not* symmetric in the sense of the above definition.

We are going to show in this section that every game is, in a sense, equivalent to a symmetric game, so that a number of questions about games in general can be reduced to consideration of the special symmetric case.

We first note

Lemma 6.1. *A symmetric game* Γ *has a solution if and only if there exists* $\bar{s}$ *in* S *such that* $\phi(\bar{s}, s) \geqq 0$, *for all* s *in* S.

Proof. If Γ has optimal strategies $\bar{s}$ and $\bar{s}'$ then $\phi(\bar{s}, s) \geqq \phi(s', \bar{s}')$ for all s and s'; so, in particular,

$$\phi(\bar{s}, s) \geqq \phi(\bar{s}', \bar{s}') = 0$$

for all s.

Conversely, if $\phi(\bar{s}, s) \geqq 0$ for all s, then $\phi(s', \bar{s}) \leqq 0$ for all s' and hence $\phi(\bar{s}, s) \geqq \phi(\bar{s}, \bar{s}) = 0 \geqq \phi(s', \bar{s})$ for all s and s'; so $(\bar{s}, \bar{s}; 0)$ is a solution of Γ.

Definition. If $\Gamma = (S, T; \phi)$ in any game, the *symmetrization* $\hat{\Gamma}$ of Γ is the game $\hat{\Gamma}$ whose strategies consist of all pairs (s, t) where $s \, \varepsilon \, S$ and $t \, \varepsilon \, T$, and whose payoff $\hat{\phi}$ is defined by

$$\hat{\phi}[(s, t), (s', t')] = \phi(s, t') - \phi(s', t)$$

Clearly $\hat{\Gamma}$ is symmetric, for

$$\hat{\phi}[(s, t), (s', t')] = \phi(s, t') - \phi(s', t)$$
$$= -[\phi(s', t) - \phi(s, t')] = -\hat{\phi}[(s', t'), (s, t)]$$

Interpretation. The definition of symmetrization given above is simply a formalization of what is often done in actual games, typically in chess, where a random device is used to determine which player shall play the "white pieces." In general, suppose in any game, the players are assigned one of the two roles by tossing a true coin. It is then necessary for each player to select in advance a pair of strategies, one from S, the other from T, so as to be prepared for either eventuality. If P_1 picks the pair (s, t) and P_2 the pair (s', t'), then the expected payoff to P_1 will be

$$\tfrac{1}{2}[\phi(s, t') - \phi(s', t)]$$

which, except for the irrelevant factor $\tfrac{1}{2}$, agrees with our formal definition.

From the above discussion, it is intuitively clear that knowing an optimal strategy for $\hat{\Gamma}$ is equivalent to knowing optimal strategies for both players in the original game Γ. The precise statement is

Theorem 6.4. *The game Γ has a solution if and only if $\hat{\Gamma}$ has a solution.*

Proof. The strategies $(\bar{s}, \bar{t})$ are optimal in Γ if and only if

$$\phi(\bar{s}, t) \geq \phi(s, \bar{t}) \qquad \text{for all } s, t$$

which means

$$\hat{\phi}[(\bar{s}, \bar{t}), (s, t)] = \phi(\bar{s}, t) - \phi(s, \bar{t}) \geq 0 \qquad \text{for all } s, t$$

and by Lemma 6.1, this is equivalent to the existence of a solution for $\hat{\Gamma}$.

As one would expect, an analogous result to the above is also true for mixed strategies, but a separate argument is needed for this case.

Theorem 6.5. *The game Γ has a solution in mixed strategies if and only if its symmetrization $\hat{\Gamma}$ has a solution in mixed strategies.*

Proof. Let $(\bar{\sigma}, \bar{\tau}; \omega)$ be a solution of Γ so that

$$\phi(\bar{\sigma}, t') = \sum_s \bar{\sigma}(s)\phi(s, t') \geq \omega \qquad \text{for all } t'$$

$$-\phi(s', \bar{\tau}) = -\sum_t \bar{\tau}(t)\phi(s', t) \geq -\omega \qquad \text{for all } s' \tag{1}$$

Let $\overline{\sigma\tau}$ be the mixed strategy for $\hat{\Gamma}$ defined by

$$\overline{\sigma\tau}(s, t) = \bar{\sigma}(s)\bar{\tau}(t)$$

Clearly $\overline{\sigma\tau}$ is a mixed strategy, for

$$\sum_{s,t} \overline{\sigma\tau}(s, t) = \sum_{s,t} \bar{\sigma}(s)\bar{\tau}(t) = \sum_s \left[\bar{\sigma}(s) \sum_t \bar{\tau}(t)\right]$$

$$= \sum_s \bar{\sigma}(s) = 1$$

To show that $\overline{\sigma\tau}$ is optimal, let (s', t') be any pure strategy for P_2 in $\hat{\Gamma}$. Then

$$\hat{\phi}[\overline{\sigma\tau}, (s', t')] = \sum_{s,t} \bar{\sigma}(s)\bar{\tau}(t)\,\hat{\phi}[(s, t), (s', t')]$$

$$= \sum_{s,t} \bar{\sigma}(s)\bar{\tau}(t)[\phi(s, t') - \phi(s', t)]$$

$$= \sum_{s} \bar{\sigma}(s)\phi(s, t') - \sum_{t} \bar{\tau}(t)\phi(s', t) \geqq 0$$

the last inequality being obtained by adding the two expressions (1).

Conversely, suppose $\bar{\rho}$ is optimal in $\hat{\Gamma}$ so that

$$0 \leqq \hat{\phi}[\bar{\rho}, (s', t')] = \sum_{s,t} \bar{\rho}(s, t)[\phi(s, t') - \phi(s', t)] \tag{2}$$

We now define $\bar{\sigma}$ and $\bar{\tau}$ by the rules

$$\bar{\sigma}(s) = \sum_{t} \bar{\rho}(s, t)$$

$$\bar{\tau}(t) = \sum_{s} \bar{\rho}(s, t)$$

Then (2) gives

$$0 \leqq \sum_{s} \bar{\sigma}(s)\phi(s, t') - \sum_{t} \bar{\tau}(t)\phi(s', t) \qquad \text{for all } s', t'$$

or
$$\phi(\bar{\sigma}, t') \geqq \phi(s', \bar{\tau}) \qquad \text{for all } s', t'$$

and hence Γ has the solution $(\bar{\sigma}, \bar{\tau}; \omega)$, where $\omega = \phi(\bar{\sigma}, \bar{\tau})$.

8. Proof of the Fundamental Theorem

In view of Theorem 6.5 of the preceding section, we can prove the fundamental theorem of game theory by proving it for symmetric matrix games only. This in turn is a very simple consequence of Theorem 2.10, as we shall see. We first observe that if a matrix game is symmetric its payoff matrix $A = (\alpha_{ij})$ is *skew-symmetric*, that is,

$$\alpha_{ij} = -\alpha_{ji}$$

for $\alpha_{ij} = \phi(s_i, t_j) = -\phi(t_j, s_i) = -\alpha_{ji}$. It follows at once that

$$xA = -Ax \qquad \text{for any vector } x \qquad (1)$$

for $xA = (xa^j)$ and $xa^j = \sum_i \xi_i \alpha_{ij} = - \sum_i \xi_i \alpha_{ji} = -a_j x$, which is the jth coordinate of $-Ax$.

We now have

Theorem 6.6.   *Every symmetric matrix game has a solution in mixed strategies.*

Proof.   It is clearly sufficient to show that there is a mixed strategy $\bar{x}$ such that $\bar{x}A \geq 0$.   If no such $\bar{x}$ exists, then the inequality

$$xA \geq 0 \qquad (2)$$

has no semipositive solution.   But then according to Theorem 2.10 (page 49) there is a nonnegative vector y such that $Ay < 0$.   Since $y \neq 0$, y must, in fact, be semipositive.   But then from (1) above we have $yA > 0$ contrary to the assumption that (2) has no semipositive solution, completing the proof.

Corollary (Fundamental Theorem).   *Every matrix game has a solution in mixed strategies.*

Thus, in this simple manner, the minimax theorem is disposed of. Of course, the key result was the inequality theorem 2.10, which was in turn a direct consequence of Theorem 2.6, the theorem of the separating hyperplane, which, as we have mentioned, is the key theoretical result for all our applications.

In the next chapter we shall give another proof of the fundamental theorem from the duality theorem of linear programming.   We have given the present proof via symmetrization here so that this chapter could be kept independent of the chapters on programming.

Appendix to Chapter Six.   A Geometric "Proof" of the Fundamental Theorem of Game Theory

The proof we have given of the fundamental theorem, while algebraically quite simple, is somewhat formal, and it is perhaps not clear why the particular manipulations we have used lead us to the desired goal.   In this appendix we shall present a geometric argument which is intended to make the validity of the theorem intuitively clear. It will be seen in this argument exactly why Theorem 2.10 comes into the proof.

For graphical reasons we shall consider a game in which P_1 has 2 pure strategies and P_2 has 5, so that the columns of the payoff matrix A are the 2-vectors $a^1, \ldots, a^5$ which are plotted in the plane

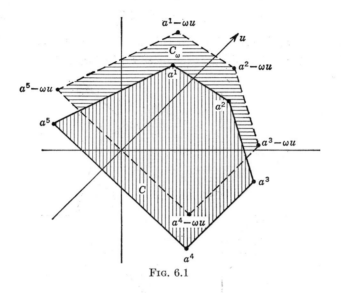

FIG. 6.1

in Fig. 6.1. Let $C = \langle a^1, \ldots, a^5 \rangle$ be the convex polytope (in this case a polygon) generated by the a^j and indicated by the vertically shaded region in the figure.

Now "translate" the set C along the 45-deg line until it just touches the negative quadrant. More precisely, let u be the vector $(1, 1)$ and let C_λ be the set of all vectors $x' = x - \lambda u$, where x is in C. If λ is very large, the C_λ lies entirely in the negative quadrant and if λ is very small then C_λ lies in the positive quadrant. Let ω be the smallest value of λ such that C_λ meets N, the nonpositive quadrant. (It is the existence of this minimum whose proof is omitted, but we expect the reader will be willing to take this on faith.) We have now

$$C_\omega = \langle a^1 - \omega u, \ldots, a^5 - \omega u \rangle$$

and the important thing to note is that, because of our choice of ω,

C_ω touches N, hence contains a nonpositive vector, but no negative vector.   Algebraically, this means the inequalities

$$\Sigma\eta_j(a^j - \omega u) \leqq 0 \tag{1}$$

have a nonnegative solution $\bar{y} = (\bar{\eta}_1, \ldots , \bar{\eta}_5)$ such that $\Sigma\bar{\eta}_j = 1$. On the other hand, the inequalities

$$\Sigma\eta_j(a^j - \omega u) < 0 \tag{2}$$

have no nonnegative solution, for this would mean that C_ω contains a negative vector.   The situation is pictured in Fig. 6.2.

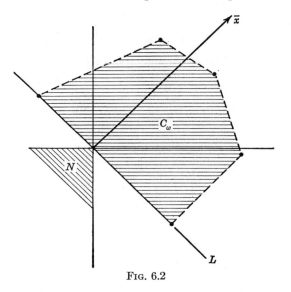

FIG. 6.2

Geometrically, one sees from the figure that it is possible to choose a line L through the origin which "separates" C_ω from N, that is, C_ω and N lie on opposite sides of L.   If $\bar{x}$ is a vector normal to L and on the same side of L as C_ω then $\bar{x}$ makes a nonobtuse angle with all points of C_ω and a nonacute angle with all points of N.   The first statement means

$$\bar{x}(a^j - \omega u) \geqq 0 \qquad \text{for all } j \tag{3}$$

and the second is clearly equivalent to the assertion that $\bar{x}$ is semipositive.   The geometric argument just given has already been given algebraically in Chap. 2 in the proof of Theorem 2.10, which states precisely that, since (2) has no nonnegative solution, (3) must have a semipositive solution $\bar{x}$. We may obviously choose this $\bar{x} = (\xi_i)$ so that $\Sigma \bar{\xi}_i = 1$.

It is now but a matter of adjusting notation to see that (1) and (3) together constitute a proof of the minimax theorem, for in matrix form (1) becomes

$$A\bar{y} = \Sigma \bar{\eta}_j a^j \leqq \Sigma \bar{\eta}_j(\omega u) = \omega u \tag{4}$$

since $\Sigma \bar{\eta}_j = 1$. And similarly, (3) becomes

$$\bar{x} a^j \geqq \omega(\bar{x}u) = \omega \qquad \text{for all } j \tag{5}$$

since $\Sigma \bar{\xi}_i = 1$, or if $v = (1, 1, 1, 1, 1)$ then

$$\bar{x} A \geqq \omega v \tag{6}$$

and (6) and (4) together give for all mixed strategies x and y

$$\bar{x} A y \geqq \omega(vy) = \omega = \omega(ux) \geqq x A \bar{y}$$

which is the desired theorem.

The proof sketched here is essentially that given by von Neumann and Morgenstern based on the proof of Ville. We shall return to this geometric picture later in order to get some insight into the structure of optimal strategies.

Bibliographical Notes

The theory of two-person games as presented in this chapter is essentially the creation of von Neumann, his first published work on the subject appearing in 1928 [1]. More extensive treatments of the theory have been given by von Neumann and Morgenstern [1] and McKinsey [1], among others. The game of bluffing of Example 4 is based on an example in Vajda [1], p. 3. For information on behavior strategies, the reader is referred to Kuhn [1].

The history of the minimax theorem is interesting. Von Neumann's original proof [1] (1928) was highly involved and depended on a rather difficult fixed-point theorem of topology. In 1941, Kakutani [1] gave a short and elegant proof of the result which, however, still depended on the fixed-point theorem. Meanwhile, Ville [1] (1938) presented the first "elementary" proof of the result, requiring nothing more advanced than a few simple facts about convex sets. The proof given by von Neumann and Morgenstern [1] is essentially a modification of Ville's proof, which in turn is much like the geometric proof presented in the appendix to this chapter. The proof via symmetrization given in Sec. 8 is due to Gale, Kuhn, and Tucker [1].

Exercises

1. Compute the number of pure strategies for each player in n-card goofspiel. (Assume that a player's choice in the kth move depends only on the cards which still remain in his and his opponent's hand.)

$$\text{Answer: } \prod_{k=0}^{n-1} (n - k)^{\binom{n}{k}}.$$

2. Consider 3-card goofspiel in which $a_1 = 1$, $a_2 = 2$, $a_3 = 3$. Show that the strategy "play card i on the ith move" is optimal. Is this strategy also optimal if $a_1 = 1$, $a_2 = 2$, but $a_3 = 4$? For $a_1 = 2$, $a_2 = 3$, $a_3 = 4$?

3. Find the payoff matrix for the following game, called *baseball*.

Rules. P_2, the pitcher, has a choice of two strategies called *fast ball* and *curve*. P_1, the batter, may either *swing* or *take*. If P_1 swings on a curve or takes a fast ball, he is "out" and loses 1. If he swings on a fast ball, he wins an amount $p > 0$. If he takes a curve, the game is played a second time and if he again takes a curve, he "walks" and wins 1.

Answer:

p	-1	-1
-1	p	-1
-1	-1	1

4. Find the payoff matrix for the following simplified *poker*.

Rules. P_1 draws either the card Hi or Lo with equal probability, and may then either "bet" or "pass." If P_1 bets, P_2 may "fold" and lose a or "call" and win or lose b according as P_1 holds Lo or Hi. If P_1 passes, then P_2 may also pass, giving payoff zero, or P_2 may bet, in which case he wins a if P_1 holds Lo and loses b if P_1 holds Hi.

Answer:

0	0	a	a
$\dfrac{b-a}{2}$	$\dfrac{b}{2}$	0	$\dfrac{a}{2}$
0	$-\dfrac{b}{2}$	$\dfrac{a+b}{2}$	$\dfrac{a}{2}$
$\dfrac{b-a}{2}$	0	$\dfrac{b-a}{2}$	0

5. Solve the following game. Each player is dealt at random one of the cards A, B, or C. Then P_1, having seen his own card, announces his guess as to which card is still in the deck. P_2, having seen his own card and heard P_1's guess, also announces his guess as to the third card. If either player guesses correctly, he wins 1 from his opponent.

6. Show that the optimal strategies in Examples 4 and 5 of the text are unique.

7. Find the strategy sets and payoff for the "noisy" duel of Example 7.

$$\text{Answer: } \phi(x,y) = 1 - 2p_2(y) \quad \text{for } x < y$$
$$= 2p_1(x) - 1 \quad \text{for } y < x$$
$$= p_1(x) - p_2(x) \quad \text{for } x = y$$

8. For a "noisy" duel in which the players have the same accuracies show that an optimal strategy is to fire when the probability of a hit is $\frac{1}{2}$. Show that this strategy is not optimal for the corresponding "silent" duel.

9. Write down the payoff for the infinite games high number and low number, Examples 9 and 10.

10. Show that an optimal strategy for the game low number, Example 10, is to guess the numbers 1, 2, 3, 4, 5, with relative frequencies 1, 5, 4, 5, 1, respectively.

11. Let $\Gamma_1, \ldots, \Gamma_n$ be n games all defined on the same strategy sets S and T; thus $\Gamma_i = (S, T; \phi_i)$. Suppose Γ_i has value ω_i and sets of optimal strategies S_i and T_i. Prove that, if the intersection of the sets S_i is S_0, and of the sets of T_i is T_0, both nonempty, then the game $\Gamma_0 = (S, T; \phi_1 + \cdots + \phi_n)$ has value $\omega_1 + \cdots + \omega_n$.

12. Let Γ be an $n \times n$ matrix game whose payoff matrix contains exactly n distinct numbers $\alpha_1, \ldots, \alpha_n$ and each α_i occurs in every row and every column. Find a solution of Γ.

13. An $n \times n$ matrix game is called *diagonal* if there is exactly one nonzero term in every row and every column. Obtain a formula for the value of a diagonal game in which all payoffs are nonnegative.

Answer: If $\alpha_1, \ldots, \alpha_n$ are the nonzero entries, $\omega = (\Sigma \, 1/a_i)^{-1}$.

14. Let $\Gamma = (S, T; \phi)$ have value ω. Show if α and β are real numbers and $\alpha \geq 0$, then $\Gamma = (S, T; \alpha\phi + \beta)$ has value $\alpha\omega + \beta$.

15. Use results (13) and (14) to solve the baseball game of Exercise 3.

$$\text{Answer: } \omega = \frac{p - 3}{p + 5}.$$

16. The pure strategy s in S is said to be *dominated* by the mixed strategy σ if $\phi(\sigma, t) > \phi(s, t)$ for all t in T. Prove that the game Γ has

the same solutions as the game Γ' obtained by removing the strategy s from the set S.

17. Prove Theorem 6.3.

18. Solve the bomber-submarine game of Example 8a by the methods used in solving Example 8.   Answer: $\omega = \frac{1}{3}$.

19. If the strategy sets S and T are closed intervals of real numbers, and ϕ is continuous, show that minimax ϕ and maximin ϕ exist but need not be equal.

20. Suppose ϕ is a function of s and t such that

$$\min_{S} \phi(s, t) \text{ and } \max_{S} \phi(s, t) \text{ exist for all } t$$
$$\min_{T} \phi(s, t) \text{ and } \max_{T} \phi(s, t) \text{ exist for all } s$$

Does it follow that minimax ϕ and maximin ϕ exist?

21. Let $\Gamma = (S, T; \phi)$ be a game with $\phi(s, t) > 0$ for all s, t. We define a symmetric game Γ_θ as follows: The strategy set for Γ_θ consists of the union of S and T, and an additional strategy θ. The payoff ϕ_θ is defined by the rules

$$\phi_\theta(s, t) = -\phi_\theta(t, s) = \phi(s, t) \qquad \text{for } s \text{ in } S, t \text{ in } T$$
$$\phi_\theta(s, \theta) = -\phi_\theta(\theta, s) = -1 \qquad \text{for } s \text{ in } S$$
$$\phi_\theta(\theta, t) = -\phi_\theta(t, \theta) = -1 \qquad \text{for } t \text{ in } T$$
$$\phi_\theta = 0 \qquad\qquad\qquad \text{otherwise}$$

Show that Γ_θ has a solution if and only if Γ has.

22. If Γ is an $n \times n$ matrix game, define the game Γ^n by the rules that the players must play Γ exactly n times using a different pure strategy on each play. After each play, each player is told which strategy was used by his opponent on that play. The payoff is the sum of the payoffs of the individual plays. Show that an optimal strategy for either player consists in playing his n strategies in random order. Find the value of Γ^n in terms of the numbers $\alpha_{ij} = \phi(s_i, t_j)$. (Hint: Argue by induction on n.)

Use the above result to solve n-card goofspiel for the special case where all the prizes a_i are equal.

23. The following game of *hide and seek* is due to von Neumann. Given an $n \times n$ positive matrix A, P_2 chooses an entry α_{ij}. P_1 chooses either a row a_i or column a^j. If α_{ij} is in the row or column chosen by P_1, then he wins α_{ij} from P_2. Otherwise the payoff is zero.

The game is solved as follows: Let $B = (\beta_{ij})$ be the matrix such that $\beta_{ij} = 1/\alpha_{ij}$.   Let S be a set of n entries of A, one in each row and column such that the corresponding β_{ij} give an optimal assignment in B.   Show that an optimal strategy for P_2 is to play α_{ij} in S with probability proportional to $1/\alpha_{ij}$ and that the value of the game is $1/\mu$, where μ is the value of the optimal assignment in B.

(Hint: Use Theorem 5.5 to get an optimal strategy for P_1.)

CHAPTER SEVEN

Solutions of Matrix Games

This chapter will be devoted to a detailed study of the properties of matrix games and related matters. In the first section we describe the relation between games and linear programs, obtaining a new proof of the minimax theorem as a special case of the standard duality theorem. It is then shown that one can go in the other direction and set up a game which corresponds in a natural way to a pair of dual standard programs. Having converted the game problem into a linear program one can then proceed to solve it by the simplex method, and this is illustrated in Sec. 2.

The next group of sections is devoted to a study of the nature of sets of optimal strategies. It is shown that for a given game these sets for the two players are convex polytopes whose dimensions must be related in a particular way. The extreme points of these strategy sets are characterized in terms of the payoff matrix. A section is devoted to the problem of game "synthesis"; that is, given a pair of polytopes, how does one construct a game having these sets as its sets of optimal strategies? In the final section we describe an iterative procedure for approximating the value of a game which while not practical from a computational point of view is of considerable theoretical interest.

1. Relation between Matrix Games and Linear Programming

One of the most striking events in connection with the emergence of modern linear economic model theory was the simultaneous but independent development of linear programming on the one hand and game theory on the other, and the eventual realization of the very close relationship that exists between the two subjects. In this section we shall describe this relationship in detail.

At the end of the preceding chapter we proved the fundamental theorem of game theory by proving it first for games with a skew-symmetric payoff matrix. We shall now give a proof using the duality theorem of linear programming for the case where the payoff matrix is positive (i.e., all its coordinates are positive). The proof for the general case will be a trivial consequence, for let $A = (\alpha_{ij})$ be any $m \times n$ matrix and let $A' = (\alpha_{ij} + \alpha)$ be the positive matrix obtained by adding a sufficiently large positive number α to all coordinates of A. Now if we assume the fundamental theorem is true for the matrix A' then there are mixed strategies $\bar{x}$ and $\bar{y}$ such that

$$\bar{x}A'y \geqq \omega' \geqq xA'\bar{y} \qquad \text{for all mixed strategies } x \text{ and } y$$

But a simple calculation shows that $\bar{x}A'y = \bar{x}Ay + \alpha$ and $xA'\bar{y} = xA\bar{y} + \alpha$ so that

$$\bar{x}Ay \geqq \omega = \omega' - \alpha \geqq xA\bar{y}$$

so $(\bar{x}, \bar{y}; \omega)$ is a solution of the original game.

Second Proof of Fundamental Theorem of Game Theory. Let A be the positive payoff matrix of a game and consider the standard minimum problem of finding a nonnegative m-vector x such that

$$xu \text{ is a minimum} \tag{1}$$

subject to

$$xA \geqq v \tag{2}$$

where u and v are, of course, the unit vectors in R^m and R^n, respectively.

Since A is positive the problem is clearly feasible and so is the dual problem of finding a nonnegative n-vector y such that

$$yv \text{ is a maximum} \tag{1*}$$

subject to

$$Ay \leqq u \tag{2*}$$

(a feasible vector is $y = 0$).

From the duality theorem, therefore, there exist optimal vectors x_0 and y_0 such that

$$x_0 u = y_0 v = \mu \tag{3}$$

where μ is the value of the pair of programs, which is clearly positive.

We assert that a solution $(\bar{x}, \bar{y}; \omega)$ of the original game is given by

$$\bar{x} = \frac{x_0}{\mu} \qquad \bar{y} = \frac{y_0}{\mu} \qquad \omega = \frac{1}{\mu}$$

The fact that $\bar{x}$ and $\bar{y}$ are mixed strategies follows at once from (3). Also from (2) if y is a mixed strategy then

$$\bar{x} A y \geqq \frac{1}{\mu} v y = \omega$$

and symmetrically

$$x A \bar{y} \leqq \omega \qquad \text{for all mixed strategies } x$$

completing the proof.

We have thus seen how an arbitrary matrix game can be solved by solving a certain related linear program. We shall now show that it is possible to go in the other direction and associate with any pair of dual standard programs a certain symmetric game whose solutions provide solutions of the given programs if such exist. We remind the reader, however, that, while games always have solutions, programs need not, and the correspondence between the two models must take account of this fact.

Let A, b, and c be the usual matrix and vectors belonging to a pair of standard programs. We shall denote this pair briefly by the symbol (A, b, c). The *equivalent game* $\Gamma_{(A,b,c)}$ will be a symmetric game with $m + n + 1$ pure strategies which we shall denote by $u_1, \ldots, u_m$, $v_1, \ldots, v_n$, and w. The payoff function ϕ is then defined by the following rules:

$$\phi(u_i, v_j) = -\phi(v_j, u_i) = -\alpha_{ij}$$
$$\phi(u_i, w) = -\phi(w, u_i) = \gamma_i$$
$$\phi(v_j, w) = -\phi(w, v_j) = -\beta_j$$

and all other payoffs are zero.

Letting A^* denote the *transpose* of the matrix A $[A^* = (\alpha_{ij}^*)$, where $\alpha_{ij}^* = \alpha_{ji}$ (see Chap. 2, Exercise 31)], the reader will easily verify that the payoff matrix corresponding to the function ϕ is the following:

	w	$u_1 \ldots u_m$	$v_1 \ldots v_n$
w	0	$-c$	b
u_1 . . . u_m	c	0	$-A$
v_1 . . . v_n	$-b$	A^*	0

Theorem 7.1. *The dual problems (A, b, c) have solutions if and only if $\Gamma_{(A,b,c)}$ has an optimal strategy $z = (\zeta_0, \zeta_1, \ldots, \zeta_{m+n})$ with $\zeta_0 > 0$. In this case there is a one-to-one correspondence between such strategies and solutions of (A, b, c).*

Proof. Let us denote the payoff matrix above by M. If $x = (\xi_i)$ and $y = (\eta_j)$ are optimal vectors for the dual problems (A, b, c), we define the $(m + n + 1)$-vector z by the rule

$$z = (1, \xi_1, \ldots, \xi_m, \eta_1, \ldots, \eta_n)$$

and we assert that $zM \geqq 0$. To see this, note that the first coordinate of zM is $xc - yb$, and this is zero since $xc = yb =$ the value of the program, by the duality theorem. The next m coordinates of zM are given by the vector

$$-c + yA^* = -c + Ay$$

and this term is nonnegative because y is a feasible vector for the dual problem. The last n coordinates of zM are given by the vector

$$b - xA$$

and this vector is nonnegative because of the feasibility of the vector x.

It now follows (see Lemma 6.1) that the vector

$$\bar{z} = \frac{z}{1 + \Sigma\xi_i + \Sigma\eta_j}$$

is an optimal strategy for the game satisfying the conditions of the theorem. We leave it to the reader to show that each pair of optimal vectors x and y of (A, b, c) corresponds in this way to one and only one optimal strategy for the game.

Conversely, let $z = (\zeta_0, \ldots, \zeta_{m+n})$ be an optimal strategy for the game with payoff matrix M such that $\zeta_0 > 0$. Then, letting $x = (\zeta_1, \ldots, \zeta_m)/\zeta_0, y = (\zeta_{m+1}, \ldots, \zeta_{m+n})/\zeta_0$, it is a matter of mechanical verification to show that x and y are feasible vectors for the dual programs, and since

$$xc - yb \geq 0$$

it follows that x and y are in fact optimal, completing the proof.

2. Solving Games by the Simplex Method

In the preceding section it was seen that the problem of solving a game with a positive payoff matrix A was equivalent to solving a pair of dual programs

$$\text{minimize } xu \tag{1}$$

subject to

$$xA \geq v \tag{2}$$

and

$$\text{maximize } yv \tag{1*}$$

subject to

$$Ay \leq u \tag{2*}$$

If we examine the proof of this fact it will be seen that it is not necessary for A to be positive but only that the value of the game be positive.

Having found this equivalent linear programming problem one may apply the simplex algorithm to it and thus obtain a solution of the original game. As an illustration of the method let us solve the game of *poker* given in Exercise 4 of the previous chapter. Reviewing the rules of the game we see that it involved two payoffs of size a and b, and it will be seen that no generality is lost if we assume $a = 1$.   Also, to avoid fractions we multiply all entries of the matrix by 2, obtaining the matrix

$$A = \begin{pmatrix} 0 & 0 & 2 & 2 \\ b-1 & b & 0 & 1 \\ 0 & -b & b+1 & 1 \\ b-1 & 0 & b-1 & 0 \end{pmatrix}$$

and it will be assumed that b is greater than 1 (otherwise the game is trivial).   It is then clear that the game has a positive value, for any mixture of the first two strategies will guarantee P_1 a positive expectation.   We shall now use the simplex method to solve the maximum problem of finding a nonnegative vector $y = (\eta_1, \eta_2, \eta_3, \eta_4)$ which

$$\text{maximizes } yv \tag{3}$$

subject to

$$Ay \leqq u \tag{4}$$

Recall that in order to use the simplex method we must transform our program from a standard to a canonical maximum problem by the usual introduction of additional nonnegative variables.   Inequality (4) then becomes

$$Ay + \Sigma \xi_i u_i = u \tag{4'}$$

In game problems, as we see from (4'), we are always in the fortunate position of being able to use the unit vectors u_i as an initial basis.   Our initial tableau for the game under consideration is seen to be

		a^1	a^2	a^3	a^4	u	u_1	u_2	u_3	u_4
	u_1	0	0	2	②	1	1	0	0	0
	u_2	$b-1$	b	0	1	1	0	1	0	0
T_0	u_3	0	$-b$	$b+1$	1	1	0	0	1	0
	u_4	$b-1$	0	$b-1$	0	1	0	0	0	1
$z-v$		-1	-1	-1	-1	0	0	0	0	0

By this time the reader is sufficiently familiar with the simplex method so that it should not be necessary to present explanatory material with each change of tableau.   It will be noted here that we may initially bring into the new basis any of the vectors a^j. When confronted by such alternatives we have tried to choose the pivot so as to minimize the computational complexities. The sequence of tableaus given here seems to be the simplest for this particular problem. As indicated by the circled element above, our first replacement operation substitutes a^4 for u_1. The remaining tableaus are shown below:

		a^1	a^2	a^3	a^4	u	u_1	u_2	u_3	u_4
	a^4	0	0	1	1	$\frac{1}{2}$	$\frac{1}{2}$	0	0	0
	u_2	$\boxed{b-1}$	b	-1	0	$\frac{1}{2}$	$-\frac{1}{2}$	1	0	0
T_1	u_3	0	$-b$	b	0	$\frac{1}{2}$	$-\frac{1}{2}$	0	1	0
	u_4	$b-1$	0	$b-1$	0	1	0	0	0	1
	$z-v$	-1	-1	0	0	$\frac{1}{2}$	$\frac{1}{2}$	0	0	0
	a^4	0	0	1	1	$\frac{1}{2}$	$\frac{1}{2}$	0	0	0
	a^1	1	$\dfrac{b}{b-1}$	$\dfrac{-1}{b-1}$	0	$\dfrac{1}{2(b-1)}$	$\dfrac{-1}{2(b-1)}$	$\dfrac{1}{b-1}$	0	0
T_2	u_3	0	$-b$	b	0	$\frac{1}{2}$	$-\frac{1}{2}$	0	1	0
	u_4	0	$-b$	$\boxed{b}$	0	$\frac{1}{2}$	$\frac{1}{2}$	-1	0	1
	$z-v$	0	$\dfrac{1}{b-1}$	$\dfrac{-1}{b-1}$	0	$\dfrac{1}{2}\left(\dfrac{b}{b-1}\right)$	$\dfrac{b-2}{2(b-1)}$	$\dfrac{1}{b-1}$	0	0
	a^4					$\dfrac{b-1}{2b}$				
	a^1					$\dfrac{b+1}{2b(b-1)}$				
T_3	u_3					0				
	a^3					$\dfrac{1}{2b}$				
	$z-v$	0	0	0	0	$\dfrac{b^2+1}{2b(b-1)}$	$\dfrac{b-1}{2b}$	$\dfrac{1}{b}$	0	$\dfrac{1}{b(b-1)}$

In the final tableau we have computed only the row and column which give the solution to the problem and the dual. The value ω of the game is the reciprocal of ζ_0 and is therefore

$$\omega = \frac{2b(b-1)}{b^2+1}$$

and the optimal strategies are found by normalizing the optimal vectors x and y of the final tableau, giving

$$\bar{x} = \frac{1}{b^2 + 1} [(b - 1)^2, 2(b - 1), 0, 2]$$

$$\bar{y} = \frac{1}{b^2 + 1} [b + 1, 0, b - 1, (b - 1)^2]$$

By way of a check we have

$$\frac{1}{b^2 + 1} [(b - 1)^2, 2(b - 1), 0, 2] \begin{bmatrix} 0 & 0 & 2 & 2 \\ b - 1 & b & 0 & 1 \\ 0 & -b & b + 1 & 1 \\ b - 1 & 0 & b - 1 & 0 \end{bmatrix}$$

$$= \frac{2b(b - 1)}{b^2 + 1} v = \omega v$$

and

$$\begin{bmatrix} 0 & 0 & 2 & 2 \\ b - 1 & b & 0 & 1 \\ 0 & -b & b + 1 & 1 \\ b - 1 & 0 & b - 1 & 0 \end{bmatrix} \frac{1}{b^2 + 1} [b + 1, 0, b - 1, (b - 1)^2] = \omega u$$

It will be well worth the reader's while to look back at the rules of the game of poker and interpret the above result in terms of these rules (see Exercise 6).

3. *Optimal Strategies*

In this section we concern ourselves with the following question: What sets of mixed strategies can occur as the set of optimal strategies of a game? The answer can be given very simply: any convex polytope in the set of mixed strategies. In the next section we shall consider a similar but more complicated question: Under what circumstances can a pair of convex polytopes $\bar{X}$ and $\bar{Y}$ be the sets of optimal strategies for P_1 and P_2, respectively, in some matrix game? The answer to this question will be more involved.

It will be convenient to adopt some simple notation. We shall denote by U_m the set consisting of the m unit vectors in R^m. Thus,

$$U_m = \{u_1, \ldots, u_m\}$$

Then the convex set $<u_1, \ldots, u_m>$ will be denoted by $<U_m>$. If $u_1, \ldots, u_m$ are thought of as pure strategies of a game then $<U_m>$ is precisely the set of mixed strategies for this game.   Similarly,

$$V_n = \{v_1, \ldots, v_n\}$$
and
$$<V_n> = <v_1, \ldots, v_n>$$

We shall denote by $\bar{X}$ and $\bar{Y}$, respectively, the set of all optimal strategies for the two players of a game.   A *solution* of a game is therefore a triple $(\bar{X}, \bar{Y}; \omega)$, where ω is the value of the game.

For many purposes one may make the simplifying assumption that the value ω is zero.   Namely, if $A = (\alpha_{ij})$ is the payoff matrix of a game with solution $(\bar{X}, \bar{Y}; \omega)$ then clearly the new game with matrix $A' = (\alpha_{ij} - \omega)$ will have the solution $(\bar{X}, \bar{Y}; 0)$ (see Exercise 14, Chap. 6).   In fact, the game A' can be thought of as the same as the game A except that before play begins P_1 pays P_2 the amount ω. For our present purposes, we may think of the solution of a game as simply the sets $\bar{X}$ and $\bar{Y}$.

Theorem 7.2. *The set of optimal strategies $\bar{X}$ (or $\bar{Y}$) of a matrix game is a convex polytope.*

Proof.   Since we are assuming $\omega = 0$ the set $\bar{X}$ consists of all vectors $\bar{x}$ in R^m satisfying

$$\bar{x} \geq 0 \tag{1}$$
$$\bar{x}A \geq 0 \tag{2}$$
$$\Sigma\xi_i = 1 \tag{3}$$

Letting $\hat{X}$ be all vectors satisfying (1) and (2), it follows from Theorem 2.13 (page 58) that $\hat{X}$, being the set of solutions of a system of homogeneous inequalities, is a finite cone, that is,

$$\hat{X} = (x_1) + \cdots + (x_k)$$

and since from (1) above each $x_r = (\xi_{r1}, \ldots, \xi_{rm})$ is semipositive, we may also assume that $\displaystyle\sum_{i=1}^{m} \xi_{ri} = 1$.   It follows that

$$\bar{X} = <x_1, \ldots, x_k> \tag{4}$$

for if $\bar{x}\,\varepsilon\,\bar{X}$, then since $\bar{X}\subset\hat{X}$ we know that $\bar{x}=\sum_{r=1}^{k}\lambda_r x_r,\ \lambda_r\geqq 0.$

Also, from (3) we have

$$1 = u\bar{x} = \Sigma\lambda_r(ux_r) = \Sigma\lambda_r$$

and hence $\bar{x}$ is a convex combination of the points x_r so

$$\bar{x}\,\varepsilon\,<x_1,\ \ldots\ ,\ x_k>$$

Since, conversely, every convex combination of the x_r satisfies (1), (2), and (3), assertion (4) is proved.

We remark that this theorem could have been proved directly using the result of Exercise 38, Chap. 2 (page 73). It seemed preferable, however, to give an independent proof.

We now prove, conversely,

Theorem 7.3. *If $\bar{X}$ is any convex polytope in $<U_m>$ then there exists a matrix game having $\bar{X}$ as the set of all optimal strategies for P_1.*

Proof. Let $\bar{X} = <x_1,\ \ldots\ ,\ x_k>$ and let $\hat{X}$ be the finite cone generated by the $x_r,\ r = 1,\ \ldots\ ,\ k$, that is,

$$\hat{X} = (x_1) + \cdots + (x_k)$$

Now, we know from Theorem 2.14 (see page 59) that $\hat{X}$ is the set of solutions of some system of inequalities $xa^j \geqq 0,\ j = 1,\ \ldots\ ,\ n$, for some number n. We assert that $\bar{X}$ is precisely the set of all solutions of the game Γ whose matrix A has columns $a^0,\ a^1,\ \ldots\ ,\ a^n$, where $a^0 = 0$ and a^j are as above for $j > 0$. First of all, Γ has value $\omega = 0$ since P_1 can achieve payoff at least 0 by playing any strategy $\bar{x}$ in $\bar{X}$, and P_2 can achieve payoff zero by playing a^0. Furthermore, P_1 is guaranteed a payoff of zero if and only if he plays $\bar{x}$ in $\bar{X}$, for if x is a mixed strategy which is not in $\bar{X}$, then x is not in $\hat{X}$ and hence $xa^j < 0$ for some j.

As an illustration of the above, let us construct a game having three pure strategies for P_1 and such that the set of optimal strategies $\bar{X}$ consists of the segment $[x_1,\ x_2]$ where

$$x_1 = (\tfrac{1}{3},\ \tfrac{2}{3},\ 0) \qquad x_2 = (\tfrac{1}{4},\ \tfrac{1}{4},\ \tfrac{1}{2})$$

Then $\hat{X}$ is generated by $(1, 2, 0)$ and $(1, 1, 2)$.   The problem is now to express $\hat{X}$ as the set of solutions of a set of inequalities.   The cone $\hat{X}$ is pictured in Fig. 7.1.

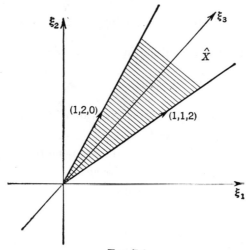

FIG. 7.1

We assert that $\hat{X}$ is the set of all nonnegative solutions of the inequalities

$$4\xi_1 - 2\xi_2 - \ \xi_3 \geqq 0$$
$$-4\xi_1 + 2\xi_2 + \ \xi_3 \geqq 0$$
$$\xi_1 + 3\xi_2 - 2\xi_3 \geqq 0$$

The appropriate columns for the payoff matrix are therefore

$$a^1 = (4, -2, -1)$$
$$a^2 = (-4, 2, 1)$$
$$a^3 = (1, 3, -2)$$

In this case, it is not even necessary to use the zero vector a^0.   We claim that the game with payoff

$$A = \begin{bmatrix} 4 & -4 & 1 \\ -2 & 2 & 3 \\ -1 & 1 & -2 \end{bmatrix}$$

has $\bar{X}$ as the optimal set for P_1.   Clearly by playing $\bar{x}$ in $\bar{X}$, P_1 achieves a nonnegative payoff.   On the other hand, P_2 by playing $(\frac{1}{2}, \frac{1}{2}, 0)$

is assured of payoff zero; so $\omega = 0$.   We leave it to the reader to show that $\bar{X}$ includes all optimal strategies for P_1.

4. Solutions

In order to describe the solution sets we introduce a useful and important concept.

Definition.   The kth pure strategy u_k for P_1 is called *essential* if there exists an optimal strategy $\bar{x} = (\xi_1, \ldots, \xi_m)$ such that $\xi_k > 0$.

In words, a strategy is essential if it is used with positive probability in an optional strategy.   As an example, in the game of morra (Example 2, Chap. 6) it was shown that s_2 and s_3 were essential strategies, but s_1 and s_4 were not.   In fact, it was shown that, if either player used s_1 or s_4 with positive probability, then his opponent, by choosing an appropriate *optimal* strategy, could achieve a positive payoff (see page 192).   This illustrates the important property of essential strategies, which gives the key to the structure of solutions.

Lemma 7.1.   *The pure strategy u_k is essential for P_1 if and only if $u_k A \bar{y} = \omega$ for all optimal $\bar{y}$ of P_2 (in words, the essential pure strategies are precisely those which achieve the value of the game against all optimal strategies of the opponent).*[1]

Proof.   In accordance with our previous remarks, the reader will easily verify that it is sufficient to prove the theorem for the case $\omega = 0$.

First, suppose u_k is essential and $\bar{x}$ is an optimal strategy with $\xi_k > 0$. Then for $\bar{y} \, \varepsilon \, \bar{Y}$

$$0 = \bar{x} A \bar{y} = \sum_{i=1}^{m} \xi_i (a_i \bar{y}) \tag{1}$$

Since $\xi_i \geqq 0$ and $a_i \bar{y} \leqq 0$ for all i it follows from (1) that $\xi_i(a_i \bar{y}) = 0$ for all i.   Hence, since $\xi_k > 0$, we must have $a_k \bar{y} = 0$, but $a_k = u_k A$; hence $u_k A \bar{y} = 0$ as asserted.

Conversely, if u_k is not essential this means that the inequalities

$$xA \geqq 0 \qquad xu_k \geqq 1 \tag{2}$$

[1] Note that since we are now concerned only with matrix games we identify pure strategies with the unit vectors and denote them by u_i and v_j instead of s_i and t_j.

have no nonnegative solution; so from Theorem 2.8 (page 47) there exists $\bar{y} \geq 0$ in R^n and $\eta \geq 0$ such that

$$A\bar{y} + \eta u_k \leq 0 \quad \text{and} \quad 0\bar{y} + \eta > 0$$

or
$$A\bar{y} \leq -\eta u_k \quad \text{and} \quad \eta > 0 \tag{3}$$

This shows that $\bar{y}$ is not zero, and hence by multiplying by a positive scalar, we may suppose $\sum\limits_{j=1}^{n} \bar{\eta}_j = 1$. Now (3) shows that $A\bar{y} \leq 0$; hence $\bar{y}$ is optimal for P_2, and taking scalar product of (3) with u_k gives

$$u_k A\bar{y} \leq -\eta u_k^2 = -\eta < 0$$

showing that u_k does not achieve the value of the game against $\bar{y}$, completing the proof.

We can now state our main structure theorem for solutions of games. Let Γ be a game with optimal sets $\bar{X}$ and $\bar{Y}$ and let $\bar{m}$ and $\bar{n}$ be the number of essential pure strategies for P_1 and P_2, respectively.

Theorem 7.4 (structure of solutions). *For any matrix game* $\bar{m} - \text{rank } \bar{X} = \bar{n} - \text{rank } \bar{Y}$.

The theorem shows that, as mentioned previously, the sets of optimal strategies for the two players cannot be arbitrary polytopes. An important special case of the above result states:

Corollary. *If the solution* $(x_0, y_0; \omega)$ *of* Γ *is unique, then* $\bar{m} = \bar{n}$.

One more auxiliary result will be needed for the proof of the theorem.

Lemma 7.2. *For any matrix game with value* ω *there exists an optimal strategy* $\bar{x} = (\bar{\xi}_i)$ *such that*

$$\bar{x}u_i > 0 \qquad \textit{for all essential } u_i \tag{1}$$
$$\bar{x}Av_j > \omega \qquad \textit{for all nonessential } v_j \tag{2}$$

Proof. For each essential u_i there exists by definition an optimal strategy $\bar{x}_i$ such that $\bar{x}_i u_i > 0$. Also, from the previous lemma, for each nonessential v_j there is an optimal $\bar{x}_j'$ such that $\bar{x}_j' A v_j > \omega$. We then define

$$\bar{x} = \frac{1}{2\bar{m}} \sum \bar{x}_i + \frac{1}{2(n - \bar{n})} \sum \bar{x}_j'$$

and verify that $\bar{x}$ is an optimal strategy with the asserted properties.

As a final notational device, we define the *essential submatrix* $\bar{A}$ of A to consist of all coordinates α_{ij} of A such that u_i and v_j are essential. In words, $\bar{A}$ is the payoff matrix of Γ if both players restrict themselves to essential pure strategies.

Proof of Theorem 7.4. We again assume $\omega = 0$ and we shall show that $\bar{m} - \text{rank } \bar{X} = \text{rank } \bar{A} = \bar{n} - \text{rank } \bar{Y}$.

We let $R^{\bar{m}}$ be the subspace for P_1 generated by the essential vectors u_i. By definition, $\bar{X}$ is in $R^{\bar{m}}$ and the matrix $\bar{A}$ multiplies vectors in $R^{\bar{m}}$ on the right. Now let $\tilde{X}$ be the linear space generated by $\bar{X}$, i.e., $\tilde{X}$ is the set of all linear combinations of vectors in $\bar{X}$, so that rank $\tilde{X} = $ rank $\bar{X}$. We shall show that

$$\bar{m} - \text{rank } \tilde{X} = \text{rank } \bar{A} \tag{1}$$

and since by symmetry the corresponding relation must hold for P_2 our result will be proved.

To establish (1) we shall show that $\tilde{X}$ consists of all solutions of the equation

$$x\bar{A} = 0 \qquad x \, \varepsilon \, R^{\bar{m}} \tag{2}$$

whence (1) will follow from Theorem 2.4 (page 39). Now clearly every x in $\tilde{X}$ satisfies (2), since $x\bar{A}v_j = 0$ for all essential v_j by Lemma 7.1 (using, of course, the fact that $\omega = 0$). Conversely, suppose x satisfies (2) and let $\bar{x}$ be an optimal strategy satisfying the conclusion of Lemma 7.2. Then we can choose the number λ sufficiently large so that $x' = x + \lambda\bar{x}$ satisfies

$$x'u_i > 0 \qquad \text{for all essential } u_i \tag{3}$$
$$x'Av_j > 0 \qquad \text{for all nonessential } v_j \tag{4}$$

Next, since x' is semipositive it follows that $\bar{x}' = x'/\Sigma\xi_i'$ is a mixed strategy, and $\bar{x}' \, \varepsilon \, \bar{X}$ from (2) and (4). But then $x = (\Sigma\xi_i')\bar{x}' - \lambda\bar{x}$ and hence x is in $\tilde{X}$ and thus $\tilde{X}$ coincides with the solutions of (2) as asserted. The rest of the argument has already been given.

It can be shown that Theorem 7.4 completely characterizes solutions of games. That is, if $\bar{X}$ and $\bar{Y}$ are arbitrary polytopes in $<U_{\bar{m}}>$ and $<V_{\bar{n}}>$ and if $\bar{m} - \text{rank } \bar{X} = \bar{n} - \text{rank } \bar{Y}$, then there is a game having $\bar{X}$ and $\bar{Y}$ as its solution. It may be necessary, however, to introduce additional nonessential strategies for both players in order for $\bar{X}$ and $\bar{Y}$ to be the given polytopes. The number of these additional strategies will depend on the number of "faces" of the polytopes $\bar{X}$ and $\bar{Y}$. We shall not attempt to give a formal statement or proof of this result, but in a later section we shall show by examples how one can construct a game with given solution sets.

We conclude this section by noting a further useful property of the essential submatrix of a game. In practice, most small games are solved by guesswork. One tries to guess which will be the essential pure strategies for the two players. If one manages to guess correctly, then one can find the value of the game by simply solving a set of simultaneous equations. The precise statement follows.

Theorem 7.5. *Let $\bar{A}$ be the essential submatrix of the game Γ and let x and λ be solutions of the equations*

$$\Sigma \xi_i = 1 \qquad x\bar{a}^j = \lambda \qquad j = 1, \ldots, \bar{n} \tag{1}$$

Then λ is the value of the game.

Proof. We may rewrite (1) in the form

$$xu = 1 \qquad x\bar{A} = \lambda v \tag{2}$$

where $u = \Sigma u_i$ and $v = \Sigma v_j$ for u_i and v_j essential. Now from Lemma 7.1, if $\bar{y}$ is optimal for P_2, then $\bar{A}\bar{y} = \omega u$; hence

$$0 = 0\bar{y} = (x\bar{A} - \lambda v)\bar{y} = \omega(xu) - \lambda(v\bar{y}) = \omega - \lambda$$

so that $\lambda = \omega =$ value of Γ, as asserted.

The above theorem enables us, in theory at least, to find the value of a game in a finite number of steps. The method consists in trying all possible sets of essential strategies for the two players. For each such guess, one determines a trial value λ. With this value λ one now seeks a nonnegative solution of Eqs. (2), and all basic nonnegative solutions can be found once more in a finite number of trials. Next, each of these solutions $\bar{x}$ must be tried against *all* pure strategies of P_2 (not just the essential ones). Simultaneously, one must carry out the same computations for the second player. Eventually, one is certain to uncover a solution $(\bar{x}, \bar{y}; \omega)$. Of course, this process is hopelessly inefficient for practical purposes.

5. Examples

We shall illustrate the structure theorem by a pair of examples. Consider first the following.

Example 1. Evasion Game. P_1 and P_2 choose integers x and y, respectively, between 1 and 4. The payoff to P_1 is $|x - y|$.

The payoff matrix is

	1	2	3	4
1	0	1	2	3
2	1	0	1	2
3	2	1	0	1
4	3	2	1	0

The name "evasion game" is suggested by the fact that P_1 is trying to keep as far away from P_2 as possible. For this reason, one might try a strategy for P_1 in which he plays only the end point 1 or 4. Let us therefore assume the essential submatrix to consist of the first and fourth rows and columns, respectively. We then look at the submatrix

$$\begin{array}{cc} 0 & 3 \\ 3 & 0 \end{array}$$

and obviously this game has value $\frac{3}{2}$ and optimal strategies $(\frac{1}{2}, \frac{1}{2})$ for both players. This suggests trying the strategies $\bar{x}_1 = \bar{y}_1 = (\frac{1}{2}, 0, 0, \frac{1}{2})$ for the original game, and one verifies by simple computation that $(\bar{x}_1, \bar{y}_1; \frac{3}{2})$ is indeed a solution. However, note that both $\bar{x}_1$ and $\bar{y}_1$ achieve the value $\frac{3}{2}$ against *all* pure strategies of the opponent. Hence, from Lemma 7.1, at least one of the two players must have additional optimal strategies. As one immediately verifies, the strategy $\bar{y}_2 = (0, \frac{1}{2}, \frac{1}{2}, 0)$ is also optimal for P_2. Now, however, note that if P_1 plays u_2 or u_3 against $\bar{y}_2$ he will achieve a payoff of only $\frac{1}{2}$, which is less than the value of the game. Hence, u_2 and u_3 are not essential; so the essential submatrix is

$$A = \begin{array}{cccc} 0 & 1 & 2 & 3 \\ 3 & 2 & 1 & 0 \end{array}$$

Every optimal strategy for P_1 is of the form $\lambda u_1 + (1 - \lambda)u_4$ and the reader will easily show that, in fact, λ must be $\frac{1}{2}$ (see Exercise 13). Hence the optimal strategy for P_1 is unique and rank $\bar{X} = 1$. We also know that $\bar{m} = 2$ and $\bar{n} = 4$; so we conclude from the structure theorem that rank $\bar{Y} = 3$. Therefore, besides $\bar{y}_1$ and $\bar{y}_2$ there must be an additional optimal strategy for P_2 which is independent of $\bar{y}_1$ and $\bar{y}_2$. Such strategies turn out to be

$$\bar{y}_3 = (\tfrac{1}{4}, 0, \tfrac{3}{4}, 0) \qquad \bar{y}_4 = (0, \tfrac{3}{4}, 0, \tfrac{1}{4})$$

Of course, the strategies $\bar{y}_1$, $\bar{y}_2$, $\bar{y}_3$, $\bar{y}_4$ must be dependent and in fact we have

$$\bar{y}_1 + 3\bar{y}_2 = 2\bar{y}_3 + 2\bar{y}_4$$

We shall see later that, in fact,

$$\bar{Y} = \langle \bar{y}_1, \bar{y}_2, \bar{y}_3, \bar{y}_4 \rangle$$

Example 2.   A Five-step Silent Duel.   This is a finite version of the silent duel described in Chap. 6, Example 7. The players advance toward each other in five steps. After each step, a player is allowed to fire or not but he may fire only once during the game, and the probability that a player will hit his opponent if he fires after moving in k steps is $k/5$.

The payoff matrix is easily calculated. If P_1 decides to fire at step i and P_2 at step j where $i < j$ then the payoff is given by

$$\frac{i}{5} - \left(1 - \frac{i}{5}\right)\frac{j}{5} = \frac{5(i - j) + ij}{25}$$

The payoff matrix multiplied by the constant 25 is seen to be

$$\begin{array}{rrrrr}
0 & -3 & -7 & -11 & -20 \\
3 & 0 & 1 & -2 & -5 \\
7 & -1 & 0 & 7 & 5 \\
11 & 2 & -7 & 0 & 15 \\
20 & 5 & -5 & -15 & 0
\end{array}$$

Now the first strategy for both players is *dominated* (see Exercise 16, Chap. 6); hence it cannot be essential (see Exercise 15, this chapter). We may now try to guess which the essential strategies are. Among

the various possibilities we will eventually test the submatrix consisting of rows and columns 2, 3, and 5, giving

$$\begin{array}{|rrr|} 0 & 1 & -5 \\ -1 & 0 & 5 \\ 5 & -5 & 0 \end{array}$$

and this game is easily seen to have the unique solution $\bar{x}_1 = \bar{y}_1 =$
$(\frac{5}{11}, \frac{5}{11}, \frac{1}{11})$.   If we now try the strategies

$$\bar{x} = \bar{y} = (0, \tfrac{5}{11}, \tfrac{5}{11}, 0, \tfrac{1}{11})$$

in the original game, it is seen that $\bar{x}$ achieves the payoff 10 against v_4
so that u_4 and v_4 are not essential and hence $(\bar{x}, \bar{y}; 0)$ is the only solution.

It is of some interest to look at this result from the point of view
of the rules of the game.   It says that a duelist should never fire after
1 step, fire with equal probability after 2 or 3 steps, never fire after
4 steps, and just occasionally hold the fire until the very end.   This
answer is rather curious and could hardly have been guessed in
advance.

6. The Structure of Symmetric Games

Example 2 of the previous section was a symmetric game and since
for such games the optimal and essential strategies for the two players
are the same, the condition of the structure theorem will be satisfied
automatically.   One might then ask if every convex polytope $\bar{X}$ in
$<U_m>$ can be the set of solutions of a symmetric game.   The answer
is in the negative, for we shall show

Theorem 7.6 (structure of solutions of symmetric games).   *For a
symmetric game $\bar{m} - $ rank $\bar{X}$ is even.*

The theorem follows from a classical result on matrices.

Lemma 7.3.   If A is skew-symmetric then the rank of A is even.

Proof.   Let X be the set of all solutions of the equation $xA = 0$
and let $x_1, \ldots, x_k$ be a basis for X.   Then rank $A = m - k$ and we
wish to show that $m - k$ is even.

It follows directly from the definition of skew symmetry that
$xAx = 0$ for all $x \,\varepsilon\, R^m$.   Choose, now, a maximal set of vectors

$y_1, \ldots, y_s$ such that

$$\text{the vectors } x_1, \ldots, x_k, y_1, \ldots, y_s \text{ are independent} \quad (1)$$
$$y_i A y_j = 0 \qquad \text{for all } i, j \quad (2)$$

Now, let $b_i = y_i A$, $i = 1, \ldots, s$. The vectors b_i are independent for if $\Sigma \lambda_i b_i = 0$ then $\Sigma \lambda_i (y_i A) = (\Sigma \lambda_i y_i) A = 0$; so $\Sigma \lambda_i y_i \, \varepsilon \, X$, giving a dependence between the x_i and the y_i, contrary to (1) above.

Next let Y be the set of all solutions of the equations $x b_i = 0$, $i = 1, \ldots, s$. Then clearly $x_i, y_i \, \varepsilon \, Y$ for all i. Conversely, if $y \, \varepsilon \, Y$ then y is a linear combination of the x_i and y_i, for if not, by letting $y = y_{s+1}$ we could increase the set satisfying (1) and (2), contradicting maximality. It follows from Theorem 2.4 (page 39) that rank $Y = m - s = k + s$ so $m - k = 2s$.

Now to prove Theorem 7.6 one simply observes that for a symmetric game the essential submatrix is also skew-symmetric since both players have the same essential pure strategies. But we saw in the proof of the structure theorem that for games with value zero $\bar{m} - \text{rank } \bar{X} = \text{rank } \bar{A}$ and this last term is even in the symmetric case.

Example 3. We consider the familiar game of "scissors, paper, rock." For those not acquainted with the precise rules of the game, it will suffice to give its payoff matrix,

$$\begin{array}{|rrr|}
\hline
0 & 1 & -1 \\
-1 & 0 & 1 \\
1 & -1 & 0 \\
\hline
\end{array}$$

Because of the obvious symmetry among the strategies as well as the players we find by inspection the optimal strategy

$$\bar{x} = \bar{y} = (\tfrac{1}{3}, \tfrac{1}{3}, \tfrac{1}{3})$$

Thus $\bar{m} = 3$ and since rank $A = 2$, it follows that $\bar{x}$ is the only optimal strategy for this game.

A four-strategy variation of this game is the following.

Example 4. Each player chooses a number from 1 to 4. A player wins 1 from his opponent if his number is one greater than his opponent's or he has chosen 1 and his opponent 4. Otherwise the game is a draw.   The matrix is

	1	2	3	4
1	0	−1	0	1
2	1	0	−1	0
3	0	1	0	−1
4	−1	0	1	0

The strategy $(\frac{1}{4}, \frac{1}{4}, \frac{1}{4}, \frac{1}{4})$ is clearly a solution, but since the matrix has even rank there must be others.   Two such are the strategies $\bar{x}_1 = (0, \frac{1}{2}, 0, \frac{1}{2})$ and $\bar{x}_2 = (\frac{1}{2}, 0, \frac{1}{2}, 0)$.   Since rank $A = 2$ and $\bar{m} = 4$ it follows that all solutions are linear combinations of $\bar{x}_1$ and $\bar{x}_2$; hence $\bar{X} = <\bar{x}_1, \bar{x}_2>$.

7. Constructing a Game with Prescribed Solutions

In this section we show that the condition of Theorem 7.4 gives a sufficient as well as necessary condition for the polytopes $\bar{X}$ and $\bar{Y}$ to be solutions of some matrix game.   We shall not give a complete proof of the fact but content ourselves with illustrating by numerical examples how to construct the desired game, given the pair of polytopes.

We first consider some special cases.   A game is called *completely mixed* if it has a unique solution and every strategy for both players is essential.

Theorem 7.7.   Let $\bar{x} = (\bar{\xi}_i)$ and $\bar{y} = (\bar{\eta}_j)$ be mixed strategies with $\xi_i, \eta_j > 0$ $(i, j = 1, \ldots, m)$.   Then there exists a completely mixed game having $(\bar{x}, \bar{y}; 0)$ as its unique solution.

Proof.   Let the payoff matrix be

$$A = \begin{bmatrix} 1 & 0 & \cdots & 0 & -\dfrac{\bar{\eta}_1}{\bar{\eta}_m} \\[2mm] 0 & 1 & \cdots & 0 & -\dfrac{\bar{\eta}_2}{\bar{\eta}_m} \\[1mm] \cdots & \cdots & \cdots & \cdots & \cdots \\[1mm] 0 & 0 & \cdots & 1 & -\dfrac{\bar{\eta}_{m-1}}{\bar{\eta}_m} \\[2mm] -\dfrac{\bar{\xi}_1}{\bar{\xi}_m} & -\dfrac{\bar{\xi}_2}{\bar{\xi}_m} & \cdots & -\dfrac{\bar{\xi}_{m-1}}{\bar{\xi}_m} & \dfrac{1}{\bar{\xi}_m \bar{\eta}_m} \displaystyle\sum_{i=1}^{m-1} \bar{\xi}_i \bar{\eta}_i \end{bmatrix}$$

By direct computation one sees that $(\bar{x}, \bar{y}; 0)$ is a solution. On the other hand, A has rank $m - 1$ (why?), and therefore by Theorem 7.4, $\bar{X}$ and $\bar{Y}$ have rank 1; so this solution is unique.

We shall now introduce a convenient graphical device for representing the sets $<U_m>$ and $<V_n>$. We consider the case of four pure strategies and represent $<U_m>$ by a regular tetrahedron Δ of altitude one. Now, it is an easily proved fact of solid geometry that for any point in Δ the sum of the distances of this point from the four

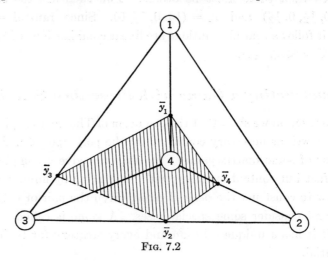

Fig. 7.2

faces is one. If we label the vertices of Δ, 1, 2, 3, and 4, then it is also true that for $x = (\xi_1, \ldots , \xi_4) \, \varepsilon \, <U_4>$ there is a unique point of Δ whose distance from the face opposite the vertex i is ξ_i. We do not prove these statements since no use will be made of them in the development of the theory. They are simply a justification for the pictorial representation we are about to use.

Let us make use of this representation to picture the optimal strategies for player 2 in Example 1 of Sec. 5.

In Fig. 7.2, the circled numbers are the pure strategies at the vertices of the tetrahedron. The extreme optimal strategies $\bar{y}_1, \ldots , \bar{y}_4$ are represented by dots and the shaded area is their convex hull $\bar{Y}$. As noted, the strategies $\bar{y}_i$ are dependent since $\bar{y}_1 + 3\bar{y}_2 = 2\bar{y}_3 + 2\bar{y}_4$, and therefore the shaded area is a two-dimensional region. (The term dimension is used here in an intuitive sense, as it has not yet been formally defined.) In fact, one sees from the figure that $\bar{Y}$ is the intersection of Δ with a two-dimensional plane. It is now clear that $\bar{Y}$ must include *all* optimal strategies, for if there were an optimal strategy not in $\bar{Y}$, then the set of optimal strategies would be at least three-dimensional so that the set of optimal strategies would have rank 4. On the other hand, subtracting the value $\omega = \frac{3}{2}$ from all coefficients of the essential matrix $\bar{A}$ we get

$$\bar{A} = \begin{pmatrix} -\frac{3}{2} & -\frac{1}{2} & \frac{1}{2} & \frac{3}{2} \\ \frac{3}{2} & \frac{1}{2} & -\frac{1}{2} & -\frac{3}{2} \end{pmatrix}$$

which has rank 1. Since $\bar{n} = 4$, we have by Theorem 7.4

$$\text{rank } \bar{Y} = 4 - 1 = 3$$

and hence there can be no optimal strategies besides those in the figure.

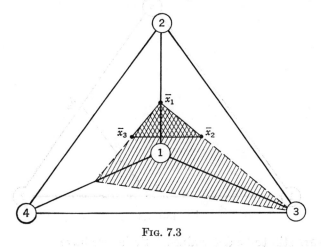

FIG. 7.3

Example 5. Let us try to construct a game whose optimal strategies are given by

$$\bar{X} = <\bar{x}_1, \bar{x}_2, \bar{x}_3> \qquad \bar{Y} = <\bar{y}_1, \bar{y}_2> \qquad \omega = 0$$

where

$$\bar{x}_1 = (\tfrac{1}{2}, \tfrac{1}{2}, 0, 0) \qquad \bar{x}_2 = (\tfrac{1}{3}, \tfrac{1}{3}, \tfrac{1}{3}, 0) \qquad \bar{x}_3 = (\tfrac{1}{2}, \tfrac{1}{4}, 0, \tfrac{1}{4})$$

and

$$\bar{y}_1 = (\tfrac{1}{2}, \tfrac{1}{2}, 0) \qquad \bar{y}_2 = (0, \tfrac{1}{2}, \tfrac{1}{2})$$

Figures 7.3 and 7.4 give the geometrical representation of $\bar{X}$ and $\bar{Y}$.

In Fig. 7.3, $\bar{X}$ is represented by the crosshatched area. The vertically shaded area is the intersection of the tetrahedron with the plane through the points $\bar{x}_1$, $\bar{x}_2$, $\bar{x}_3$.

We start by trying to construct the essential submatrix of the game. Since rank $\bar{X} = 3$ and there are 4 essential strategies, it follows that the rank of the essential submatrix must be 1.

Letting a^1 be the first column vector of the essential submatrix we have from Lemma 7.1

$$\bar{x}_i a^1 = 0 \qquad i = 1, 2, 3$$

One solution of these equations for a^1 gives

$$a^1 = (1, -1, 0, -1)$$

and since $\bar{A}$ must have rank 1 it follows that $a^2 = \lambda a^1$, $a^3 = \mu a^1$, where

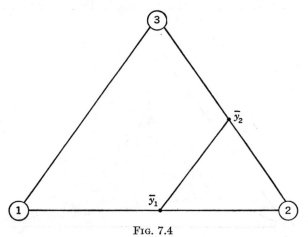

FIG. 7.4

λ and μ are still to be determined. So far we have

$$\bar{A} = \begin{pmatrix} 1 & \lambda & \mu \\ -1 & -\lambda & -\mu \\ 0 & 0 & 0 \\ -1 & -\lambda & -\mu \end{pmatrix}$$

But now since all strategies are essential for P_1, we have again, by Lemma 7.1,

$$a_1 \bar{y}_1 = (1, \lambda, \mu)(\tfrac{1}{2}, \tfrac{1}{2}, 0) = 0 \qquad \text{so } \lambda = -1$$

and

$$a_2 \bar{y}_2 = (1, \lambda, \mu)(0, \tfrac{1}{2}, \tfrac{1}{2}) = 0 \qquad \text{so } \mu = 1$$

Hence

$$\bar{A} = \begin{pmatrix} 1 & -1 & 1 \\ -1 & 1 & -1 \\ 0 & 0 & 0 \\ -1 & 1 & -1 \end{pmatrix}$$

We have now constructed a satisfactory essential subgame, but the problem is not yet solved since, in the game whose payoff is $\bar{A}$, all strategies in the vertically shaded area (Fig. 7.3) are optimal, whereas we want only the crosshatched region to be optimal. It is necessary therefore by some means to cut off the undesired portion of the vertically shaded area. We shall attempt to do this by passing a hyperplane through the vectors $\bar{x}_2$ and $\bar{x}_3$ so that $\bar{x}_1$ lies on the "positive" side of the hyperplane. More precisely, if a^4 is the normal to this hyperplane, we want to satisfy the conditions

$$a^4\bar{x}_2 = 0 \qquad a^4\bar{x}_3 = 0 \qquad \text{and} \qquad a^4\bar{x}_1 > 0$$

Here one looks for an a^4 satisfying the first two equations, changing the sign if necessary so that the inequality condition is also satisfied. In this case $a^4 = (-1, 2, -1, 0)$ satisfies the condition and if we now introduce a fourth nonessential strategy for P_2 we get the payoff matrix

$$A = \begin{pmatrix} 1 & -1 & 1 & -1 \\ -1 & 1 & -1 & 2 \\ 0 & 0 & 0 & -1 \\ -1 & 1 & -1 & 0 \end{pmatrix}$$

One now verifies easily (see Exercise 20) that this game has precisely the given sets as its optimal strategies.

The procedure used above can be described roughly as follows: First, construct the essential submatrix. This matrix will have optimal strategies which include the given sets and have the proper rank but may be too large. To obtain the desired polytope one then introduces additional nonessential strategies for the opposing player which have the effect of "cutting down" the optimal set to the desired polytope. Let us illustrate the procedure with one more example.

Example 6. Let $\bar{X} = <\bar{x}_1, \bar{x}_2, \bar{x}_3>$, $\bar{Y} = <\bar{y}_1, \bar{y}_2>$, where

$$\bar{x}_1 = (1, 0, 0) \qquad \bar{x}_2 = (\tfrac{1}{2}, \tfrac{1}{2}, 0) \qquad \bar{x}_3 = (\tfrac{1}{3}, \tfrac{1}{3}, \tfrac{1}{3})$$

and $$\bar{y}_1 = (1, 0) \qquad \bar{y}_2 = (\tfrac{1}{2}, \tfrac{1}{2})$$

The pictures are shown in Figs. 7.5 and 7.6, where the crosshatched area in Fig. 7.5 and the heavy line in Fig. 7.6 represent the sets of optimal strategies.

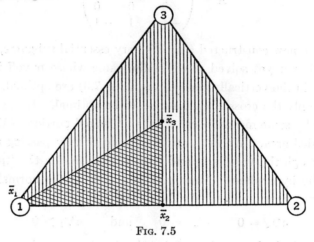

FIG. 7.5

Since rank $\bar{X} = \bar{m} = 3$ and rank $\bar{Y} = \bar{n} = 2$ it follows, assuming $\omega = 0$, that

$$\text{rank } \bar{A} = 0$$

so the essential matrix must be identically zero.   Thus,

$$\bar{A} = \begin{pmatrix} 0 & 0 \\ 0 & 0 \\ 0 & 0 \end{pmatrix}$$

Now, in order to cut down the set of optimal strategies for P_1 to the given triangle we must introduce two additional strategies for P_2

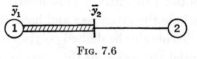

FIG. 7.6

corresponding to the edges $\bar{x}_1\bar{x}_3$ and $\bar{x}_2\bar{x}_3$ in Fig. 7.5.   Thus, we first find a^3 such that

$$a^3\bar{x}_1 = 0 \qquad a^3\bar{x}_3 = 0 \qquad \text{and} \qquad a^3\bar{x}_2 > 0$$

An obvious solution to this system is $a^3 = (0, 1, -1)$.

Next we solve

$$a^4\bar{x}_2 = 0 \qquad a^4\bar{x}_3 = 0 \qquad \text{and} \qquad a^4\bar{x}_1 > 0$$

and here we use $a^4 = (1, -1, 0)$.

We now have the matrix

$$A' = \begin{pmatrix} 0 & 0 & 0 & 1 \\ 0 & 0 & 1 & -1 \\ 0 & 0 & -1 & 0 \end{pmatrix}$$

This is not yet a solution of the problem since there are still too many optimal strategies for P_2, namely, any combination of the first two strategies. In order to cut off P_2's optimal strategies at the point y_2 we introduce a fourth row $a_4 = (-1, 1, 0, 0)$ and get

$$A = \begin{pmatrix} 0 & 0 & 0 & 1 \\ 0 & 0 & 1 & -1 \\ 0 & 0 & -1 & 0 \\ -1 & 1 & 0 & 0 \end{pmatrix}$$

which has the desired solution (Exercise 21).

We have not, of course, shown that the method illustrated above will always work, nor, in fact, have we attempted to give a precise description of what the method is. We wished here to make plausible the sufficiency of the condition given by the structure theorem. The proof of sufficiency, while not especially difficult, is rather tedious and does not seem of sufficient importance to be included here. Suffice it to say that a procedure does exist for constructing a game with pre-assigned solution sets even when there are more than four pure strategies, in which case the graphical method of this section is, of course, not applicable.

8. Basic Optimal Strategies

Since we have shown that the sets $\bar{X}$ and $\bar{Y}$ are convex polytopes, it follows that in order to find all solutions of a game it suffices to find all extreme points of these polytopes. Such extreme points are called *basic optimal strategies* or *basic solutions* and by the theory of Chap. 2 all other optimal strategies are convex combinations of these. We shall here give a characterization of the extreme optimal strategies which enables one, at least in theory, to discover in a finite number of steps all such strategies.

For present purposes a few additional conventions will be useful.

Definitions.   The $m \times m$ matrix A is called *regular* if its rank is m. A matrix which is not regular is called *singular*[1] (see Chap. 2, Exercise 9).

If A is an $m \times n$ matrix, S a subset of $M = \{1, \ldots, m\}$, and T a subset of $N = \{1, \ldots, n\}$, then the *submatrix* A_{ST} is the array of coordinates α_{ij} with $i \, \varepsilon \, S, j \, \varepsilon \, T$.

We remind the reader that we have agreed to say that the m-vector $x = (\xi_i)$ *depends* on the set S, if $\xi_i = 0$ for i not in S.

We can now give our characterization of basic optimal strategies.

Theorem 7.8.   *Let Γ have value $\omega \neq 0$. Then the optimal strategy $\bar{x}$ is basic if and only if there are sets $S \subset M$ and $T \subset N$ such that A_{ST} is regular, $\bar{x}$ depends on S, and*

$$\bar{x}a^j = \omega \qquad \text{for all } j \, \varepsilon \, T \tag{1}$$

Before proving this theorem, let us discuss it briefly.   We have seen already that, by correctly guessing which the essential strategies are, we can by means of Theorem 7.6 compute the value of the game. Using the present result we can now in a finite number of steps obtain all optimal strategies.   First, we may assume $\omega \neq 0$ for if $\omega = 0$ we simply add a fixed number to all the coordinates of A.   Next, examine all regular submatrices A_{ST} of A and solve Eq. (1) above for $\bar{x}$ (since A_{ST} is regular, this solution will be unique).   Then if $\bar{x}$ is an optimal strategy (and this is easily checked) it will be basic and in this way all basic strategies will be obtained.

Proof of Theorem.   The proof will be based on the characterization of extreme solutions of inequalities given in Theorem 2.16 (page 65). We first note that all optimal strategies for P_1 are solutions of

$$\begin{aligned} \bar{x}u_i &\geq 0 \qquad \text{for all } i \\ \bar{x}(a^j - \omega u) &\geq 0 \qquad \text{for all } j \end{aligned} \tag{2}$$

---

[1] We are here attempting to reform conventional usage.   The usual term for regular is "nonsingular," which seems an unfortunate use of the double negative. Why distinguish a normal object by its lack of abnormality?

According to Theorem 2.16, $\bar{x}$ is an extreme solution of (2) if and only if the set of relations above in which $\bar{x}$ yields equality has rank $m - 1$. We must show that this will be the case if and only if $\bar{x}$ satisfies the conditions of our theorem.

Suppose first that these conditions are satisfied; that is,

$$\begin{aligned} \bar{x}u_i &= 0 \qquad \text{for } i \text{ not in } S \\ \bar{x}(a^j - \omega u) &= 0 \qquad \text{for } j \text{ in } T \end{aligned} \tag{3}$$

Since A_{ST} is a square matrix, the above system is a set of m equations in m unknowns, and hence its rank is at most $m - 1$ since it possesses the nonzero solution $\bar{x}$. Now, if the rank of (3) were less than $m - 1$, then we could find a second solution x' of (3) independent of $\bar{x}$. We distinguish two cases.

Case 1. $x'u = 0$.

Then from (3) we have

$$\begin{aligned} x'u_i &= 0 \qquad \text{for } i \text{ not in } S \\ x'a^j &= 0 \qquad \text{for } j \text{ in } T \end{aligned} \tag{4}$$

The reader will verify that these equations are precisely the statement that the rows of the matrix A_{ST} are dependent. This, however, contradicts the assumption that A_{ST} is regular.

Case 2. $x'u \neq 0$.

Then we may assume that $x'u = 1$ (multiplying by a suitable scalar) but then $\bar{x} - x'$ will satisfy (4) above, which we have seen is impossible. Therefore, the system (3) has rank $m - 1$ and $\bar{x}$ is extreme.

Conversely, suppose $\bar{x}$ is extreme. Then let us suppose in inequalities (2) we have (reordering if necessary)

$$\begin{aligned} \bar{x}u_i &= 0 \qquad \text{for } i = r, r + 1, \ldots, m \\ \bar{x}(a^j - \omega u) &= 0 \qquad \text{for } j = 1, \ldots, s \end{aligned} \tag{5}$$

and these are the only places in which equality holds. Since $\bar{x}$ is extreme, the system (5) has rank $m - 1$. We assert that the vectors $u_r, \ldots, u_m, a^1, \ldots, a^s$ have rank m, for if they have lower rank there exists $x' = (\xi_i') \neq 0$ with $\xi_i = 0$, $i \geq r$, and $x'a^j = 0$ for $j \leq s$. Then choose an optimal strategy $\bar{y} = (\bar{\eta}_j)$ for P_2. For $j > s$ we know that $\bar{x}a^j > \omega$; hence v_j is not essential for P_2 (Lemma 7.1), and hence

$\bar{\eta}_j = 0$ for $j > s$. Then

$$x'A\bar{y} = \sum_{j=1}^{s} (x'a^j)\bar{\eta}_j = 0 \tag{6}$$

and, on the other hand,

$$x'A\bar{y} = \sum_{i=1}^{r-1} \xi_i'(a_i\bar{y}) = \left(\sum_{i=1}^{r-1} \xi_i'\right)\omega \tag{7}$$

since strategy u_i is essential for $i < r$. Since $\omega \neq 0$ this means $\sum_{i=1}^{r-1} \xi_i' = \sum_{i=1}^{m} \xi_i' = 0$, or $x'u = 0$, and therefore $\bar{x} - x'$ is also a solution of (5). But we have noticed that (5) has rank $m - 1$ so that $\bar{x} - x'$ and $\bar{x}$ are dependent; hence x' is a multiple of $\bar{x}$, and this is impossible since $\bar{x}$ has coordinate sum 1 and x' has coordinate sum zero.

Having seen that the vectors $u_r, \ldots, u_m, a^1, \ldots, a^s$ have rank m we choose from them a basis, say $a^1, \ldots, a^k, u_{k+1}, \ldots, u_m$, and it is now a simple matter to see that if $S = T = \{1, \ldots, k\}$ then A_{ST} is regular and satisfies the conditions of the theorem.

To illustrate this theorem, let us look once more at the evasion game, Example 1, whose essential submatrix was

$$\begin{array}{|cccc|}\hline 0 & 1 & 2 & 3 \\ 3 & 2 & 1 & 0 \\ \hline \end{array}$$

The four basic optimal strategies for P_2 correspond to the four regular submatrices

$$\begin{array}{|cc|}\hline 0 & 3 \\ 3 & 0 \\ \hline \end{array} \qquad \begin{array}{|cc|}\hline 1 & 2 \\ 2 & 1 \\ \hline \end{array} \qquad \begin{array}{|cc|}\hline 0 & 2 \\ 3 & 1 \\ \hline \end{array} \qquad \begin{array}{|cc|}\hline 1 & 3 \\ 2 & 0 \\ \hline \end{array}$$

as one immediately verifies.

We close this section with some additional numerical illustrations of the above result. First, consider the game of morra, Example 2 of Chap. 6. The matrix of the game is

$$A = \begin{pmatrix} 0 & 2 & -3 & 0 \\ -2 & 0 & 0 & 3 \\ 3 & 0 & 0 & -4 \\ 0 & -3 & 4 & 0 \end{pmatrix}$$

Since this game has value zero Theorem 7.8 is not directly applicable. However, by adding 1 to all entries in the matrix we get a game with the same optimal strategies, namely,

$$A' = \begin{pmatrix} 1 & 3 & -2 & 1 \\ -1 & 1 & 1 & 4 \\ 4 & 1 & 1 & -3 \\ 1 & -2 & 5 & 1 \end{pmatrix}$$

The regular submatrices corresponding to basic solutions

$$\bar{x}_1 = (0, \tfrac{3}{5}, \tfrac{2}{5}, 0) \quad \text{and} \quad \bar{x}_2 = (0, \tfrac{4}{7}, \tfrac{3}{7}, 0)$$

are, respectively,

$$\begin{pmatrix} -1 & 1 \\ 4 & 1 \end{pmatrix} \quad \text{and} \quad \begin{pmatrix} 1 & 4 \\ 1 & -3 \end{pmatrix}$$

as one easily verifies.

Let us now consider Example 5 of the previous section. Here again the value of the game was zero, but if we add 1 to each entry in the payoff matrix we get

$$A' = \begin{pmatrix} 2 & 0 & 2 & 0 \\ 0 & 2 & 0 & 3 \\ 1 & 1 & 1 & 0 \\ 0 & 2 & 0 & 1 \end{pmatrix}$$

Corresponding to the basic optimal strategies

$$\bar{x}_1 = (\tfrac{1}{2}, \tfrac{1}{2}, 0, 0) \quad \bar{x}_2 = (\tfrac{1}{3}, \tfrac{1}{3}, \tfrac{1}{3}, 0) \quad \bar{x}_3 = (\tfrac{1}{2}, \tfrac{1}{4}, 0, \tfrac{1}{4})$$

we have the regular submatrices

	1	2
1	2	0
2	0	2

	2	3	4
1	0	2	0
2	2	0	3
3	1	1	0

	1	3	4
1	2	2	0
2	0	0	3
4	0	0	1

Note that the submatrix corresponding to a given basic strategy is not unique. For example, corresponding to $\bar{x}_3$ one could also choose

	1	2	4
1	2	0	0
2	0	2	3
4	0	2	1

or

	2	3	4
1	0	2	0
2	2	0	3
4	2	0	1

In each of the above cases, one could examine all regular sub-matrices. If this is done it will be found that no additional basic strategies appear.

9. *A Method of "Learning" a Game*

These final sections treat a topic which is almost completely independent of the material presented so far. By way of introducing the subject, let us imagine the following situation. Two people quite ignorant of game theory are about to play a matrix game a large number of times. Not knowing anything in advance about the nature of his opponent, each player decides to make careful observations of the other's choices as play proceeds and to choose his own strategy on each play from information he gets in this way. There are many ways in which he might do this. A very naïve procedure would be to assume that on each play the opponent will choose the same strategy he used on the previous play. A player would then choose his best counter-strategy to his opponent's previous choice. There are two immediate objections one could raise to this procedure. First, it does not make full use of the information one has concerning one's opponent but only uses what he did on his last play. Second, there is no reason to expect a player to repeat a strategy; in fact quite the contrary would seem reasonable. A scheme which overcomes these objections is the following: Suppose the game has been played k times and P_1, having kept records, observes that P_2 has played his first strategy k_1 times, his second k_2 times, and so on. A somewhat less naïve procedure for P_1 is to assume that the probability that P_2 will play his jth strategy is k_j/k. This is clearly equivalent to the assumption that P_2 will play the mixed strategy $x^k = (k_1/k, \ldots, k_n/k)$, and accordingly, P_1 chooses a pure strategy giving the maximum expectation against x^k. We have described a very simple formula for "learning from experience." This procedure would indeed be extremely reasonable if one knew that the opponent was committed in advance to playing some given mixed strategy. A game against nature would be an example where such an assumption seems justified.

Carrying the above illustration one step further, suppose that both players decide to proceed in the experimental manner we have just described. It is then clear that, after each player has chosen his initial strategy, the strategies chosen on all future plays are essentially determined. A simple example will illustrate the point. Consider the game of baseball (Chap. 6, Exercise 3) where $p = 2$ so that the payoff matrix becomes

	t_1	t_2	t_3
s_1	2	−1	−1
s_2	−1	2	−1
s_3	−1	−1	1

In order to get started we suppose that on the first play both players use their first strategies. We record this in the following way:

		P_1				P_2		
1	s_1	2	−1	−1	t_1	2	−1	−1

The 1 on the left hand indicates the number of the play. The s_1 in the second place means that on the first play P_1 used s_1. In the third column we enter the row of the payoff matrix corresponding to the strategy chosen by P_1. The reason for this will become clear. The last two columns give the strategy chosen by P_2, namely, t_1, and the corresponding column in the matrix.

Now, according to the simple scheme of play we have described P_1 chooses his strategy for the next play as follows: He observes that P_2 used t_1 on the first play, and assuming he will do so again on the second, he decides to play s_1, which will give him a payoff of 2. On the other hand, P_2 wishes to minimize the payoff (to P_1), and observing that P_1 used s_1 on the first play, he sees that assuming P_1 will use s_1 on the second play, P_2 is best off by playing either t_2 or t_3. In order to be specific we shall assume that in case of ties a player always chooses the strategy with the smallest subscript. From what we have just said, the choices on the second play look as follows:

		P_1				P_2		
2	s_1	2	−1	−1	t_2	−1	2	−1

It is convenient to form a composite table from the first two plays. Thus

		P_1				P_2		
1	s_1	2	-1	-1	t_1	2	-1	-1
2	s_1	4	-2	-2	t_2	1	1	-2

Note that in the second row and third column we have entered not the row corresponding to s_1 but the *sum* of the rows corresponding to the strategies chosen on the first and second plays. These happened to be s_1 in both cases. For the second player the entry in the last column, second row, is the sum of the first and second columns of the matrix. The reason for tabulating in this manner will now be explained. Which strategy will P_1 choose on the third play? According to our rules, he must now assume that P_2 will choose t_1 or t_2 with equal probability. His expected payoff for each of his three strategies is then given by dividing the entry in the last row and column above by 2, giving $(\frac{1}{2}, \frac{1}{2}, -1)$. In order to choose his next strategy he must find the largest coordinate in this vector and play the corresponding strategy. Note that, for this purpose, it is not necessary to divide by 2. P_1 simply notes that the first and second coordinates of the vector $(1, 1, -2)$ are maximal, and therefore he must again play s_1. Similarly, P_2 observes that the second and third coordinates are the smallest in the vector $(4, -2, -2)$ (second row, third column, of the table) and accordingly he uses t_2 on the third play, giving

		P_1				P_2		
3	s_1	6	-3	-3	t_2	0	3	-3

where again the vectors for P_1 and P_2 are obtained by adding to the previously obtained totals the first row and second column of the payoff matrix, respectively. The method of procedure should now be clear. At the kth stage we are confronted with a vector u^k for P_1 and a vector v^k for P_2. The new vector u^{k+1} for P_1 is obtained by adding to u^k the ith row a_i of the payoff matrix, where i corresponds to the maximum coordinate of v^k. Similarly $v^{k+1} = v^k + a^j$, where j corresponds to the minimum coordinate of u^k. The table which follows gives the first 21 values of u^k and v^k for the game of baseball.

		P_1				P_2		
1	s_1	2	−1	−1	t_1	2	−1	−1
2	s_1	4	−2	−2	t_2	1	1	−2
3	s_1	6	−3	−3	t_2	0	3	−3
4	s_2	5	−1	−4	t_2	−1	5	−4
5	s_2	4	1	−5	t_3	−2	4	−3
6	s_2	3	3	−6	t_3	−3	3	−2
7	s_2	2	5	−7	t_3	−4	2	−1
8	s_2	1	7	−8	t_3	−5	1	0
9	s_2	0	9	−9	t_3	−6	0	1
10	s_3	−1	8	−8	t_3	−7	−1	2
11	s_3	−2	7	−7	t_3	−8	−2	3
12	s_3	−3	6	−6	t_3	−9	−3	4
13	s_3	−4	5	−5	t_3	−10	−4	5
14	s_3	−5	4	−4	t_1	−8	−5	4
15	s_3	−6	3	−3	t_1	−6	−6	3
16	s_3	−7	2	−2	t_1	−4	−7	2
17	s_3	−8	1	−1	t_1	−2	−8	1
18	s_3	−9	0	0	t_1	0	−9	0
19	s_1	−7	−1	−1	t_1	2	−10	−1
20	s_1	−5	−2	−3	t_1	4	−11	−2
21	s_1	−3	−3	−3	t_1	6	−12	−3

Of course, the question is what has this method to do with game theory? The remarkable fact is that, by behaving in this naïve experimental manner, the average payoff (to P_1) will approach the value of the game! Let us examine the data in the preceding table with this fact in mind. In the course of the 21 plays, P_1 has used s_1 6 times, s_2 6 times, and s_3 9 times, corresponding to a mixed strategy $(2/7, 2/7, 3/7)$ for which the payoff vector is $(-1/7, -1/7, -1/7)$, which of course could have been obtained by dividing the vector u^{21} by 21. This tells us at once that the value $\omega \geqq -1/7$. Following the same argument for P_2 and dividing v^{21} by 21 gives $(2/7, -4/7, -1/7)$, which shows that $\omega \leqq 2/7$. Actually we can do much better than this, for note that after 18 plays the average payoff for P_2 is $(0, -1/2, 0)$, which shows that the value of the game is nonpositive. We have thus shown that

$$-1/7 \leqq \omega \leqq 0$$

giving an estimate of the game's value (the reader will easily compute the true value of the game so we shall not spoil his fun by telling him what it is). This estimate is not especially good, and indeed the method is not recommended for practical computational purposes. Nevertheless, in view of our remarks above, we know that if we play a sufficiently large number of times we will get arbitrarily good estimates of the value, and this fact is of considerable theoretical interest. It shows that after a large number of plays the payoffs will "stabilize," becoming asymptotically close to the value of the game.   This is the first instance we have encountered of a *stability theorem*, a type of result that comes up frequently in connection with economic models, and we shall have more to say on the subject in later chapters.

10. *Convergence of the Learning Method*

In the previous section we have described and illustrated what we have called the "learning method" for solving a game. In this section we give a precise formulation of the method and prove its convergence.

Definition. If Γ is a game with payoff matrix A, a *learning sequence* for Γ is a sequence of pairs of nonnegative vectors (x^0, y^0),

$(x^1, y^1), \ldots , (x^k, y^k), \ldots$

where x^0 and y^0 are the zero vectors in R^m and R^n (1)

$x^{k+1} = x^k + u_i$ where i is the index of a maximum coordinate of Ay^k (2)

$y^{k+1} = y^k + v_j$ where j is the index of a minimum coordinate of $x^k A$ (3)

The motivation for this definition has been given in the previous section, and no further comments should be necessary at this point.

In terms of learning sequences, the convergence theorem takes the following simple form.

Theorem 7.9 (convergence theorem). *If (x^k, y^k) is a learning sequence for a game Γ with matrix A and value ω then*

$$\lim_{k \to \infty} \min_j \left(\frac{x^k A}{k} \right) = \lim_{k \to \infty} \max_i \left(\frac{Ay^k}{k} \right) = \omega$$

What does this result imply? First, note that the vector x^k/k is a mixed strategy and hence the theorem asserts that for large k the strategy x^k/k guarantees P_1 a payoff which is arbitrarily close to ω. Similarly, y^k/k guarantees P_2 a payoff arbitrarily close to $-\omega$. Therefore, after a large number of plays the payoff will get as close as we wish to the value ω, which amounts to the verbal statement made in the last section.

The proof of the convergence theorem is quite difficult. One simplification is to symmetrize, as was done in proving the minimax theorem. The symmetrized version runs as follows.

Let A be a skew-symmetric matrix. A *learning sequence* $z^0, z^1, \ldots, z^k, \ldots,$ is a sequence of nonnegative m-vectors such that

$$z^0 = 0 \tag{1}$$
$$z^{k+1} = z^k + u_i \tag{2}$$

where i is the index of some minimum coordinate of $z^k A$.

We now have the following simple statement of convergence for this symmetric case.

Theorem 7.10

$$\lim_{k \to \infty} \min_j \frac{z^k A}{k} = 0$$

Our first task is to show that the symmetric Theorem 7.10 implies the general Theorem 7.9. To see this let Γ be a game with matrix A, and let $\hat{A}$ be the skew-symmetric matrix corresponding to the symmetrized game $\hat{\Gamma}$. The reader will see by referring to Chap. 6, Sec. 7, that $\hat{A}$ is an $mn \times mn$ matrix and the entry in row ij and column kl is

$$\alpha_{ij:kl} = \alpha_{il} - \alpha_{kj}$$

We now make some simple observations. If $z = (\zeta_{ij}), i = 1, \ldots, m, j = 1, \ldots, n,$ is an mn-vector we may define an m-vector $x_z = (\xi_i)$ and an n-vector $y_z = (\eta_j)$ by the rules

$$\xi_i = \sum_j \zeta_{ij} \qquad \eta_j = \sum_i \zeta_{ij}$$

If we now compute the ijth coordinate of the vector $z\hat{A}$ we have

$$\sum_{k,l} \zeta_{kl}\alpha_{kl:ij} = \sum_{k,l} \zeta_{kl}(\alpha_{kj} - \alpha_{il})$$

$$= \sum_{k} \xi_k\alpha_{kj} - \sum_{l} \eta_l\alpha_{il} = x_z a^j - y_z a_i \qquad (1)$$

In order to show that Theorem 7.10 implies Theorem 7.9 let (x^k, y^k) be a learning sequence for Γ and define a sequence (z^k) for $\hat{\Gamma}$ by the rules

$$z^0 = 0 \qquad (2)$$
$$z^{k+1} = z^k + w_{ij} \qquad (3)$$

where w_{ij} is the ijth unit vector in R^{mn} and i is the maximum coordinate of Ay^k and j is the minimum coordinate of $x^k A$.

The sequence (z^k) was so constructed that $x_{z^k} = x^k$ and $y_{z^k} = y^k$, as the reader will readily check. This means in view of (1) that the ijth coordinate of $z^k \hat{A}$ is $x^k a^j - y^k a_i$, and this expression attains its minimum over all ij when $x^k a^j = \min x^k A$ and $y^k a_i = \max Ay^k$. This shows therefore that (z^k) is a learning sequence for $\hat{A}$. Now assuming Theorem 7.10 we know that

$$\min_{ij} \frac{z^k \hat{A}}{k} = \min_{i,j} \frac{x^k a^j - y^k a_i}{k}$$

$$= \frac{\min\limits_{j} x^k a^j - \max\limits_{i} y^k a_i}{k}$$

$$= \min_{j} \frac{x^k A}{k} - \max_{i} \frac{Ay^k}{k}$$

approaches zero with k. Combining this with the fact that $\min\limits_{j} \dfrac{x^k A}{k} \leqq$

$\omega \leqq \max\limits_{i} \dfrac{Ay^k}{k}$ (why is this?) we obtain at once the conclusion of Theorem 7.9.

The above formalism perhaps obscures the simple intuitive idea in the symmetrization argument. Recall that the symmetrized game can be thought of as a single person playing two games, or rather the same game twice, using the "white pieces" in one play and the "black pieces" in the other. It is almost obvious that the learning method for this "double game" is a sort of composite of what each player would do in the unsymmetrized game.

We must now get on to the business of proving Theorem 7.10. It turns out that one must actually prove something a little more general.

Definition.   A *vector sequence* (z^k) for the skew-symmetric matrix A is the same as a learning sequence except that the vector z^0 may be any nonnegative vector.

Notation.   If A is a matrix, the *absolute value* of A, written $|A|$, is defined by

$$|A| = \max_{ij} |\alpha_{ij}|$$

In words, the absolute value of A is the maximum of the absolute values of its coordinates.

We now give a lemma which implies Theorem 7.10.

Lemma 7.4.   *If (z^k) is a vector sequence for the $m \times m$ skew-symmetric matrix A with absolute value $|A|$ then for any positive ϵ there is a positive integer N depending only on m and $|A|$ such that*

$$\frac{\min z^0 A - \min z^n A}{n} \leqq \epsilon |A| \tag{1}$$

for $n > N$.

It is easy to see that this lemma implies Theorem 7.10 for in case (z^k) is a learning sequence, then $z^0 = 0$ and (1) becomes

$$\frac{\min z^n A}{n} \geqq -\epsilon |A| \qquad \text{for } n > N \tag{2}$$

On the other hand, we know, since A is skew-symmetric, that $\min z^n A \leqq 0$ (for if $z^n A > 0$ then we would have $z^n A z^n > 0$ contrary to the fact that $zAz = 0$ for all z).   Hence

$$-\epsilon |A| \leqq \frac{\min z^n A}{n} \leqq 0$$

and thus $$\lim_{n \to \infty} \frac{\min z^n A}{n} = 0$$

In order to prove Lemma 7.4, we need another simple fact.

Lemma 7.5.   If (z^k) *is a vector sequence for* A *then*

$$\max z^k A \geq \min z^0 A \qquad (3)$$

for all k.

Proof.   The lemma simply asserts that $(z^k - z^0)A$ cannot be negative and since $z^k - z^0$ is nonnegative and A is skew-symmetric this follows at once (see parenthetical argument in the paragraph above).

Proof of Lemma 7.4.   The proof proceeds by induction on m where m is the number of rows (and columns) of A.   For $m = 1$, $A = 0$ and the proof is immediate.   For $m = 2$, $A = \begin{pmatrix} 0 & \alpha \\ -\alpha & 0 \end{pmatrix}$ and again convergence is trivial (see Exercise 28).   Assume the theorem true for a matrix with m rows and let A be a matrix with $m + 1$ rows, and ϵ a positive number.   By induction hypothesis there is a number N' such that for any skew-symmetric submatrix A' of A and vector sequence (z^k), for $n > N'$ we have

$$\frac{\min z^0 A' - \min z^n A'}{n} \leq \frac{\epsilon}{3} |A'| \qquad (4)$$

We now choose $N \geq \dfrac{3}{\epsilon} N'$ and must show that N satisfies the conclusion of the lemma.

Let us then choose $n > N$.   Now by definition, we know that $z^k - z^{k-1}$ is some unit vector which we shall denote by u^k.   Next, let s be the largest integer such that the vectors u^s, u^{s-1}, . . . , $u^{s-N'}$ include all the $m + 1$ unit vectors.   In game theoretic language, this means that in the course of N' plays all $m + 1$ of the strategies were used.   Of course, there may be no such integer s, in which case we let $s = 0$.

We shall first show that

$$\min z^0 A - \min z^s A \leq N' |A| \qquad (5)$$

and this will follow from the previous Lemma 7.5 if we can show

$$\max z^{s-N'} A - \min z^s A \leq N' |A| \qquad (6)$$

for combining (6) and (3) gives (5).

To establish (6), suppose the ith coordinate of $z^{s-N'}A$ is maximal and denote it by $\eta_i^{s-N'}$ and suppose the jth coordinate of $z^s A$ is minimal and denote it by η_j^s. Now by assumption, the ith strategy was used in the sequence $z^{s-N'}, \ldots, z^s$; hence

$$\eta_i^p \leqq \eta_j^p \qquad \text{for some } p \text{ between } s - N' \text{ and } s \qquad (7)$$

On the other hand, $|\eta_i^{k+1} - \eta_i^k| \leqq |A|$ for all k; hence

$$\eta_i^p \geqq \eta_i^{s-N'} - (p - s + N')|A| \qquad (8)$$

and $$\eta_j^p \leqq \eta_j^s + (s - p)|A| \qquad (9)$$

and combining (7), (8), and (9), we have

$$\eta_i^{s-N'} - (p - s + N')|A| \leqq \eta_j^s + (s - p)|A|$$

or $$\eta_i^{s-N'} - \eta_j^s \leqq N'|A|$$

which is, in fact, (6).

Now because of the choice of s it follows that the sequence u^s, $u^{s+1}, \ldots, u^{s+N'}$ leaves out at least one unit vector, say u_i. Letting A' be the matrix obtained from A by deleting the ith row and column, we see that the vectors $z'^s, z'^{s+1}, \ldots, z'^{s+N'}$ form a vector sequence for A' where z'^k is obtained from z^k by deleting the ith coordinate. By induction hypothesis then

$$\min z^s A - \min z^{s+N'} A \leqq N'|A| \frac{\epsilon}{3} \qquad (10)$$

where we can remove primes since $|A| \geqq |A'|$ and the ith coordinate of z^s, z^{s+1}, etc., remains constant. Similarly,

$$\min z^{s+N'} A - \min z^{s+2N'} A \leqq N'|A| \frac{\epsilon}{3} \qquad (11)$$

etc.

To complete the proof we write $n - s = qN' + r$, where q and r are integers with $r < N'$. Then

$$\begin{aligned}
\min z^0 A - \min z^n A &= (\min z^0 A - \min z^s A) \\
&\quad + (\min z^s A - \min z^{s+N'} A) + \cdots \\
&\quad + (\min z^{s+qN'} A - \min z^n A) \\
&\leqq N'|A| + qN'|A| \frac{\epsilon}{3} + r|A|
\end{aligned}$$

but $q \leqq n/N'$, $r < N' \leqq \epsilon N/3 \leqq \epsilon n/3$, giving

$$\min z^0 A - \min z^n A \leqq \left(\frac{\epsilon n}{3} + \frac{\epsilon n}{3} + \frac{\epsilon n}{3}\right) |A| = \epsilon n |A|$$

or $$\frac{\min z^0 A - \min z^n A}{n} \leqq \epsilon |A|$$

which completes the proof.

We conclude the section with a few final remarks concerning the learning method.

Originally, the learning method was proposed as a means for actually computing the value of a game. As a computational procedure, as already mentioned, the method is impractical since the rate of convergence is so extremely slow. A number of variants of the method have been proposed which seem to have better convergence properties. The situation here, however, is still in an uncertain state.

Concerning terminology, what we have referred to as the learning method has been popularly called the "method of fictitious play," the idea being that, in order to find the value of the game, the computer pretends to play both sides in accordance with the rules we have given. We prefer our "learning" terminology as it emphasizes the theoretical rather than the computational aspect of the method.

Bibliographical Notes

The proof of the equivalence of games and programs was given by Dantzig [2]. The theorems on the structure of solutions of games were first proved by Bohnenblust, Karlin, and Shapley [1]. The presentation here is based on a paper of Gale and Sherman [1]. The structure theorem for symmetric games is due to Gale, Kuhn, and Tucker [1]. The characterization of basic optimal strategies is due to Shapley and Snow [1].

The "learning method" for solving a game was proposed by Brown [1]. The proof of convergence is due to Robinson [1].

Exercises

1. Prove that the problem of solving a game with payoff matrix A is equivalent to the following general maximum problem: Find a

nonnegative vector x and a number ω such that

$$\omega \text{ is a maximum} \tag{1}$$

subject to

$$xA \geqq \omega v \tag{2}$$
$$xu = 1$$

2. By applying the general duality theorem to the program of Exercise 1, give another proof of the minimax theorem.

3. Let (A, b, c) stand for a standard maximum problem with value μ. Show that the game whose payoff matrix is

$$M = \begin{pmatrix} -A & c \\ b & -\mu \end{pmatrix}$$

has value zero.

4. Show that, if the game with matrix M of Exercise 3 has value zero and the last strategies for both players are essential, then the program (A, b, c) has value μ.

5. Find all optimal strategies for the game of poker treated in Sec. 2 for the case $b = 3$. (It will be found that there are two basic optimal strategies for each player.)

6. Analyze the solution of the game of poker by determining as a function of the "bet" b: (a) the value of the game; (b) the probability that P_1 "bluffs," i.e., bets when he holds the low card; (c) the probability that P_1 "underplays," i.e., does not bet when he holds the high card.

7. *Rules.* P_2 chooses two integers between 1 and 4. P_1 chooses an integer i between 1 and 4 and wins or loses i according as i is or is not one of the integers chosen by P_2. Solve by the simplex method.

8. The general has 4 divisions, the enemy 5. There are two roads leading to the town, and the general will capture the town if his troops outnumber the enemy's along either road. What should he do?

9. P_1 and P_2 choose integers x and y between 0 and 3. If $x \geqq y$ then P_1 wins $x - y$. If $x < y$ then P_1 wins $x + y$. Solve by the simplex method.

10. We describe another *evasion game.*

Rules. P_1 and P_2 choose integers $i, j \leqq n$. If $i \neq j$, P_1 wins i, but if $i = j$, P_2 wins λi.

Show that this game is completely mixed if $\lambda > n - 1 - \sum_{i=1}^{n} \frac{1}{i} > 0$,

and find its general solution.

11. Use the simplex method to solve the game of Exercise 10 when $n = 5$ and $\lambda = 2$.

12. The players choose integers i and j between 1 and n and P_1 wins $|i - j|$. Assuming n is odd: (a) Show that the game has value $\omega = (n - 1)/2$. (b) Show that P_2 has a pure optimal strategy. (c) Find all essential pure strategies for P_1. (d) Show that P_1 has a unique optimal strategy. (e) Find all essential pure strategies for P_2.

13. If n is even in the game of Exercise 12, show that (a) and (d) above are still true, but (b) is false.

14. Find all optimal strategies for both players in the game of Exercise 12 when $n = 5$.

15. Show that a dominated pure strategy cannot be essential.

16. Let A be a matrix, A_s the submatrix consisting of the first s rows of A, A^t the submatrix consisting of the first t columns of A.

Suppose the jth column of A_s is dominated for $j > t$, and the ith row of A^t is dominated for $i > s$. Prove that u_i and v_j are not essential for $i > s$, $j > t$. (If $s = t = 1$ this says that A has a unique saddle point.)

17. For any number α between 0 and 1 construct a 2×2 game such that the optimal strategies for P_1 are

$$\bar{X} = \{(\xi, 1 - \xi)|\xi \leqq \alpha\}$$

18. For any numbers $0 < \alpha < \beta < 1$ construct a 2×3 game such that

$$\bar{X} = \{(\xi, 1 - \xi)|\alpha \leqq \xi \leqq \beta\}$$

What must the set $\bar{Y}$ be in this game?

19. If in a matrix game every optimal strategy uses all pure strategies, then show that the game is completely mixed (i.e., A is square and optimal strategies are unique).

20. Show in detail that the game of Example 5 of the text has no optimal strategies other than those listed.

21. The same as Exercise 20 for Example 6 of the text.

22. Construct a game whose basic optimal strategies are

$$
\begin{array}{lll}
x_1 = (\tfrac{1}{2}, \tfrac{1}{2}, 0, 0) & x_2 = (0, \tfrac{1}{2}, \tfrac{1}{2}, 0) & x_3 = (0, 0, \tfrac{1}{2}, \tfrac{1}{2}) \\
y_1 = (\tfrac{1}{2}, \tfrac{1}{2}, 0) & y_2 = (\tfrac{1}{3}, \tfrac{1}{3}, \tfrac{1}{3}) &
\end{array}
$$

23. If a, b, c are not zero, show that the symmetric game with matrix

$$\begin{array}{|ccc|} 0 & a & b \\ -a & 0 & c \\ -b & -c & 0 \end{array}$$

has a unique solution.

When will the game have one essential strategy? Two? Three? Give the solution in each case.

24. Consider the general game corresponding to Examples 3 and 4. *Rules.* The players choose integers i and j between 1 and n.

$$P_1 \text{ wins if } i = j + 1 \quad \text{or} \quad i = 1 \quad \text{and} \quad j = n$$
$$P_2 \text{ wins if } j = i + 1 \quad \text{or} \quad j = 1 \quad \text{and} \quad i = n$$

Otherwise the game is a draw.

(*a*) Show that solutions are unique for n odd.

(*b*) If n is even, show solutions are not unique and find all solutions.

25. List all square submatrices in Examples 5 and 6 which correspond to basic optimal strategies.

26. For the game of morra, compute the first 200 terms in the learning sequence (the amount of computation involved is surprisingly small, as the reader will see). What are the bounds on the value obtained?

27. Show that, in the learning sequence of morra, all strategies are used infinitely often (this is surprising since we know that the first and fourth strategies are not essential).

28. Show that for a 2×2 symmetric game the bounds on the value after n iterations of the learning sequence are

$$-\frac{|A|}{n} < \omega < \frac{|A|}{n}$$

29. If a game Γ has a unique optimal strategy $\bar{x}$ for P_1, show that, if (x^k) is a learning sequence for Γ, then

$$\lim_{k \to \infty} \frac{x^k}{k} = \bar{x}$$

(Here one must use the fact that a bounded infinite sequence of vectors has a limit point.)

CHAPTER EIGHT

Linear Models of Exchange

In our study of linear programming and matrix games we have become familiar with two economic models for which rather extensive theories have been developed. In this chapter and the next we shall consider a number of other linear models. Unlike the game and programming models, those which we are about to take up will have more the flavor of the problems which occur in ordinary courses in economics. In this chapter we shall be concerned with such matters as balance of trade, flow of income, price equilibrium, and other concepts familiar to economics students. The reader should be warned, however, that we intend to remain within the framework of linear theory and therefore we shall be treating rather special types of exchange situations. Nevertheless, these linear exchange models have received considerable attention in recent years, and an understanding of them is not only useful in itself but also a prerequisite for the analysis of more general models.

As in the previous chapters we begin our discussion with some illustrations.

1. Examples

Example 1. The Simple Exchange Model. The Price Problem. We consider an *economy* in which there are n *producers* P_1, . . . , P_n and n *goods* G_1, . . . , G_n, where producer P_i produces only the good G_i. We shall be considering a fixed period of time, say a year, and for convenience we choose our units so that each producer P_i produces exactly one unit of G_i per year.

Now, in addition to producing the good G_i, producer P_i will also consume certain amounts of one or more of the other goods. Specifically, let α_{ij} be the amount of G_j consumed by P_i per year where, of course,

$$\alpha_{ij} \geqq 0 \tag{1}$$

We shall also assume that our model is *closed*, which simply means there is no flow of goods to or from the model from outside, and hence for each good, total production equals total consumption, giving the equation

$$\sum_{i=1}^{n} \alpha_{ij} = 1 \tag{2}$$

It may appear that we are making a strong assumption here in supposing that everything which P_i produces will be consumed. Actually, however, (2) will be true by definition if we simply agree that P_i consumes all of G_i which remains after the other producers have taken their shares α_{ij}. Consumption in this case may consist of P_i's simply disposing of the amount α_{ii} of G_i which is left over.

The matrix $A = (\alpha_{ij})$ formed from the coefficients α_{ij} will be called the *exchange matrix* of the model. More generally, we shall call any matrix $A = (\alpha_{ij})$ whose entries α_{ij} satisfy (1) and (2) above an *exchange matrix*.[1]

Now, suppose the price of one unit of G_i to be π_i. Then the annual *income* of P_i will also be π_i since P_i produces and sells (including possible sales to himself) exactly one unit of G_i per year. The annual *expenditure* of P_i is obviously given by the expression

$$\sum_{j=1}^{n} \alpha_{ij}\pi_j$$

We shall say that the prices $p = (\pi_1, \ldots, \pi_n)$ yield *equilibrium* if

---

[1] In probability theory such matrices are termed "stochastic." We prefer the alternative terminology as being more suggestive in our present context.

$$\sum_j \alpha_{ij}\pi_j \leq \pi_i \qquad \text{for all } i \tag{3}$$

This is simply the requirement that no producer spends more than he earns. The word "equilibrium" is intended to convey this simple budgetary condition.

Problem. Given an exchange matrix A, do there exist prices π_j satisfying inequalities (3)?

In vector-matrix language we have: Given a matrix A such that

$$A \geq 0 \tag{1}$$

$$\sum_i a_i = v \tag{2}$$

does there exist a semipositive vector p such that

$$Ap \leq p \tag{3}$$

It is clear that we are dealing with a typical equation-inequality problem of the type studied in Chap. 2. Before proceeding to the complete analysis of the problem we can make one simple preliminary observation. If (3) above holds then, in fact, we have the stronger statement

$$Ap = p \tag{4}$$

To see this, note that from (3) and (2) we have

$$\Sigma\pi_i \geq \Sigma a_i p = (\Sigma a_i)p = vp = \Sigma\pi_i$$

Hence $\Sigma\pi_i = \Sigma(a_i p)$ and therefore $\pi_i = a_i p$ for all i.

This algebraic result is equivalent to the following simple economic fact: If at prices p some producer is making a profit then at least one other producer is taking a loss. Stated formally we have:

Lemma 8.1. If A is an exchange matrix and p a vector such that $Ap \leq p$ then $Ap = p$.

The price problem is now reduced to finding a semipositive vector p satisfying (4). (Such a vector is generally called a *characteristic vector* or *eigen-vector* of the matrix A.) In the next section we shall discuss the solutions of this problem in complete detail. Before doing so let us give a second example which though different in economic content leads to the same algebraic problem.

Example 2.   The Simple Linear Model of International Trade.   Consider n countries $C_1, \ldots, C_n$ which are engaged in trade with each other, and assume there is a single common unit of currency, say the dollar.   In this example, unlike the previous one, we assume that all prices are given in advance and remain constant. The *income* η_j to country C_j is assumed to come entirely from sale of its own goods either internally or to other countries.   We now make the strong

Assumption of Linearity.   The fraction of C_j's income η_j which will be spent on imports from C_i is a fixed number α_{ij} which does not depend on η_j.

This assumption is admittedly a rather special one.   In order to see how it could be violated one might think of an individual who spends the fraction α_F of his income on food, α_C on clothes, and α_E on entertainment.   Now if the individual's income becomes small one would expect that the fraction spent on entertainment would decrease and if his income became very small his entire income might have to go for food.   The linearity assumption is more likely to be approximately satisfied for larger aggregates of individuals such as countries, though even here it should be recognized that the condition is quite restrictive.   Nevertheless, such linear models have been quite extensively studied, partly for their own sake and partly in the hope of gaining insight into more difficult nonlinear problems.

Since the numbers α_{ij} are defined as fractions of the income η_j it follows by definition that $\alpha_{ij} \geqq 0$ and $\displaystyle\sum_{i=1}^{n} \alpha_{ij} = 1$ and hence the matrix $A = (\alpha_{ij})$ is again an *exchange matrix*.

We wish next to determine the income of each country C_i which, as we have agreed, is the total value of sales by C_i to itself and other countries.   Now, we have assumed that the value of exports from C_i to C_j is equal to $\eta_j \alpha_{ij}$.   Hence the total income η_i of C_i satisfies the equation

$$\eta_i = \sum_{j=1}^{n} \eta_j \alpha_{ij} \tag{1}$$

and (1) above must be satisfied for all countries C_i.   In vector language the nonnegative income vector $y = (\eta_1, \ldots, \eta_n)$ must satisfy

$$Ay = y$$

where A is the given exchange matrix. The algebraic problem is thus formally identical with that of Example 1.

2. Equilibrium for the Exchange Model

The two examples of the previous section both lead to the following algebraic problem:

Given an exchange matrix A, does there exist a semipositive n-vector y such that $Ay = y$?

In this section we shall give the complete solution to this problem, including a full discussion of existence and uniqueness as well as the economic interpretation of the results in terms of our examples.

The question of existence is quickly disposed of by the following

Theorem 8.1 (existence theorem). *If A is an exchange matrix then there exists a semipositive vector y such that $Ay = y$.*

Proof. Letting I be the identity matrix (see Chap. 2, Exercise 8) we seek $y \geq 0$ such that $(I - A)y = 0$. From Theorem 2.9 (page 48) this system has no solution only if there is a vector x such that $x(I - A) > 0$, or

$$\sum_{i=1}^{n} \xi_i a_i < x \qquad \text{where } x = (\xi_1, \ldots, \xi_n) \tag{1}$$

Since A is an exchange matrix we have

$$\sum_{i=1}^{n} a_i = v \tag{2}$$

Now let $\mu = \min(\xi_i)$, say $\mu = \xi_1$. Then multiplying (2) by ξ_1 and subtracting from (1) gives

$$\sum_{i=2}^{n} (\xi_i - \xi_1)a_i < x - \xi_1 v$$

and in particular

$$\sum_{i=2}^{n} (\xi_i - \xi_1)\alpha_{i1} < 0$$

but this is impossible since both $\xi_i - \xi_1$ and α_{i1} are nonnegative for all i. Therefore, no such vector x exists, and the conclusion of the theorem follows.

This result shows that there always exists a solution to the problems of Examples 1 and 2. Let us call the solution vector y an *equilibrium vector*. The next question which naturally suggests itself is whether one can make the stronger assertion that the equilibrium vector will actually be positive. In the price problem this would mean that there are no *free goods*, and in the international-exchange problem it would mean that each country realizes a positive income. This problem turns out to be closely related to that of uniqueness. In this connection we note that if y is an equilibrium vector so also is λy for any $\lambda > 0$. Economically, this simply means that in our models it is only the *relative* prices and incomes which are determined, for clearly, multiplying all prices or incomes by the same positive constant corresponds to choosing a new unit of measurement of currency. It is possible, however, for a nontrivial kind of nonuniqueness to occur. In the international-trade model suppose the countries C_i break up into two or more disjoint groups in such a manner that the countries in a given group trade only with other countries in the same group. In this case we are actually considering two or more completely independent models and it is clear that the incomes of all countries in one of the groups may change by some nonnegative multiple without affecting the countries of other groups. The remaining theorems of this section show that this is in fact the only kind of nonuniqueness that can occur.

For the sake of being specific we shall think henceforth in terms of the trade model of Example 2, though our results have analogous interpretations in the other case. The following definition is motivated by the discussion of the paragraph above.

Definition. Let S be a subset of the indices $N = \{1, 2, \ldots, n\}$ and let S' be its complement. The countries C_i, $i \in S$, are called an *independent subset* if in the exchange matrix $A = (\alpha_{ij})$, $\alpha_{ij} = 0$ for $j \in S$, $i \in S'$. We shall abbreviate by saying in this case that the indices themselves form the *independent subset*.

This definition says precisely that the countries of S import only from each other. If by suitable reordering we make S consist of the first k indices then the exchange matrix A takes the following form:

$$A = \begin{pmatrix} A_1 & A_2 \\ 0 & A_3 \end{pmatrix}$$

in which there is an $(n - k) \times k$ block of zeros in the lower left corner of the matrix.

We remark that the set N itself is an independent subset.

Definition. The exchange matrix A is called *irreducible* if there are no nonempty independent subsets of N other than N itself.

The irreducibility of an exchange matrix has an important economic interpretation. It implies that every country trades with every other country at least "indirectly." That is, for any two countries C_i and C_j there exists a sequence of indices $i_1, \ldots, i_k$ such that C_i imports from C_{i_1}, C_{i_1} from C_{i_2}, $\ldots$, C_{i_k} from C_j. The proof that this is equivalent to irreducibility is left to the exercises (see Exercise 1).

For irreducible exchange matrices we have the following concise result:

Theorem 8.2. *If the exchange matrix A is irreducible then any equilibrium vector y is positive and unique up to multiplication by a positive number.*

Proof. We first show that y is positive. If not then, say, $y = (\eta_1, \ldots, \eta_n)$ and $\eta_j > 0$ for $j \varepsilon S$, $\eta_j = 0$ for $j \varepsilon S'$. Then if $i \varepsilon S'$ we have

$$a_i y = \eta_i = 0 = \sum_{j=1}^{n} \alpha_{ij}\eta_j = \sum_{j \varepsilon S} \alpha_{ij}\eta_j$$

and therefore $\alpha_{ij} = 0$ for $i \varepsilon S'$ and $j \varepsilon S$; hence S is an independent subset, and since A is irreducible it follows that $S = N$ and therefore $\eta_j > 0$ for all j, or $y > 0$.

Next, if $y' = (\eta_1', \ldots, \eta_n')$ is also an equilibrium vector, then let $\lambda = \min \eta_j/\eta_j'$, say $\lambda = \eta_1/\eta_1'$. Then $\lambda > 0$ and $\eta_j - \lambda\eta_j' \geqq 0$; so $y'' = y - \lambda y' \geqq 0$ and $Ay'' = y''$. But y'' is not positive since $\eta_1'' = 0$. From the first part of the proof, therefore, $y'' = 0$; so $y = \lambda y'$, as asserted in the theorem.

The irreducible case having been disposed of, it remains to consider the situation when A is reducible.

Definition. An independent subset $S \subset N$ is called *irreducible* if there is no other independent subset S_1 properly contained in S (i.e., contained in but distinct from S).

From the definition it is clear that for every exchange matrix there is at least one irreducible subset, possibly the set N itself. The following result gives further information on the structure of the matrix A.

Lemma 8.2.   If S and T are independent subsets, so are $S \cap T$ and $S \cup T$.

Proof. Suppose $j \, \varepsilon \, S \cap T$ and $i \notin S \cap T$. Then either $i \notin S$ or $i \notin T$ and in either case, since S and T are independent subsets and j belongs to both, it follows that $\alpha_{ij} = 0$, and hence $S \cap T$ is independent. The second conclusion is equally trivial.

Corollary.   Distinct irreducible subsets of N are disjoint.

The proof is left as an exercise (see Exercise 2).

Let us once more interpret the above result both economically and matrically. In our trade model the result states that we may partition the set N of countries into irreducible blocks, $S_1, S_2, \ldots, S_k$, plus possibly some additional countries which belong to no irreducible block which we may lump together in a set T. A country in a given block S_i imports only from other countries in the same block.

We illustrate with a numerical example. Let the trade matrix A be given by

	1	2	3	4	5	6	7
1	0.2	0.1		0.3			
2		0.2					0.5
3		0.2	0.5		0.9		
4						0.4	
5			0.5		0.1		0.2
6	0.8			0.7		0.6	
7		0.5					0.3

where the absence of an entry stands for a zero. This matrix contains two irreducible subsets $S_1 = \{1,\ 4,\ 6\}$ and $S_2 = \{3,\ 5\}$. The countries 2 and 7 belong to no irreducible subset. If we reorder the indices the matrix becomes

	1	4	6	3	5	2	7
1	0.2	0.3	0			0.1	0
4	0	0	0.4			0	0
6	0.8	0.7	0.6			0	0
3				0.5	0.9	0.2	0
5				0.5	0.1	0	0.2
2						0.2	0.5
7						0.5	0.3

and the irreducible subsets correspond to the two square blocks along the main diagonal.

The process of "untangling" the exchange matrix into its irreducible subsets, as we have done in this example, is achieved in a straightforward manner. Starting with the index 1, or the country C_1, we look for all countries C_j from which C_1 imports. These correspond to the nonzero entries in the first column of A. In our example these correspond to the indices 1 and 6. We then look for the countries from which these C_j import. In the example we note that C_6 imports from C_4. We continue in this way until no new countries are obtained. The example shows that the only countries we get in this way are C_1, C_4, and C_6. These countries form an independent subset, possibly the whole set. This subset will not necessarily be irreducible, and one must repeat the procedure for the different countries in the subset. After finding all irreducible subsets of the first independent subset one now picks a country not in the original independent set, if there are any, and goes through the procedure again.

In general, the reader will easily verify that by suitable reordering any exchange matrix may be given the form

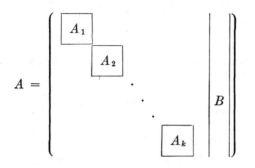

$$A =$$

where the A_i correspond to the irreducible subsets S_i, and B corresponds to the remaining indices.

From the above discussion we can construct equilibrium vectors in the following way: Let A_r be the submatrix corresponding to the irreducible subset S_r consisting of s_r indices $i_1, \ldots , i_{s_r}$. Now A_r is itself an irreducible exchange matrix and hence has a positive equilibrium vector $y_r = (\eta_{i_1}, \ldots , \eta_{i_{s_r}})$. If we now define an n-vector $\bar{y}_r$ whose coordinates η_j agree with those of y_r for $j \, \varepsilon \, S_r$ and are zero otherwise, then it is clear that $\bar{y}_r$ is an equilibrium vector for the whole matrix A. If the vectors $\bar{y}_1, \ldots , \bar{y}_k$ correspond in this way to equilibrium vectors of the submatrices $A_1, \ldots , A_k$ then any vector $y = \sum_{r=1}^{k} \lambda_r \bar{y}_r$, where the λ_r are nonnegative and not all zero, will be an equilibrium vector for A. We shall now show that *every* equilibrium vector for A is of this form.

Theorem 8.3. *Let A be an exchange matrix with irreducible subsets $S_1, \ldots , S_k$, and let $y = (\eta_j)$ be an equilibrium vector. Then*

$$y = \sum_{r=1}^{k} y_r, \text{ where } y_r \text{ is an equilibrium vector which depends on the set } S_r.$$

Proof. Define the n-vector $y_r = (\eta_{r1}, \ldots , \eta_{rn})$ by the rules

$$\eta_{rj} = \eta_j \quad \text{for } j \, \varepsilon \, S_r$$
$$\eta_{rj} = 0 \quad \text{otherwise}$$

Now $y_r \leqq y$; hence $a_i y_r \leqq a_i y$ for all i.   In particular

$$\text{if } i \ \varepsilon \ S_r \text{ then } a_i y_r \leqq a_i y = \eta_i = \eta_{ri}$$

and $\quad\quad\quad$ if $i \ \notin S_r$ then $a_i y_r = 0$

Hence $\quad\quad\quad\quad\quad\quad\quad\quad A y_r \leqq y_r$

but from Lemma 8.1 this means $A y_r = y_r$; hence y_r is an equilibrium vector.

It remains to show that $y = \sum\limits_{r=1}^{k} y_r$.   Let T be the set of indices i belonging to no irreducible subset S_r and let $y' = (\eta'_1, \ldots, \eta'_n) = y - \Sigma y_r$. Then clearly $A y' = y'$ and further $\eta'_i > 0$ only if $i \varepsilon T$. Letting Q be all indices i such that $\eta'_i > 0$ it follows just as in the proof of Theorem 8.2 that Q is an independent subset of T, but this would mean that T contains an irreducible subset contrary to assumption.   It follows that $\eta'_i = 0$ for all i, or $y' = 0$, completing the proof.

Let us now apply Theorem 8.3 to find all equilibrium vectors y for the matrix of our previous numerical example.   We have seen that there are two independent subsets consisting of the indices 1, 4, 6 and 3, 5.   The set of equations corresponding to the first of these sets is

$$0.2\eta_1 + 0.3\eta_4 \quad\quad\quad = \eta_1$$
$$0.4\eta_6 = \eta_4$$
$$0.8\eta_1 + 0.7\eta_4 + 0.6\eta_6 = \eta_6$$

and the solution is

$$\eta_1 = 0.15\alpha \quad\quad \eta_4 = 0.4\alpha \quad\quad \eta_6 = \alpha$$

where α is any positive number.   The equations for the second independent subset are

$$0.5\eta_3 + 0.9\eta_5 = \eta_3$$
$$0.5\eta_3 + 0.1\eta_5 = \eta_5$$

and the solution is

$$\eta_3 = 1.8\beta \quad\quad \eta_5 = \beta$$

for any positive number β.

According to our theorem every equilibrium vector y is of the form

$$y = (0.15\alpha,\ 0,\ 1.8\beta,\ 0.4\alpha,\ \beta,\ \alpha,\ 0)$$

Corollary.   If i belongs to no independent subset then $\eta_i = 0$ for all solutions of $Ay = y$.

We summarize the material of this section.   To "solve" a linear trade model one first breaks it up into its irreducible subsets.   Each of these may be solved as an independent model having a solution which is unique up to a positive multiple.   The general solution is then any nonnegative combination of these subsolutions.

3. Dynamic Theory

In this section we concentrate our attention on the model of Example 2.   We have seen in the previous section that there exist incomes $y = (\eta_1, \ldots, \eta_n)$ which give equilibrium in the sense that if each country behaves in accordance with the exchange matrix then the incomes will maintain themselves at the values η_i.   We shall now investigate the situation in which the countries start out with an arbitrary distribution of incomes which will then shift as a result of exchange between countries.   It will turn out that except for certain well-defined exceptional situations the incomes will converge toward the equilibrium values.

The theorem we shall prove is well known in probability theory as the fundamental convergence theorem for Markov chains.   It is interesting that this same theorem occurs here in a context having nothing to do with uncertainty.

In a very naïve formulation we may think of the countries C_i as n players sitting around a table, the jth player initially equipped with η_j dollars.   On each "play," player j hands player i the fraction α_{ij} of the amount he is holding, and play is repeated indefinitely.   We wish to determine whether the amounts held by the players approach limiting values and if so what these values are.   More precisely, let $y_0 = (\eta_1, \ldots, \eta_n)$ give the initial amounts held by the n countries.   Then clearly $y_1 = Ay_0$ gives the amount held by each country after one round of exchange, $y_2 = Ay_1 = A(Ay_0) = A^2 y_0$ gives the amount after two rounds, and in general $y_k = A^k y_0$ gives the distribution of income after k rounds of exchange. The question is then to determine whether the vectors $y_k = A^k y_0$ approach a limit, whether this limit depends on y_0, and so forth. We now formulate these notions exactly.

Definition. If $y_1, y_2, \ldots$ is a sequence of n-vectors,

$$y_k = (\eta_{1k}, \ldots, \eta_{nk})$$

we say the sequence *converges* to $y = (\eta_1, \ldots, \eta_n)$ if the sequence of numbers η_{jk} converges to η_j for $j = 1, \ldots, n$. We write $y_k \to y$.

The exchange matrix A is called *stable* if there exists a nonnegative vector $\bar{y}$, such that for any semipositive vector y_0 satisfying $y_0 v = \bar{y} v$ the sequence $A^k y_0$ converges to $\bar{y}$.

We remark that if $A^k y_0$ converges to $\bar{y}$ then $\bar{y}$ is an equilibrium vector for the matrix A (see Exercise 9).

It is easy to construct matrices which are not stable. The simplest example is the matrix $\begin{pmatrix} 0 & 1 \\ 1 & 0 \end{pmatrix}$. This corresponds to a two-country model in which each country spends its entire income on importing from the other. If initially one of the countries has, say, one dollar and the other nothing, then clearly the dollar will simply be passed back and forth between the countries indefinitely. One can generalize this situation as follows: Suppose the n countries break up into m disjoint subsets $S_1, \ldots, S_m$ in such a way that countries in S_r import only from countries in S_{r+1} for $r < m$, and countries in S_m import only from S_1. It is then clear that if all the income is initially held by S_1 it will pass successively to each of the other groups, returning to S_1 after every m rounds of exchange, and therefore there will be no stability. We express the above as follows:

Definition. An exchange matrix A is called *periodic* if the set N can be partitioned into m subsets $S_1, \ldots, S_m$ such that $\alpha_{ij} = 0$ unless $j \varepsilon S_r$ and $i \varepsilon S_{r+1}$ for $r < m$, or $j \varepsilon S_m$ and $i \varepsilon S_1$. In this case m is called a *period* of A.

If we order the indices i so that $S_1 = \{1, \ldots, n_1\}$, $S_2 = \{n_1 + 1,$

. . . , n_2}, etc., then a periodic matrix takes the following form:

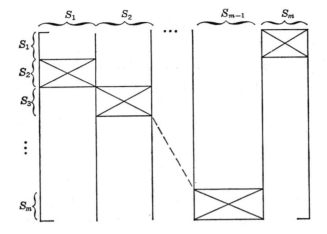

where all entries not in one of the marked rectangles are zero.

In what follows we shall restrict ourselves to the case in which the exchange matrix A is irreducible. We could formally reduce the general case to the irreducible case, but we prefer to give a rough verbal argument. First, recall that, in general, the set of countries breaks up into irreducible subsets $S_1, \ldots, S_k$ and a set T of the remaining countries. Now, all money initially in the set T will gradually flow out into the sets S_i, and since there is no flow into T from the sets S_i the amount of money in T approaches zero. Also since the sets S_i are independent subsets all money which flows into them remains in them. Thus the limiting amount of money in S_i is the initial amount plus some fraction of the initial amount in the set T. Let ζ_i be the limiting amount of money in S_i; the question of its distribution among the members of S_i is solved by looking at the irreducible submatrix A_i. Thus the general problem is reduced to the one with A irreducible.

As a matter of convenience we shall choose our unit of money so that initially $\sum_{j=1}^{n} \eta_j = 1$, and hence the sum of the coordinates of $A^k y$ is 1 for all k. In view of Theorem 8.2 there is then a unique positive equilibrium vector $\bar{y}$ whose coordinate sum is 1. We now state the fundamental theorem of this section as follows:

Theorem 8.4. *An irreducible exchange matrix is either stable or periodic.*

We shall prove the theorem in several steps. We first introduce a "norm" in the space R^n.

Definition. If $y = (\eta_1, \ldots, \eta_n)$ ε R^n we define the *norm* of y, written $|y|$, by the rule $|y| = \sum_{j=1}^{n} |\eta_j|$.

One immediately verifies that the norm has the following properties:

$$|\lambda y| = |\lambda| \, |y| \tag{i}$$
$$|y + y'| \leq |y| + |y'| \tag{ii}$$

Here since λ is a scalar the symbol $|\lambda|$ means the ordinary absolute value.

We also note that $y_k \to \bar{y}$ if and only if $|\bar{y} - y_k| \to 0$, for the expression $\sum_{j=1}^{n} |\bar{\eta}_j - \eta_{jk}|$ goes to zero if and only if each term $|\bar{\eta}_j - \eta_{jk}|$ goes to zero.

Now let A be an irreducible exchange matrix and let $\bar{y}$ be its equilibrium vector. Let Y be all semipositive vectors $y = (\eta_1, \ldots, \eta_n)$ such that $\Sigma \eta_j = 1$. We shall say that A is a *shrinking* matrix if there exists a number γ, $0 < \gamma < 1$, such that $|Ay - \bar{y}| \leq \gamma |y - \bar{y}|$ for all y ε Y. In words, A is shrinking if it moves all vectors of Y toward the stable vector $\bar{y}$. We then have the following simple and intuitively plausible result:

Lemma 8.3. *If A is shrinking then A is stable.*

Proof. Let γ be the constant of "shrinkage" of A. Then for any y ε Y we assert $|A^k y - \bar{y}| \leq \gamma^k |y - \bar{y}|$, which is true by definition if $k = 1$. Letting $y_k = A^k y$ we have

$$|A^{k+1} y - \bar{y}| = |Ay_k - \bar{y}| \leq \gamma |y_k - \bar{y}|$$
$$= \gamma |A^k y - \bar{y}| \leq \gamma^{k+1} |y - \bar{y}|$$

and thus, by induction, the assertion follows. But $0 < \gamma < 1$; so $\gamma^k \to 0$ and A is stable.

Lemma 8.4. *If A has a positive row then A is shrinking.*

In economic terms this lemma states that, if there is some country which exports to all the others, then A is stable.

Proof. Let us assume the first row a_1 of A is positive. We must now determine the shrinking constant γ. Let $\bar\gamma = \min_j \alpha_{1j}$. The constant which works is $\gamma = 1 - \bar\gamma$, as we shall now show. For $y \, \varepsilon \, Y$ let $z = y - \bar y = (\zeta_1, \ldots, \zeta_n)$. Since y and $\bar y$ are in Y it follows that $\sum_{j=1}^{n} \zeta_j = 0$. Let $\zeta_j^+ = \max(\zeta_j, 0)$; let $\zeta_j^- = \min(\zeta_j, 0)$. Then $\Sigma \zeta_j^+ = -\Sigma \zeta_j^-$ and $\Sigma \zeta_j^+ - \Sigma \zeta_j^- = \Sigma |\zeta_j| = |z|$, and hence

$$- \sum \zeta_j^- = \frac{|z|}{2} \tag{1}$$

We may assume that $\sum_j \alpha_{1j} \zeta_j \geqq 0$, for if not we could simply replace z by $-z$ in the following argument. Now

$$|Az| = \sum_i \left| \sum_j \alpha_{ij} \zeta_j \right| = \sum_{i=2}^{n} \left| \sum_j \alpha_{ij} \zeta_j \right| + \sum_j \alpha_{1j} \zeta_j$$

$$\leqq \sum_{i=2}^{n} \left(\sum_j \alpha_{ij} |\zeta_j| \right) + \sum_j \alpha_{1j} \zeta_j$$

$$= \sum_{i,j} \alpha_{ij} |\zeta_j| + \sum_j \alpha_{1j} \zeta_j - \sum_j \alpha_{1j} |\zeta_j|$$

$$= \sum_j |\zeta_j| \left(\sum_i \alpha_{ij} \right) + \sum_j \alpha_{1j} \zeta_j - \sum_j \alpha_{1j} |\zeta_j|$$

$$= |z| + \sum_j \alpha_{1j} \zeta_j - \sum_j \alpha_{1j} |\zeta_j|$$

$$= |z| + \sum_j \alpha_{1j} \zeta_j - \sum_j \alpha_{1j} \zeta_j^+ + \sum_j \alpha_{1j} \zeta_j^-$$

$$= |z| + 2 \sum_j \alpha_{1j} \zeta_j^-$$

$$\leqq |z| + 2\bar\gamma \sum_j \zeta_j^- = |z| - \bar\gamma |z| = \gamma |z|$$

from (1).

Since by assumption a_1 is positive, it follows that $\bar\gamma > 0$; hence $\gamma = 1 - \bar\gamma < 1$ and A is shrinking.

Corollary. If A has a positive row then A is stable.

We shall proceed by gradually weakening the hypotheses on A until we obtain a sufficient condition for stability that is also necessary.

We first make the obvious remark that if A is an exchange matrix so also is A^k, for an exchange matrix is characterized by the properties $A \geqq 0$ and $uA = u$, both of which are preserved when A is raised to some power.   But the following is also true.

Lemma 8.5.   *If A^m is stable for some positive integer m, then A is stable.*

Proof.   First note that, for any $y \, \varepsilon \, Y$,

$$|Ay - \bar{y}| = |A(y - \bar{y})| = \sum_{i=1}^{n} \left| \sum_{j=1}^{n} \alpha_{ij}(\eta_j - \bar{\eta}_j) \right| \leqq \sum_{i,j} \alpha_{ij}|\eta_j - \bar{\eta}_j|$$

$$= \sum_{j=1}^{n} \left(|\eta_j - \bar{\eta}_j| \sum_{i=1}^{n} \alpha_{ij} \right) = \sum_{j} |\eta_j - \bar{\eta}_j| = |y - \bar{y}|$$

Now, if A^m is stable then given $\epsilon > 0$, we have $|A^{km}y - \bar{y}| \leqq \epsilon$ for k greater than some number N_1.   Letting $N = N_1 m$, if $k > N$ then $k = N_1 m + r$ and $|A^{N_1 m + r}y - \bar{y}| = |A^r(A^{N_1 m}y - \bar{y})| \leqq |A^{N_1 m}y - \bar{y}| \leqq \epsilon$.

Combining this result with that of Lemma 8.4 we have

Corollary.   *The exchange matrix A is stable if some power of A has a positive row.*

To complete the proof of Theorem 8.4 we must show that if no power of A has a positive row then A is periodic.

Let the ijth coordinate of A^r be denoted by $\alpha_{ij}^{(r)}$.   From the definition of matrix multiplication

$$\alpha_{ik}^{(r+s)} = \alpha_{ij}^{(r)}\alpha_{jk}^{(s)} + \text{other terms which are nonnegative}$$

so we have

$$\text{if } \alpha_{ij}^{(r)} > 0 \quad \text{and} \quad \alpha_{jk}^{(s)} > 0 \quad \text{then } \alpha_{ik}^{(r+s)} > 0 \qquad (1)$$

We also note:

Lemma 8.6.   *If A is irreducible then for any i and j there exists r such that $\alpha_{ij}^{(r)} > 0$.*

Proof.   It suffices to prove this for $i = 1$.   Let S be the set of all j such that $\alpha_{1j}^{(r)} = 0$ for all r.   If $j \, \varepsilon \, S$ and $i \, \varepsilon \, S'$ then $\alpha_{1i}^{(r)} > 0$ for some r and therefore $\alpha_{ij} = 0$; otherwise from (1), $\alpha_{1j}^{(r+1)} > 0$, contrary to assumption.   It follows that S is an independent subset.   Clearly S is not all of N for then $\alpha_{1j} = 0$ for all j, and $\{2, \ldots, n\}$ would be independent. Therefore, since A is irreducible, S is empty, proving the assertion.

Proof of Theorem 8.4. Since A is irreducible $\alpha_{11}^{(r)} > 0$ for some integer r. Let $R = \{r|\alpha_{11}^{(r)} > 0\}$ and let p be the greatest common divisor of the numbers in R.

Case 1. $p > 1$. First note that if $\alpha_{1j}^{(r)} > 0$ and $\alpha_{1j}^{(s)} > 0$ then $r \equiv s \pmod{p}$ (that is, p divides $r - s$), for by the previous lemma $\alpha_{j1}^{(k)} > 0$ for some k, and hence $\alpha_{11}^{(r+k)} > 0$ and $\alpha_{11}^{(s+k)} > 0$ so that p divides $r + k$ and $s + k$ and therefore also $r - s$. Now, for $r = 1$, $2, \ldots, p$ let S_r be all indices i such that $\alpha_{1i}^{(r+kp)} > 0$ for some k. From the previous observation the sets $S_1, \ldots, S_p$ are disjoint. If $\alpha_{ij} > 0$ and $i \varepsilon S_r$ then $\alpha_{1i}^{(r+kp)} > 0$ for some k; hence from (1), $\alpha_{1j}^{(r+1+kp)} > 0$; so $j \varepsilon S_{r+1}$ if $r < p$ and $j \varepsilon S_1$ if $r = p$, and this shows that A is periodic with period p.

Case 2. $p = 1$. We need the following result from number theory.

Lemma 8.7. *If R is a set of positive integers whose greatest common divisor is 1 then there exists an integer ρ such that if $m \geqq \rho$ then $m =$*

$$\sum_{i=1}^{r} m_i a_i,$$ *where m_i are positive integers and $a_i \varepsilon R$.*

Assuming this for the moment we complete the proof of the theorem. Choose ρ as in the lemma, where R is the set previously defined. Then for $m \geqq \rho$, $\alpha_{11}^{(m)} = \alpha_{11}^{(\Sigma m_i a_i)} > 0$, again from (1). Also since A is irreducible there exists for each index j an integer δ_j such that $\alpha_{1j}^{(\delta_j)} > 0$. Letting $\delta = \max_j \delta_j$ we assert that $\alpha_{1j}^{(m+\delta)} > 0$ for all j, for $m + \delta = m + \delta_j' + \delta_j$ and $\alpha_{11}^{(m+\delta_j')} > 0$ and $\alpha_{1j}^{(\delta_j)} > 0$. But this shows that $A^{(m+\delta)}$ has its first row positive, and therefore from the previous lemmas A is stable.

Proof of Lemma 8.7. First consider the case in which R contains two numbers a and b whose greatest common divisor is 1. If $k \geqq N = (b - 1)a$ then the nonnegative integers k, $k - a$, $k - 2a$, $\ldots$, $k - (b - 1)a$ have distinct remainders when divided by b, for if $k - ma$ and $k - na$, $n \neq m$, had the same remainder then b would divide $(n - m)a$, which is impossible since b is prime to a and $n - m < b$. Since there are b such remainders and all are less than b, one of them is zero, i.e., b divides $k - ma$ for some $m < b$.   But then $k = ma + nb$, and the assertion is proved.

Suppose now that R contains r numbers $a_1, \ldots, a_r$ whose g.c.d. (greatest common divisor) is 1, and suppose the theorem proved for any smaller number of relatively prime elements.   If $a_1, \ldots, a_{r-1}$ have d as their g.c.d. then the numbers $a_1/d, \ldots, a_{r-1}/d$ have their g.c.d. equal to 1; so there exists N_1 such that for $k_1 \geqq N_1$ we can write

$$k_1 = \sum_{i=1}^{r-1} \frac{m_i a_i}{d}$$

In particular we can choose k_1 prime to a_r so that $dk_1 = \sum_{i=1}^{r-1} m_i a_i$ is also prime to a_r.   But we have already seen that for k greater than some N there are nonnegative integers n_1 and n_2 such that

$$k = n_1 dk_1 + n_2 a_r$$

and this proves the lemma.

4. Dynamics in the Reducible Case

We turn finally to a brief examination of the dynamic situation for a reducible model.   In case the model is *completely reducible*, i.e., every country belongs to some irreducible subset, then we easily determine the stable distribution of income by treating each submodel separately. The only case that remains is that in which some of the countries belong to no irreducible submodel.   In this case all the income initially held by these countries will eventually be distributed among the countries in the various irreducible submodels.   It is of interest to determine just what this distribution will be.

As a concrete example let us return to the numerical illustration of Sec. 2.   We noted there that countries 2 and 7 belonged to no irreducible submodel.   Suppose initially each of these countries holds one unit of money.   How will these two units eventually be distributed between the two irreducible submodels (1, 4, 6) and (3, 5)?

Instead of trying to settle this question at once let us look at the general situation.   Suppose $C_1, \ldots, C_k$ are the countries belonging to no irreducible submodel and let C_0 be some other country. Now consider the $k \times k$ submatrix B of the exchange matrix A,

$$
\begin{array}{c@{\quad}c@{\quad}c@{\quad}c}
 & C_1 & \cdots & C_k \\
C_1 & \begin{array}{|ccc|}
\hline
\alpha_{11} & \cdots & \alpha_{1k} \\
\cdot & & \cdot \\
\cdot & & \cdot \\
\cdot & & \cdot \\
\alpha_{k1} & \cdots & \alpha_{kk} \\
\hline
\end{array}
\end{array} = B
$$

Suppose further that initially C_j holds the amount η_{j0} for $j = 1, \ldots, k$, so that $y_0 = (\eta_{10}, \ldots, \eta_{k0})$ is the initial income distribution among the countries $C_1, \ldots, C_k$. Then, just as before, the income distribution after n rounds of exchange will be given by $B^n y_0$. Let us now ask how much of the wealth originally held by the countries C_j will have been passed on to the country C_0 after n rounds of exchange. This clearly depends on the numbers $\alpha_{01}, \ldots, \alpha_{0k}$, where, as always, α_{0j} is the fraction of C_j's income which is handed on to C_0. Letting η_{jn} denote the income of C_j after n rounds of exchange, it is clear that on the $(n + 1)$st round C_0 receives the amount

$$
\sum_{j=1}^{k} \alpha_{0j} \eta_{jn}
$$

and letting $a_0 = (\alpha_{01}, \ldots, \alpha_{0k})$ we have

$$
\sum_{j=1}^{k} \alpha_{0j} \eta_{jn} = a_0 B^n y_0
$$

Finally, the total amount μ_n which C_0 has received from the countries C_j after n rounds of exchange is the sum of the amounts received on each round up to the nth; thus

$$
\mu_n = a_0 (I + B + \cdots + B^n) y_0
$$

We obtain a simpler expression for μ_n by noting the identity

$$
(I - B)(I + B + \cdots + B^n) = I - B^{n+1}
$$

Hence assuming for the moment that $I - B$ is regular (see Exercise 14) we may write

$$(I + B + \cdots + B^n) = (I - B)^{-1}(I - B^{n+1})$$

Hence
$$\mu_n = a_0(I - B)^{-1}(I - B^{n+1})y_0$$
$$= a_0(I - B)^{-1}y_0 - a_0(I - B)^{-1}B^{n+1}y_0$$

On the other hand, we know that $\lim_{n \to \infty} B^{n+1}y_0 = 0$, which is again the statement that the wealth initially held by countries C_j eventually drops to zero.   Thus we have

$$\mu = \lim_{n \to \infty} \mu_n = a_0(I - B)^{-1}y_0 \tag{1}$$

which is the formula we need to obtain the desired wealth distribution.
In the example of Sec. 2 the matrix B is

	C_2	C_7
C_2	0.2	0.5
C_7	0.5	0.3

and the matrix $(I - B)^{-1}$ is

$$\begin{pmatrix} \dfrac{0.7}{0.31} & \dfrac{0.5}{0.31} \\ \dfrac{0.5}{0.31} & \dfrac{0.8}{0.31} \end{pmatrix}$$

Supposing now that C_2 and C_7 each hold one unit initially.   Then

$$(I - B)^{-1}y_0 = \left(\frac{1.2}{0.31}, \frac{1.3}{0.31}\right)$$

and we see that

$$C_1 \text{ gets } 0.1 \times \frac{1.2}{0.31} = \frac{0.12}{0.31}$$

$$C_3 \text{ gets } 0.2 \times \frac{1.2}{0.31} = \frac{0.24}{0.31}$$

$$C_5 \text{ gets } 0.2 \times \frac{1.3}{0.31} = \frac{0.26}{0.31}$$

Note that the sum of these numbers is $\dfrac{0.62}{0.31} = 2$, which is the amount initially held by C_2 and C_7.

With this information we can now calculate the stable distribution of income starting from any initial distribution (see Exercises 6, 7).

5. *Price Equilibrium for Linear Exchange Models*

For the final topic of this chapter we take up a subject which is not directly related to the material of the previous sections but which plays a very central role in general economic theory. In the house-buying example in Sec. 6 of Chap. 5 the reader was introduced to a special case of a price-equilibrium problem. In this section we shall treat another such special case. The general problem of price equilibrium is one of the most interesting and difficult in mathematical economics. Unfortunately the mathematical machinery needed for treating it goes far beyond the material we have developed in this book, and for this reason we are forced to impose some restrictive and somewhat unnatural conditions on our problem in order to include it here. Nevertheless, the ideas and methods involved are of basic importance and it has therefore seemed worthwhile to present the discussion which follows by way of introducing the reader to an important branch of economic theory.

We return to an economy in which there are n goods $G_1, \ldots, G_n$ and m *consumers* denoted by $C_1, \ldots, C_m$ and one fictitious personality whom we shall call "Production." Each year Production produces one unit of each of the goods G_j (where we have simply chosen the unit of each good to be a year's production). The annual *income* of the ith consumer C_i is assumed to be some fixed amount β_i, and it is further assumed that each C_i will spend his entire income β_i for various amounts of the goods G_j. In order to specify just how he will do this we must know what value the consumer places on each of the goods. We therefore assume that the *value* to C_i of one unit of G_j is given by a nonnegative number α_{ij}.

We pause here to point out that this value number α_{ij} is not necessarily in monetary units. We do not wish at this point to become involved in the philosophical problems of utility theory. Let us merely say that the number α_{ij} measures, in some sense, the subjective value of G_j to C_i. Of course, the number α_{ij} by itself gives no information.   On the other hand, if $\alpha_{i1} = 2$ and $\alpha_{i2} = 4$ then we know that the value to C_i of G_2 is twice that of G_1.

We now make a rather drastic assumption concerning the nature of the consumers' subjective valuations.   Let us define a *goods bundle* to be a nonnegative n-vector $y = (\eta_j)$, where η_j is the amount of G_j in the bundle y.   Let

$$a_i = (\alpha_{i1}, \ldots, \alpha_{in})$$

Assumption I.   The value μ_i of the goods bundle y to consumer C_i is given by the expression

$$\mu_i = \sum_{j=1}^{n} \alpha_{ij}\eta_j = a_i y_i$$

It need hardly be remarked that, in general, subjective valuations will not satisfy this simple linear law.   One hundred pounds of potatoes will not necessarily be one hundred times as desirable as one pound.   On the other hand, one can imagine that the linear law might be an admissible approximation to the true situation for small changes in the quantities η_j.   Assumption I is, of course, needed here to bring the problem into the domain of linear models.

Assume next that we are given a price vector $p = (\pi_1, \ldots, \pi_n)$, where π_j is the price of one unit of G_j.   It is then clear how C_i will distribute his income.   He will choose a bundle y_i which

$$\text{maximizes } a_i y_i \tag{1}$$

subject to the *budget inequality*

$$py_i \leqq \beta_i \tag{2}$$

Thus each consumer spends in such a way as to solve this very simple linear programming problem—simple because there is only one constraint on the variables.   Following the familiar terminology we shall say that a bundle which satisfies (2) is *feasible*.

Recall now that Production supplies only one unit of each good. On the other hand, the consumers are demanding m bundles $y_1, \ldots,$ y_m in accordance with (1) and (2) above, and this demand can be met only if the *total bundle* $y = \sum_{i=1}^{m} y_i$ contains no more than one unit of each good, i.e., only if

$$\sum_{i=1}^{m} y_i \leqq v \tag{3}$$

(where, as usual, v is the unit vector).

It is clear that for an arbitrary price vector p we cannot expect inequality (3) to be satisfied. In general, certain goods will be over-demanded, others oversupplied. Now, according to classical theory, when this happens the prices of overdemanded goods go up and those of underdemanded goods go down until eventually prices are attained which balance supply and demand. This eventual situation is completely described by the following

Definition. The price vector p is called an *equilibrium price vector* if there exist bundles y_i satisfying (1) and (2) for all consumers C_i, and such that

$$\Sigma y_i = v \tag{4}$$

In this case the bundles y_i are called *equilibrium bundles*.

It is interesting to note that, although the notion of equilibrium prices goes back to the very early days of economic theory, it is only in quite recent times that people have actually given proofs of the existence of such prices.

We shall prove the existence and uniqueness of equilibrium prices for our model after making a few preliminary simplifications. We first assume that in the *subjective value matrix* $A = (\alpha_{ij})$ there is at least one positive entry in each row and column. The assumption is entirely harmless, for if A contained a row of zeros this would mean that one of the consumers C_i was not in the market for any of the goods G_j. In this case we would ignore C_i entirely and consider the model to be composed only of the remaining $m - 1$ consumers. Similarly, if the jth column of A is zero this would mean there was no demand for G_j, in which case we would not consider it as being part of the model. The condition is formalized as follows:

Assumption II. The value matrix $A = (\alpha_{ij})$ has at least one positive entry in each row and column.

Next, it turns out to be convenient to pick the monetary unit in such a way that the total income of the community is one, i.e.,

$$\sum_{i=1}^{m} \beta_i = 1$$

Finally, we shall assume that Production wishes to sell the entire bundle v which it produces. In order to do this it is clear that the total monetary value of this bundle must not exceed the total income of the community. In other words we must have:

Assumption III. A price vector $p = (\pi_1, \ldots, \pi_n)$ must satisfy the condition

$$\sum_{j=1}^{n} \pi_j = 1 \qquad (5)$$

Let us now express in concise form all that has been said at some length in the preceding paragraphs.

Definition. Let $A = (\alpha_{ij})$ be a nonnegative matrix with at least one positive entry in each row and column. Let $\beta_1, \ldots, \beta_m$ be a set of positive numbers summing to one.

The nonnegative n-vector $p = (\pi_1, \ldots, \pi_n)$ is called an *equilibrium price vector* and the nonnegative n-vectors $y_1, \ldots, y_m$ are called *equilibrium bundles* provided

$$\Sigma \pi_j = 1 \qquad (a)$$
$$y_i \text{ maximizes } a_i y_i \qquad (b)$$

subject to

$$p y_i \leqq \beta_i \qquad (c)$$

and in addition

$$\sum_i y_i = v \qquad (d)$$

Bundles and prices satisfying (a) to (d) above are said to give a *price equilibrium*.

Theorem 8.5 (equilibrium theorem). *For any matrix A and numbers β_i as above there exists a price equilibrium.*

Proof. We define a function φ on bundles $y_1, \ldots, y_m$ by the rule

$$\varphi(y_1, \ldots, y_m) = (a_1 y_1)^{\beta_1} \cdots (a_m y_m)^{\beta_m} \qquad (1)$$

Let $\bar{y}_1, \ldots, \bar{y}_m$ be bundles which maximize the function φ among all bundles satisfying condition (d) above. (The fact that such maximizing bundles exist follows from the basic result that any continuous function defined on a closed bounded set in a Euclidean space attains a maximum. The proof can be found in any book on elementary analysis.) From the conditions on A we know that $a_i \neq 0$; hence φ has a positive maximum and therefore $a_i \bar{y}_i$ is positive. We can now define

$$\pi_j = \max_i \frac{\alpha_{ij} \beta_i}{a_i \bar{y}_i} \tag{2}$$

and we shall show that the bundles $\bar{y}_i = (\bar{\eta}_{ij})$ and prices π_j do in fact yield a price equilibrium. (Note that $\pi_j > 0$. See Exercise 20.)

We first observe that condition (d) is satisfied from the definition of the bundles $\bar{y}_i$.

The proof of the remaining conditions depends on the following fact: If $\bar{\eta}_{ij} > 0$ then

$$\pi_j = \frac{\alpha_{ij} \beta_i}{a_i \bar{y}_i} \tag{3}$$

Assuming this fact for the moment, we easily complete the proof. First we check the budget inequality (c). From (3) we have

$$\pi_j \bar{\eta}_{ij} = \frac{\beta_i}{a_i \bar{y}_i} \alpha_{ij} \bar{\eta}_{ij} \qquad \text{for } all \ i \text{ and } j$$

and summing on j for a fixed i gives

$$p\bar{y}_i = \sum_{j=1}^n \pi_j \bar{\eta}_{ij} = \frac{\beta_i}{a_i \bar{y}_1} \sum_{j=1}^n \alpha_{ij} \bar{\eta}_{ij} = \beta_i \tag{4}$$

which proves (c) actually we get a budget equality, as could have been predicted from the assumptions on A).

To prove (a) we sum (4) on i, giving $1 = \Sigma \beta_i = \Sigma p\bar{y}_i = pv = \sum_{j=1}^n \pi_j$.

Lastly, we must verify (b), and it is sufficient to do this for the case $i = 1$. We may suppose that $\alpha_{11}/\pi_1 = \max_j \alpha_j/\pi_{1j}$ (if not reorder the indices j). Then for any bundle y_1 satisfying the budget inequality for C_1 we have

$$a_1 y_1 = \sum_j \alpha_{1j} \eta_{1j} \leqq \frac{\alpha_{11}}{\pi_1} \sum_j \pi_j \eta_{1j} \leqq \frac{\alpha_{11}}{\pi_1} \beta_1 \tag{5}$$

On the other hand, from the definition of π_1 we have

$$\pi_1 \geqq \frac{\alpha_{i1}\beta_i}{a_i\bar{y}_i} \qquad \text{for all } i$$

or, in particular,

$$a_1\bar{y}_1 \geqq \frac{\alpha_{11}\beta_1}{\pi_1} \qquad (6)$$

From (5) and (6) we have $a_1\bar{y}_1 \geqq a_1y_1$ and hence $\bar{y}_1$ maximizes a_1y_1 subject to the budget inequality, which establishes (b).

It only remains to prove assertion (3). We argue by contradiction. Suppose, say,

$$\bar{\eta}_{11} > 0 \qquad \text{but} \qquad \pi_1 > \frac{\alpha_{11}\beta_1}{a_1\bar{y}_1} \qquad (7)$$

Now, from (2) we must have $\pi_1 = \alpha_{i1}\beta_i/a_i\bar{y}_i$ for some index i, say

$$\pi_1 = \frac{\alpha_{21}\beta_2}{a_2\bar{y}_2} \qquad (8)$$

Then from (7) and (8) we get

$$\alpha_{11}\beta_1(a_2\bar{y}_2) < \alpha_{21}\beta_2(a_1\bar{y}_1) \qquad (9)$$

and we shall show that this contradicts the fact that the bundles $\bar{y}_i$ maximize the function φ.

Let $y_1' = (\bar{\eta}_{11} - \epsilon, \bar{\eta}_{12}, \ldots, \bar{\eta}_{1n})$, $y_2' = (\bar{\eta}_{21} + \epsilon, \bar{\eta}_{22}, \ldots, \bar{\eta}_{2n})$, where $0 < \epsilon < \bar{\eta}_{11}$; then clearly the bundles y_1', y_2', $\bar{y}_3$, $\ldots$, $\bar{y}_m$ still satisfy condition (d). Now

$$\varphi(y_1', y_2', \bar{y}_3, \ldots, \bar{y}_m) - \varphi(\bar{y}_1, \bar{y}_2, \ldots, \bar{y}_m)$$
$$= [(a_1\bar{y}_1 - \alpha_{11}\epsilon)^{\beta_1}(a_2\bar{y}_2 + \alpha_{21}\epsilon)^{\beta_2} - (a_1\bar{y}_1)^{\beta_1}(a_2\bar{y}_2)^{\beta_2}](a_3\bar{y}_3)^{\beta_3} \cdots (a_m\bar{y}_m)^{\beta_m}$$

If we expand the first two terms in the brackets by the binomial theorem we get inside the brackets

$$\{(a_1\bar{y}_1)^{\beta_1-1}(a_2\bar{y}_2)^{\beta_2-1}[(a_1\bar{y}_1)\alpha_{21}\beta_2 - (a_2\bar{y}_2)\beta_1\alpha_{11}]\epsilon$$
$$+ \text{terms in higher powers of } \epsilon\}$$

but inequality (9) tells us precisely that the first term in the braces is positive; hence for ϵ sufficiently small the whole expression will be positive, and this contradicts the assumption that φ is maximized by the bundles $\bar{y}_i$. This completes the proof.

A few remarks concerning the equilibrium theorem are in order. First notice that nothing in the problem is changed if the rows in the matrix are multiplied by arbitrary positive numbers. Clearly the problem will not be affected if a consumer changes all his values proportionally since, as we have already observed, it is only relative values of goods which influence the consumer's economic behavior.

Perhaps the most interesting feature of the equilibrium theorem is the appearance of the function φ. A consequence of our proof is the following statement:

At price equilibrium, goods are distributed in such a way as to maximize the product of each individual's satisfaction raised to the power equal to his budget.

This result could hardly have been anticipated in advance, and its derivation provides an illustration of the way in which mathematical reasoning can lead to the discovery of new economic facts.

Finally, we remark that it can also be shown that every set of equilibrium bundles maximizes the function φ so that the problem of maximizing φ and that of finding a price equilibrium are equivalent.

6. An Example of Price Equilibrium

Let us consider a numerical example given by the following value matrix:

	G_1	G_2	G_3
C_1	4	3	1
C_2	2	3	2
C_3	3	1	2

where we assume each consumer has one unit of money, which means that the equilibrium prices will sum to 3 rather than 1. We assert that equilibrium prices are given by

$$\pi_1 = 1.2 \qquad \pi_2 = 1.0 \qquad \pi_3 = 0.8$$

The following simple lemma will enable us to verify that these prices give equilibrium.

Lemma 8.8.   Let $\mu_i = \max\limits_{j} (\alpha_{ij}/\pi_j)$.   A bundle y_i satisfying the budget equality maximizes $a_i y_i$ if and only if

$$\eta_{ik} > 0 \qquad implies \;\; \frac{\alpha_{ik}}{\pi_k} = \mu_i \tag{1}$$

Proof.   By definition of μ_i we have

$$\frac{\alpha_{ij}}{\pi_j} \leqq \mu_i \qquad \text{for all } j$$

Multiplying the above inequality by η_{ij} and summing on j gives

$$a_i y_i = \sum_j \alpha_{ij} \eta_{ij} \leqq \mu_i \sum_j \eta_{ij} \pi_j = \mu_i \beta_i \tag{2}$$

and equality holds in (2) if and only if (1) is satisfied.

This lemma is economically obvious and simply says that a consumer will buy only that good or those goods which give him the maximum satisfaction per dollar.   In our example C_1 will spend his entire budget on G_1 since the ratios α_{1j}/π_j are

$$\frac{4}{1.2} \qquad \frac{3}{1} \qquad \frac{1}{0.8}$$

of which the largest is $4/1.2$.   He will therefore buy $\tfrac{5}{6}$ unit of G_1. Similarly C_2 will buy only G_2 since his ratios are

$$\frac{2}{1.2} \qquad \frac{3}{1} \qquad \frac{2}{0.8}$$

so C_2 buys one unit of G_2.   Finally, C_3 is indifferent as between G_1 and G_3 since the corresponding ratios $3/1.2$ and $2/0.8$ are equal.   Thus any way of distributing his income between G_1 and G_3 will maximize his satisfaction.   If he buys $\tfrac{1}{6}$ unit of G_1 and 1 unit of G_3 then his total expenditure will be

$$\tfrac{1}{6} \times 1.2 + 0.8 = 1$$

so his budget relation is satisfied.   Also we note the bundles demanded are *equilibrium bundles*, for we have

$$y_1 = (\tfrac{5}{6}, 0, 0) \qquad y_2 = (0, 1, 0) \qquad y_3 = (\tfrac{1}{6}, 0, 1)$$

and therefore
$$y_1 + y_2 + y_3 = (1, 1, 1)$$

as required.   We have therefore found a price equilibrium.

The reader has no doubt wondered how we were able to find the price vector p in the first place and, in general, how one computes the solution of a price-equilibrium problem.   This question of calculating solutions is one which we shall not be able to take up here.   The existence theorem suggests a method of approach.   Instead of solving the original problem one goes over to the equivalent maximum problem and tries to maximize the function φ subject to the linear constraints (d).   This would be a linear programming problem except for the unfortunate fact that the function φ is not linear.   The function is, however, what is called "concave."   The subject of "concave programming" is one which has received considerable attention, though we cannot go into it here.

7. Uniqueness of Equilibrium Prices

As a final result on price equilibrium we show

Theorem 8.6.   *For a given matrix A and incomes β_i there is only one equilibrium price vector p.*

Proof.   We first observe that the prices of all goods must be positive, for if π_j were zero, then, since α_{ij} is positive for some i, C_i would demand an infinite amount of G_j, which would, of course, contradict condition (d).

Suppose, now, that p and p' are both equilibrium price vectors. Let $\theta = \max_j (\pi'_j/\pi_j)$, and let J be all indices j such that $\pi'_j/\pi_j = \theta$. We have seen in the previous section that C_i will invest in G_j only if

$$\frac{\alpha_{ij}}{\pi_j} \geqq \frac{\alpha_{ik}}{\pi_k} \qquad \text{for all } k \tag{1}$$

In case (1) holds we shall say that G_j is *preferred* by C_i.   Now let I be all indices i such that C_i prefers at least one of the goods G_j, $j \, \varepsilon \, J$, at prices p'.   Then we have

$$\sum_I \beta_i \geqq \sum_J \pi'_j = \theta \sum_J \pi_j \tag{2}$$

for the total income of the consumers C_i of I must be sufficient to pay for all the goods G_j of J at prices p'.

Next, let $i \, \varepsilon \, I$. Then by definition of I there exist $j \, \varepsilon \, J$ such that

$$\frac{\alpha_{ij}}{\pi'_j} \geqq \frac{\alpha_{ik}}{\pi'_k} \qquad \text{for all } k \tag{3}$$

Now if G_r is preferred by C_i at prices p then

$$\frac{\alpha_{ir}}{\pi_r} \geqq \frac{\alpha_{ij}}{\pi_j} = \frac{\theta \alpha_{ij}}{\pi'_j} \geqq \frac{\theta \alpha_{ir}}{\pi'_r} \tag{4}$$

Hence $\pi'_r/\pi_r \geqq \theta$, which means $r \, \varepsilon \, J$. We have thus shown that every good preferred by a member of I at prices p is among the goods of J. This means

$$\sum_I \beta_i \leqq \sum_J \pi_j \tag{5}$$

since members of I buy only goods of J at prices p and they must spend their entire income in so doing. But inequalities (2) and (5) together show that $\theta = 1$ so that $p = p'$ as asserted.

Bibliographical Notes

The simple exchange model is presented here essentially as given by Remak [1]. In more recent times the model has come to be known as the closed Leontief model from the work of Leontief [1]. An even earlier work concerning a problem which is mathematically equivalent to the price problem is due to Bray [1]. The model of international exchange was introduced by Frisch in [1]. The dynamic theorem on stability is, as we mentioned, a basic result in the theory of probability. Its relation to the exchange problem was first exploited by Solow [1]. The particular price-equilibrium problem discussed in this chapter has been treated in a somewhat different context by Eisenberg and Gale [1].

Exercises

1. Prove that the exchange matrix A is irreducible if and only if for every two indices i and j there is a sequence $i = i_1, i_2, \ldots, i_r = j$ such that $\alpha_{i_k i_{k+1}} > 0$ for $k = 1, \ldots, r - 1$.

2. Prove if S and T are distinct irreducible subsets of the indices $1, \ldots, n$, then S and T are disjoint.

3. For the following exchange matrix find the irreducible subsets and reorder the matrix accordingly:

$$\begin{pmatrix} 0 & 0 & \frac{1}{2} & 0 & 0 & 0 \\ 0 & 0 & 0 & \frac{3}{4} & 0 & \frac{1}{3} \\ \frac{2}{3} & 0 & 0 & 0 & 1 & \frac{1}{3} \\ 0 & 1 & 0 & \frac{1}{4} & 0 & \frac{1}{3} \\ \frac{1}{3} & 0 & \frac{1}{2} & 0 & 0 & 0 \\ 0 & 0 & 0 & 0 & 0 & 0 \end{pmatrix}$$

4. Find all equilibrium vectors for the above matrix.

Answer: $y = (3\alpha,\ 3\beta,\ 6\alpha,\ 4\beta,\ 4\alpha,\ 0)$.

5. If initially each country in Exercise 3 has one unit of money find the stable distribution. Answer: $(\frac{30}{39},\ \frac{24}{21},\ \frac{60}{39},\ \frac{32}{21},\ \frac{40}{39},\ 0)$.

6. In the numerical example of Sec. 2 find the stable distribution of income if the initial distribution is one unit for each country.

Answer: $(\frac{315}{961},\ 0,\ \frac{72}{31},\ \frac{840}{961},\ \frac{40}{31},\ \frac{210}{961},\ 0)$.

7. As in Exercise 6 find the stable distribution of income if the initial distribution is

$$(2, 5, 3, 4, 3, 6, 4)$$

8. If A is irreducible with equilibrium vector $\bar{y} = (\bar{\eta}_1, \ldots, \bar{\eta}_n)$, where $\Sigma \bar{\eta}_i = 1$, show that A is stable if and only if $A^k \to \bar{A} = (\bar{\alpha}_{ij})$, where $\bar{\alpha}_{ij} = \bar{\eta}_i$.

9. Prove if $A^k y \to \bar{y}$ for some semipositive vector y then $\bar{y}$ is an equilibrium vector.

10. Show that a periodic matrix cannot be stable.

11. Show that if $\alpha_{ij}^{(p)} > 0$ then there is a sequence of indices $i = i_1$, $i_2, \ldots, i_r = j$ such that $\alpha_{i_k i_{k+1}} > 0$ for $k = 1, \ldots, r-1$.

12. Prove the converse of Lemma 8.4. If for every i and j there exists k such that $\alpha_{ij}^{(k)} > 0$ then A is irreducible.

13. If

$$A \text{ is nonnegative} \tag{1}$$
$$\sum_i \alpha_{ij} < 1 \quad \text{ for all } j \tag{2}$$

prove that $A^k \to 0$. (Hint: Show $|Ax| \leq \gamma |x|$ for $0 < \gamma < 1$.)

14. Prove if $A^k \to 0$ then $(I - A)$ is regular.

15. Prove that if A is irreducible and stable then $A^k > 0$ for some integer k.

16. Let A be the exchange matrix given by

$$\begin{pmatrix} 0 & 0.7 & 0 & 0 & 0.4 & 0 & 0 \\ 0 & 0 & 0.5 & 1 & 0 & 0.2 & 0 \\ 0.2 & 0 & 0 & 0 & 0 & 0 & 0.5 \\ 0.2 & 0 & 0 & 0 & 0 & 0 & 0.2 \\ 0 & 0 & 0.5 & 0 & 0 & 0.8 & 0 \\ 0.6 & 0 & 0 & 0 & 0 & 0 & 0.3 \\ 0 & 0.3 & 0 & 0 & 0.6 & 0 & 0 \end{pmatrix}$$

Show that A is periodic and find its period.

17. Show that an irreducible exchange matrix A has period p if and only if A^p is completely reducible and has p irreducible subsets.

18. Show that an irreducible exchange matrix is stable if and only if A^k is irreducible for all k.

19. If A is reducible show that A is "stable" if and only if all its irreducible submatrices are stable, but that the limiting value of $A^k y_0$ depends on the initial vector y_0.

20. Why are the numbers π_j defined by relation (2) of Theorem 8.5 positive?

21. In the numerical example of Sec. 6 suppose the initial incomes are $\beta_1 = 3$, $\beta_2 = 2$, $\beta_3 = 4$. Show that equilibrium prices are given by $p = \frac{9}{29}(12, 9, 8)$ and find the corresponding equilibrium bundles.

22. Give an example to show that the equilibrium bundles need not be unique.

23. In a price-equilibrium model with two consumers and two goods suppose the first consumer places the same value on each of the goods. Show that if both consumers have income $\frac{1}{2}$ then the equilibrium prices will be $(\frac{1}{2}, \frac{1}{2})$ regardless of the values to the second consumer.

24. Let

$$\begin{pmatrix} \alpha_1, & 1 - \alpha_1 \\ \alpha_2, & 1 - \alpha_2 \end{pmatrix}$$

be the value matrix for a two-consumer two-goods equilibrium model (note that the most general 2×2 value matrix can be put in this form by multiplying rows appropriately), and suppose the incomes are $(\frac{1}{2}, \frac{1}{2})$. Show that the only possible equilibrium prices are (1) $(\alpha_1, 1 - \alpha_1)$, (2) $(\alpha_2, 1 - \alpha_2)$, (3) $(\frac{1}{2}, \frac{1}{2})$. Show that case (1) occurs if $\alpha_2 \geqq \alpha_1 \geqq \frac{1}{2}$, case (2) occurs if $\alpha_1 \geqq \alpha_2 \geqq \frac{1}{2}$, case (3) occurs if

$\alpha_1 \geq \frac{1}{2} \geq \alpha_2$ or $\alpha_2 \geq \frac{1}{2} \geq \alpha_1$. Find the equilibrium bundles in each case.

In solving the following numerical examples do not attempt to use the existence theorem, but rely on good guesses and trial and error.

25. Solve the 2×2 equilibrium problem whose matrix is

$$\begin{pmatrix} 3 & 2 \\ 1 & 3 \end{pmatrix}$$

if the incomes are (a) $\beta_1 = \frac{1}{3}$, $\beta_2 = \frac{2}{3}$, (b) $\beta_1 = \frac{2}{3}$, $\beta_2 = \frac{1}{3}$.

26. There are four consumers with equal incomes. Find the equilibrium prices of the two goods if the matrix is

$$\begin{pmatrix} 2 & 1 \\ 3 & 2 \\ 1 & 3 \\ 4 & 3 \end{pmatrix}$$

27. There are five goods and two consumers with equal budgets. The value matrix is

$$\begin{pmatrix} 2 & 5 & 3 & 4 & 3 \\ 4 & 2 & 1 & 2 & 1 \end{pmatrix}$$

Find the equilibrium prices.

CHAPTER NINE

Linear Models of Production

We have already devoted considerable space to the analysis of models of production in connection with linear programming problems. We were interested there in questions of maximizing revenues, minimizing costs, and the like. In this chapter we shall consider questions connected with production models which are not matters of simple optimization. Rather than attempt to describe in advance the material to be discussed let us proceed at once to the topics themselves.

1. The Simple Linear Production Model

At this point the reader should refresh his memory on the definition of a *linear production model*. He will recall that, if such a model involves n goods $G_1, \ldots, G_n$ and m activities $P_1, \ldots, P_m$, then the model is completely described by the production matrix $A = (\alpha_{ij})$, where α_{ij} is the amount of G_j consumed or produced by activity P_i according as α_{ij} is negative or positive.

The above is a description of a *linear production model*. A *simple linear production model* will naturally be a special case of the general model. The special assumptions are these:

Assumption I. *Each activity P_i produces only one good G_j.* In more familiar terms, we are assuming that there is no joint production, and there are no by-products of any activity. In terms of the matrix A the assumption means that there is only one positive entry in each row a_i, all the rest being zero or negative.

Assumption II. *Each good G_j is produced by one and only one activity P_i.*

This means, in particular, that there are the same number of activities as goods, and it is natural to label goods and activities correspondingly. We shall agree henceforth that P_i is the activity which produces G_i. The production matrix A for a simple model is square.

Because of Assumptions I and II it is convenient to modify slightly the definition of the matrix A as follows: Let us agree that α_{ij} *shall stand for the amount of G_j which it is necessary to consume in order to produce one unit of G_i.* Since consumption is now being taken as positive rather than negative it is appropriate to refer to A as the *consumption matrix* of the model. The ith row a_i of A gives the inputs of various goods required to produce one unit of G_i. We do not exclude the possibility that α_{ii} is positive; that is, it may be necessary to consume a certain amount of steel in order to produce more steel. Thus a *consumption* matrix A for a simple linear model may be any nonnegative square matrix.

We shall be concerned first of all with a simple feasibility question. Suppose the model with matrix A is asked to produce the "bill of goods" $y = (\eta_1, \ldots, \eta_n)$, that is, to produce η_1 units of G_1, η_2 units of G_2, etc. Does there exist a production program so that this demand can be met? Now if the activity P_i is operated at *level* or *intensity* ξ_i (we are using the terminology of Chap. 1) then ξ_i units of G_i will be produced. At the same time P_i will consume the vector $\xi_i a_i$ and the amounts consumed by the whole model will clearly be

$$\sum_{i=1}^{n} \xi_i a_i = xA$$

where $x = (\xi_i)$ gives the levels at which each activity is operated. Then *net production*, that is, production minus consumption, is given by the vector

$$x - xA = x(I - A)$$

and the feasibility question is simply: Given $y \geq 0$ does the equation

$$x(I - A) = y \tag{1}$$

have a nonnegative solution?

It is clear that (1) need not have a solution.   For example, let A be given by

$$A = \begin{pmatrix} 0 & 2 \\ 2 & 0 \end{pmatrix}$$

Then
$$(I - A) = \begin{pmatrix} 1 & -2 \\ -2 & 1 \end{pmatrix}$$

and certainly
$$x(I - A) \geq 0$$

has no nonnegative solution.   We could have reached this conclusion by simple common sense.   If it takes 2 units of G_1 to make 1 unit of G_2 and also 2 units of G_2 to make 1 unit of G_1 then one cannot produce positive amounts of both G_1 and G_2 simultaneously.   We see then that if our technology is going to be useful at all it must be capable of producing at least one positive output vector.   We are thus led to make the following

Definition.   A simple linear model with consumption matrix A will be called *productive* if there exists a nonnegative vector $\bar{x}$ such that $\bar{x} > \bar{x}A$.   We shall also say in this case that the matrix A itself is *productive*.

The key property of simple production models is the fact that if such a model is productive then it is capable of producing any positive output vector y, that is,

Theorem 9.1.   *If the matrix A is productive then for any $y \geq 0$ the equation*

$$x(I - A) = y$$

has a unique nonnegative solution.

The theorem will be a consequence of the following lemma:

Lemma 9.1.   If A is productive and $x \geq xA$ then $x \geq 0$.

Proof.   By definition there is a vector $\bar{x} = (\bar{\xi}_1, \ldots, \bar{\xi}_n) \geq 0$ such that $\bar{x} > \bar{x}A$.   This means that $\bar{\xi}_j > \bar{x}a^j$ and hence $\bar{\xi}_j > 0$; so $\bar{x} > 0$. Suppose now that $x = (\xi_1, \ldots, \xi_n)$ satisfies $x \geq xA$ but $x \not\geq 0$. Then some coordinate of x is negative.   Let $\theta = \max [-\xi_i/\bar{\xi}_i]$, say $\theta = -\xi_1/\bar{\xi}_1$.   Then θ is positive and $x' = x + \theta\bar{x} = (\xi'_1, \ldots, \xi'_n) \geq 0$, with $\xi'_1 = 0$.   But also $x' = x + \theta\bar{x} > xA + \theta\bar{x}A = x'A \geq 0$, which would imply $\xi'_1 > x'a^1 \geq 0$, a contradiction.

Corollary.   If A is productive then $I - A$ is regular (has rank n).

Proof.   If $x(I - A) = 0$ then $-x(I - A) = 0$, but by the lemma this means $x \geqq 0$ and $-x \geqq 0$ and therefore $x = 0$.

Proof of Theorem.   Since $I - A$ is regular there exists a unique x such that $x(I - A) = y$ and since $y \geqq 0$ the lemma implies $x \geqq 0$.

Corollary.   The matrix A is productive if and only if $(I - A)^{-1}$ is nonnegative.

Proof.   The *i*th row of the matrix $(I - A)^{-1}$ is the vector x_i such that $x_i(I - A) = u_i$, and we have just seen that x_i must be nonnegative.   Conversely, if $(I - A)^{-1}$ exists and is nonnegative then $x = u(I - A)^{-1}$ is nonnegative; so $x(I - A) = u > 0$ and A is productive (u is once again the unit vector).

This corollary gives a simple means for deciding whether A is productive.   One simply computes the inverse of $I - A$.

We call attention to the fact that Theorem 9.1 makes strong use of the condition that there is no joint production, given by Assumption I.   If, for example, we had a production matrix of the form

$$\begin{pmatrix} 1 & 1 \\ -1 & 1 \end{pmatrix}$$

where positive numbers now represent outputs, then clearly it would not be possible to produce the vector $(1, 0)$.

The reader may object to this example since here the first activity is giving us "something for nothing."   A more realistic counter-example is given in the exercises (see Exercise 4).

One might think that for the sake of greater generality one should consider not only productive matrices but also *semiproductive* ones, i.e., matrices A such that $x \geq xA$ for some $x \geqq 0$.   It turns out, however, that this case can immediately be reduced to the previous one, as we now show.

Definition.   If A is semiproductive we call the activity P_j *productive* if there is a vector $x = (\xi_1, \ldots, \xi_n) \geqq 0$ such that $x \geqq xA$ and $\xi_j > \sum_{i=1}^{n} \alpha_{ij}\xi_i$.   The corresponding good G_j is called *producible*.   The remaining activities and goods will be called *nonproductive* and *nonproducible*, respectively.

Theorem 9.2. *If P_i is productive and P_j is nonproductive then* $\alpha_{ij} = 0$.

In the terminology of the previous chapter, the indices j corresponding to productive processes form an independent subset. In more economic language, the theorem says that no nonproducible good is used in any productive process. Therefore, by reordering we may make the production matrix take the form

$$
\begin{array}{c}
\text{Productive} \left\{ \\ \\ \text{Nonproductive} \left\{ \right.
\end{array}
\left(\begin{array}{c|c} \overbrace{} \\ A_1 & 0 \\ \hline & \\ A_2 & \end{array} \right)
$$

where the matrix A_1 is square.

Proof. Since P_i is productive there exists $x = (\xi_1, \ldots, \xi_n) \geq 0$ such that

$$\xi_i > \sum_{k=1}^{n} \xi_k \alpha_{ki} \qquad \text{in particular } \xi_i > 0 \tag{1}$$

and

$$\xi_r \geq \sum_{k=1}^{n} \xi_k \alpha_{kr} \qquad \text{for all } r \tag{2}$$

Since P_j is nonproductive we must have

$$\xi_j = \sum_{k=1}^{n} \xi_k \alpha_{kj} \tag{3}$$

Now, for ϵ small and positive we may replace ξ_i by $\xi_i - \epsilon$ without disturbing inequality (1) while inequalities (2) are, if anything, strengthened; and if $\alpha_{ij} > 0$ then (3) becomes

$$\xi_j > \sum_{k=1}^{n} \xi_k \alpha_{kj} - \epsilon \alpha_{ij} \tag{4}$$

But this would mean P_j is productive contrary to hypothesis.

The economic moral of this theorem is that there is nothing to be gained by operating the nonproductive processes. Namely, let $x = (\xi_1, \ldots, \xi_n)$ be an intensity vector such that $x \geq xA$, or $\xi_j \geq \sum_{i=1}^{n} \xi_i \alpha_{ij}$.

If we set $\xi_i = 0$ for all nonproductive i then if P_j is productive we possibly strengthen the above inequalities, while if P_j is nonproductive we get $0 = 0$; so this new intensity vector is just as good as, and possibly better than, the original one.

So far our discussion has been concerned entirely with technology. We turn now to economic considerations by introducing prices.   As usual we let $p = (\pi_1, \ldots, \pi_n)$ be the price vector, where π_j is the price of one unit of G_j.   Then the *profit* of the activity P_i is given by the expression $\pi_i - \sum_{j=1}^{n} \alpha_{ij}\pi_j$, and the *profit vector* q is given by $q = (I - A)p$.   We recall that in the linearexchange models of the previous chapter it was not possible for all activities to make a profit simultaneously.   Here the situation is quite the opposite, as we now see.

Theorem 9.3.   *If A is productive then for any nonnegative (profit) vector q there exists a unique nonnegative (price) vector p such that $q = (I - A)p$.*

Proof.   Since $I - A$ is regular there exists a unique p such that $q = (I - A)p$, and it only remains to show that p is nonnegative. From Theorem 9.1 there exists $x_i \geq 0$ such that $x_i(I - A) = u_i$; so $0 \leq x_i q = x_i(I - A)p = u_i p$.   Since all coordinates of p are nonnegative, the result follows.

The theorem shows that if prices are appropriately set the profits of the various activities may be any preassigned nonnegative numbers.

2. A Dynamic Property of the Simple Model

Let us suppose now that we are dealing with a simple model whose matrix is A, and suppose further that outside consumers have demanded a set of goods given by the nonnegative vector y_0.   If we think of our model as being operated by a central planning authority then there will be no difficulty in meeting the demand y_0 assuming that A is productive.   The planning authority simply solves the equation

$$x(I - A) = y_0$$

and if the solution is $\bar{x} = (\bar{\xi}_i)$ then each activity P_i is ordered to operate at the level $\bar{\xi}_i$.

However, we may also think of the activities P_i as being operated by completely independent authorities none of whom has any control over the actions of the others. In this case we can nevertheless describe a method by which the production problem can be solved at least approximately. The method is the following: Let us denote by $y_0 = (\eta_{i0})$ the initial demand by outside consumers. Then, in particular, there is a demand for η_{10} units of G_1. Now if this amount is to be produced by P_1 then P_1 must consume the vector $\eta_{10}a_1$. Thus having received an order for η_{10} units of G_1 the operator of P_1 in turn places orders for other goods in the amounts $\eta_{10}a_1$. Similarly, all the other producers P_i place orders for the vectors $\eta_{i0}a_i$. If we think of the vector y_0 as the first round of orders we see that in order to fill these orders the producers must initiate a second round of orders for the total vector

$$y_1 = \sum_{i=1}^{n} \eta_{i0}a_i = y_0 A$$

But now, in order to fill the orders $y_1 = (\eta_{i1})$ the producers must place a third round of orders for the vector

$$y_2 = \Sigma \eta_{i1}a_i = y_1 A = y_0 A^2$$

and it is clear that this reordering process will go on indefinitely. The total bill of goods ordered will be the sum of those ordered at each stage, and we are thus led to consider the infinite series of vectors

$$y_0 + y_0 A + \cdots + y_0 A^n + \cdots$$

If we are fortunate, then this series will, in fact, converge and give us the correct amount which each P_i should produce in order for the model as a whole to supply the initial demand y_0.

Of course, in reality no such infinite sequence of reorderings could actually occur and the description above is not to be taken too literally. On the other hand, one can imagine some process like the one described taking place over a long period of time.

The theorem we shall prove is the following:

Theorem 9.4. *Let y be any vector and let $x_n = y(I + A + \cdots + A^n)$. Then if A is productive*

$$\lim_{n \to \infty} x_n(I - A) = y$$

The theorem shows that if we go through the reordering routine sufficiently many times we shall come arbitrarily close to satisfying the demand y. The proof is an easy consequence of the following

Lemma 9.2. *If A is productive then $\lim\limits_{n \to \infty} A^n = 0$.*

Proof. Since A is productive there exists $x > 0$ such that $xA < x$. In fact there exists λ such that

$$xA < \lambda x \tag{1}$$

where $0 < \lambda < 1$. From (1) it follows by induction that

$$xA^n < \lambda^n x$$

and hence $\lim\limits_{n \to \infty} xA^n = 0$. But letting $x = (\xi_i)$ we have

$$xA^n = \Sigma \xi_i(u_i A^n) \to 0$$

Since all terms in the sum are nonnegative each must approach zero; hence $(u_i A^n)$ approaches zero for all i and therefore A^n approaches zero as asserted.

Proof of Theorem. We simply observe that

$$\begin{aligned} x_n(I - A) &= y(I + A + \cdots + A^n)(I - A) \\ &= y - yA^{n+1} \end{aligned}$$

and since yA^{n+1} approaches zero, the theorem is proved.

3. *The Leontief Model*

One of the unnatural features of the simple model discussed in the preceding sections was the fact that if the model was capable of producing any positive goods vector then it could produce arbitrarily large amounts of any of the goods in any proportions. There is nothing wrong with this provided the model is given a sufficient amount of time in which to do the producing. In realistic production problems, however, time is generally of the essence. When consumers demand some goods vector y they expect to receive the goods not in the indefinite future but within some specified time, say a year.

In order to go over to a more realistic model which takes account of time, we need change nothing in our mathematical model but merely our interpretation of the quantities involved.   The consumption number α_{ij} now becomes the amount of G_j required, say *per year*, in order to obtain a *yearly* output of one unit of G_i.   In this interpretation it is obviously unreasonable to expect to be able to produce arbitrarily large quantities in a limited amount of time.   Why?   Because of limitations on *capacity*.   No matter how much is available in the way of steel, say, for making automobiles, there are only enough machines, equipment, and especially *labor* to produce a certain finite number of cars per year.

The above ideas are easily formalized.   Goods like plant equipment and labor are characterized by the following two properties:

1. They are not outputs of any of the activities of the model.

2. They are available in a limited amount.

Goods satisfying (1) and (2) are called *primary goods* (also sometimes referred to as *factors of production*).

We are now prepared to describe the *simple Leontief model*.

Definition.   The *simple Leontief model* consists of a simple production model in which there is a single primary good G_0 called *labor*.

We shall assume that labor is needed as an input to all activities; that is, the consumption coefficients α_{i0} are all positive.   We also choose the unit of labor so that the total amount available is 1.

The first question for the Leontief model which can be quickly settled is that of prices.   For the case of the simple model without primary goods we have seen that profits could be any numbers at all. For the Leontief model with labor as primary input it is natural to assume that when the cost of labor is taken into account the profit of each activity shall be zero.   In other terms, all the profit which is made from production is turned back to labor as wages.

Theorem 9.5.   *There exists a positive price vector p, unique up to multiplication by a positive number, such that at prices p the profit to each activity is zero.*

Proof.   Let us assume the price of labor π_0 to be 1.   The condition that profits be zero is then

$$\alpha_{i0} + \sum_{j} \pi_j \alpha_{ij} = \pi_i \qquad \text{for all } i > 0$$

or $$(I - A)p = a^0 \tag{1}$$

where $a^0 = (\alpha_{i0})$ and A is the consumption matrix without the column a^0. By Theorem 9.3, (1) has a unique nonnegative solution, and since a^0 is positive p must also be positive.

So far we have not made any explicit use of Assumption II. This was the condition that there be *only one* process for making each commodity. In realistic situations there might be a number of alternative ways of producing a given good. Let us define a *general* (as opposed to simple) *Leontief model* to satisfy all the conditions imposed on the simple model except that the good G_j may be producible by more than one activity. In a general model, then, there will be more activities than goods. We denote by S_j the set of all activities which produce G_j or, more conveniently, the set of all indices i such that P_i produces G_j. Then, given an intensity vector $x = (\xi_i)$ determining the various activity levels and such that the labor supply is not exceeded, the corresponding net *output vector* $y = (\eta_j)$ is given by

$$\eta_j = \sum_{i \varepsilon S_j} \xi_i - \sum_{i=1}^{m} \xi_i \alpha_{ij} \qquad \text{where } \sum_{i=1}^{m} \xi_i \alpha_{i0} \leqq 1$$

The set Y of all such vectors will be termed the *output space* of the model.

It might reasonably be expected that the analysis of the general Leontief model would be considerably more involved than that of the simple model. It turns out somewhat surprisingly, however, that almost all questions concerning general models can be reduced to questions about certain simple submodels, as the following interesting theorem shows.

Theorem 9.6 (substitution theorem). *If a general Leontief model is productive then there exists a set of n activities $P_{i_1}, \ldots, P_{i_n}$, where $i_j \ \varepsilon \ S_j$, such that the simple Leontief model formed from these activities has the same output space as the original model.*

There are a number of ways of proving this result. The most instructive method is via the duality theory of linear programming.

We digress for a moment, therefore, to reconsider the canonical minimum problem of finding a nonnegative vector x which

$$\text{minimizes } xc \tag{1}$$

subject to

$$xA = b \tag{2}$$

We call a set of independent rows a_i of A an *optimal (feasible) basis* if there is an optimal (feasible) vector x depending on these rows. The result we need is the following:

Lemma 9.3. Let a set $\mathfrak{B}$ of rows a_i of A be an optimal basis for the problem (1), (2) above and consider the new problem

$$\text{to minimize } xc \tag{1'}$$

subject to

$$xA = b' \tag{2'}$$

Then if $\mathfrak{B}$ is a feasible basis for problem (1'), (2') it is, in fact, an optimal basis for this problem also.

Proof.   Let $\bar{x}$ be an optimal vector for problem (1), (2) depending on the basis $\mathfrak{B}$ and let $\bar{y}$ be a solution of the dual.   Then we know from the Equilibrium Theorem 3.2 (page 82) that

$$\text{if } a_i\bar{y} < \gamma_i \qquad \text{then } \bar{\xi}_i = 0 \tag{3}$$

Now assume x' is a feasible vector for problem (1'), (2') depending on the set $\mathfrak{B}$.   Then we have also

$$\text{if } a_i\bar{y} < \gamma_i \qquad \text{then } \xi_i' = 0 \tag{3'}$$

since by hypothesis $\xi_i' = 0$ whenever $\bar{\xi}_i = 0$.   But this is precisely the condition that x' and $\bar{y}$ be solutions of the primal and dual problems of (1') and (2') (again by Theorem 3.2) and, in particular, x' is an optimal vector, as asserted.

Proof of Substitution Theorem.   Let $\bar{y}$ be a positive vector in the output space Y.   We consider the canonical minimum problem of producing the vector $\bar{y}$ while minimizing the amount of labor used, that is,

$$xa^0 = \text{minimum}$$

Now let $\bar{x}$ be a basic optimal vector for this problem. Then $\bar{x}$ depends on at most n rows $i_1, \ldots, i_n$ of the production matrix. Since $\bar{y}$ is positive all goods are produced by $\bar{x}$ and hence ξ_i must be positive for one index i in each of the sets S_j. Letting $\bar{A}$ be the matrix with rows a_{i_j} it remains to show that $\bar{A}$ has the output space Y. Let y' be any other vector in Y. We know that the matrix $\bar{A}$ is productive since it produced the positive vector $\bar{y}$. Hence, by Theorem 9.1, there exists a vector x' such that

$$x'(I - \bar{A}) = y'$$

but this simply says that the basis given by the rows a_{i_j} is feasible for the new linear program where the vector to be produced is y' rather than $\bar{y}$. According to the previous lemma, therefore, x' is also optimal, that is,

$$x' \text{ minimizes } xa^0$$

among all possible vectors x for the original model. Since $y' \, \varepsilon \, Y$ there is some intensity vector x which produces y' and for which $xa^0 \leqq 1$ (the labor supply is not exceeded). It now follows that

$$x'a^0 \leqq 1$$

and hence y' is producible with the matrix $\bar{A}$ and one unit of labor. The proof is now complete.

There are a number of remarks to be made concerning the above result.

Remark 1. Notice that we have actually proved more than is stated in the theorem. Not only are we able to produce everything with the simple model that we could with the general model but we can also produce just as economically with the simple model in the sense that the amount of labor required for each output vector is no greater for the simple model than for the general. Thus, in a "Leontief economy," there is nothing to be gained by having several processes for producing the same good.

Remark 2. Both the primal and dual linear programming problem used in the proof of the substitution theorem have very natural economic interpretations. The primal problem asks for a way of producing a given bill of goods with minimum labor. The dual asks for a set of prices which will maximize the cost of this bill of goods subject to the familiar condition that no activity shall show a positive profit.

Remark 3. The validity of the substitution theorem depends strongly on the assumption that there is only one primary good, as the following counter-example shows: We consider a model in which there are two primary goods, say *skilled labor* G_0 and *unskilled labor* G_0'. There are also two output goods G_1 and G_2. There is only one activity P_1 producing G_1, and this requires an input of one unit of skilled labor. There are two activities P_2 and P_2' for producing G_2. The first requires an input of 1 unit of skilled labor; the second requires an input of 2 units of unskilled labor. We leave it to the reader to show that in this example if either of the activities P_2 or P_2' are eliminated the output space becomes smaller (see Exercise 10).

Finally, we observe that the way to find the simple submodel with the properties of the substitution theorem is to solve the linear program for minimizing labor input. The reader will do well at this point to work the numerical example of Exercise 9.

4. The General Linear Production Model. Efficient Points

We turn now to the consideration of the most general linear production model in which we place no restrictions on the nature of the production activities. An activity may have any number of outputs as well as inputs, the same good may be produced by any number of activities, and there is no restriction on the allowable number of primary goods. In formulating the model it is actually more convenient not to distinguish between primary and final goods but to use an alternative description.

We consider the usual linear activity model with *production matrix* which for reasons which will soon be apparent we shall denote by B. The m rows and n columns correspond to the usual activities and goods, respectively, and for a given nonnegative *input vector* x we obtain an *output vector* y where

$$y = xB \tag{1}$$

Now, because of the existence of primary goods not all nonnegative vectors x may be possible, as we have seen, for example, in the case of the Leonteif model where we have to satisfy the condition

$$xa^0 \leqq 1$$

The generalization to more than one primary good is obvious. We are given a *consumption matrix* A and a *supply vector* b and we require that

$$xA \leqq b \tag{2}$$

The matrix A of course has m rows. The columns, however, will correspond only to those goods of which there is a limited supply.

The model described here is entirely similar to the one treated in Sec. 5, Chap. 3. The inequality (2) corresponds to what we called limitations of plant capacity in our earlier discussion. We have now given a complete description of the model and we turn to a study of some of its properties.

Definition. The nonnegative solutions of (2) above will be called the *input space* of the model, denoted by X.

The *output space* Y of the model consists of all vectors y such that $y = xB$ for x in X (we do not require that y be nonnegative).

We now recall briefly some terminology from Chap. 2. The input space above, being the set of all solutions of a set of inequalities, was called a *solution set* (see Exercise 36, Chap. 2). It follows from Exercise 40 of Chap. 2 that the output space Y is also a solution set. This means that there exist some n-rowed matrix C and some vector c such that Y is the set of all solutions of the inequalities

$$yC \leqq c \tag{3}$$

It is this characterization of the output space Y which we shall make use of in what follows.

We come now to the central economic notion of this section.

Definition. The vector y_0 in Y is called *efficient* if there is no vector y' in Y such that $y' \geq y$.

In words, y_0 is efficient if it is impossible to increase the output of any good without decreasing the output of some other.

The principal result on efficient points relates them to prices and income.   It seems intuitively obvious on economic grounds that any output vector which maximizes income at some set of prices will be efficient.   Conversely, it turns out that corresponding to each efficient vector y_0 there is a set of prices for which y_0 is an income maximizer, as we now show.

Theorem 9.7. *If Y is the output space of a general linear model then the vector y_0 in Y is efficient if and only if there exists a positive (price) vector p such that $y_0 p \geq y p$ for all $y \, \varepsilon \, Y$.*

Proof.   If p is given and $y_0 p \geq y p$ for all y in Y then clearly y_0 is efficient, for if not we would have $y' \, \varepsilon \, Y$ and $y' \geq y_0$ and therefore $y' p > y_0 p$, contrary to assumption.

Conversely, suppose y_0 is efficient.   From (3) above we have

$$y_0 c^j \leqq \gamma_j \qquad \text{for all } j$$

We now divide the indices j into two sets S and S' where

$$y_0 c^j = \gamma_j \qquad \text{for } j \, \varepsilon \, S$$
$$y_0 c^j < \gamma_j \qquad \text{for } j \, \varepsilon \, S'$$

The set S cannot be empty, for then we would have $y_0 C < c$, so that for a sufficiently small positive number ϵ we would have

$$(y_0 + \epsilon v) C \leqq c$$

and $y_0 + \epsilon v$ would be in Y, contradicting the assumption that y_0 is efficient.

We next assert that the inequalities

$$z c^j \leqq 0 \qquad \text{for all } j \, \varepsilon \, S \tag{4}$$

have no semipositive solution, for if z were such a solution then clearly we would have, for any positive number ϵ,

$$(y_0 + \epsilon z) c^j \leqq \gamma_j \qquad \text{for } j \, \varepsilon \, S$$

and for ϵ sufficiently small

$$(y_0 + \epsilon z) c^j \leqq \gamma_j \qquad \text{for } j \, \varepsilon \, S'$$

but this would mean that $y_0 + \epsilon z$ is in Y, again contradicting the efficiency of y_0.

Now since inequalities (4) have no semipositive solution we know from Theorem 2.10 (page 49) that there are numbers λ_j, $j \; \varepsilon \; S$ such that

$$\sum_{j \varepsilon S} \lambda_j c^j > 0$$

Letting $p = \sum_{j \varepsilon S} \lambda_j c^j$, the proof is completed by noting that, for y in Y,

$$yp = \sum_S \lambda_j (yc^i) \leqq \sum_S \lambda_j \gamma_j = \sum_S \lambda_j (y_0 c^i) = y_0 p$$

so that y_0 maximizes income at prices p.

The above theorem gives a mathematical justification for some of the tenets of classical price theory. It states that any efficient mode

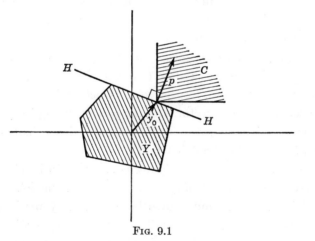

Fig. 9.1

of production can be achieved by setting prices appropriately and allowing producers to maximize their income.

There is a simple geometric picture corresponding to this theorem. Let y_0 be efficient in Y. The set of all vectors y' such that $y' \geq y_0$ clearly form a convex cone C with vertex at y_0. The efficiency of y_0 states that C and Y do not intersect (see Fig. 9.1). It is geometrically obvious then that there is a hyperplane H through y_0 which separates

C from Y, and the normal to this hyperplane in the direction of C gives the desired price vector.

Finally we remark that neither the efficient point corresponding to given prices nor the prices for a given efficient point need be unique (see Exercises 11, 12, 13).

5. von Neumann's Expanding Model

The previous sections have been concerned with the static theory of production models. We now take up the case of a model whose output varies with time and consider the possibility of a steady expansion of such a model in relation to prices of the goods involved.

As in the previous section we consider a general linear model involving n goods $G_1, \ldots, G_n$ and m activities $P_1, \ldots, P_m$. We wish now to distinguish explicitly between goods produced and consumed in a given activity. Accordingly we denote by α_{ij} the amount of G_j consumed in P_i, and by β_{ij} the amount of G_j produced by P_i. The activity P_i is accordingly represented by two nonnegative vectors, an *input vector* $a_i = (\alpha_{i1}, \ldots, \alpha_{in})$ and an *output vector* $b_i = (\beta_{i1}, \ldots, \beta_{in})$. The corresponding matrices $A = (\alpha_{ij})$ and $B = (\beta_{ij})$ are called the *input* and *output* matrices, respectively. Once again, an *intensity vector* x is a semipositive m-vector, and the corresponding input and output vectors are given by xA and xB. Henceforth we shall denote the model symbolically by the pair (A, B).

The model we are now considering is assumed to be *closed*. This means that there is no flow of goods to or from the model. All goods consumed in the model must have been previously produced by it, and the only thing one can do with the model's output is to feed it back into the model as an input at a later stage. We are therefore concerned with a sort of self-sustaining mechanism whose sole function is to perpetuate itself in some manner. Such a model is in some sense an approximation to a total economy in which labor produces consumption goods and these goods are then consumed by consumers, enabling or inducing them to give more labor, so that we have roughly the cyclic situation described by the model.

It is clear that in order for the model to function in the manner described it must be possible to choose an intensity vector x so that every good which is consumed is also produced. A condition sufficient to ensure this is

Assumption I.   For all j, $b^j \geq 0$.

This simply states that every good is an output of some activity.

We shall also make a second assumption which asserts that it is impossible to get something for nothing.

Assumption II.   For all i, $a_i \geq 0$.

This says that every activity must have at least one good as input.

Now suppose we have an intensity vector x such that $xB \geq \alpha x A$ for some number $\alpha > 0$. We then say that the *model is expanding at a rate at least equal to* α. The terminology is appropriate, for the above inequality means that $xb^j \geq \alpha x a^j$; thus the output of each good G_j is at least α times as great as its input. Note that this does not exclude the possibility that both input and output of some good be zero.

Definition.   *The technological expansion problem* for the model (A, B) is to find a semipositive m-vector x and number α such that

$$\alpha \text{ is a maximum} \tag{1}$$

subject to

$$xB \geq \alpha x A \tag{2}$$

If the maximum value of α exists it is called the *technological expansion rate*[1] of the model and is denoted by α_0. The corresponding intensity vector x_0 is then called an *optimal intensity vector*.

Theorem 9.8 (existence theorem).   *For models satisfying Assumptions* I *and* II, α_0 *exists and is positive.*

Proof.   For each positive number α, consider the problem of finding a semipositive solution x to the inequality

$$x(B - \alpha A) \geq 0 \tag{3}$$

Now, for α sufficiently small (3) has a solution, for if x is positive

---

[1] Although we use the term "expansion" throughout, we nowhere require that α be greater than unity. Thus the whole theory of these models applies equally well to "contracting" models, although the case $\alpha \geq 1$ is the one of economic interest.

it follows from Assumption I that xB is positive; hence $xB \geqq \alpha xA$ for some positive number α. On the other hand, for α very large (3) has no solutions, for since there is a positive entry in every row of A (Assumption II), we can choose α so large that the sum of the coordinates in each row of $B - \alpha A$ is negative, that is,

$$(B - \alpha A)v < 0$$

where v is the unit vector in R^n, and hence for any $x \geq 0$,

$$x(B - \alpha A)v < 0$$

so that (3) has no solution.

Let α_0 be the least upper bound of all numbers for which (3) has a solution; it is clear that α_0 is the desired technological expansion rate.[1]

Having considered so far only the technological aspects of the model, we turn now to the economic theory. We shall obtain results here which are striking analogues to the duality theorems of linear programming.

As usual, we consider a semipositive price vector $p = (\pi_1, \ldots, \pi_n)$. At prices p the *cost* of activity P_i is $a_i p$ and the *revenue* from P_i is $b_i p$. The *cost vector* is Ap; the *revenue vector* is Bp. We now describe an economic problem which will turn out to be the dual of the expansion problem previously defined.

Definition. The *economic expansion problem* for the model (A, B) is to find a semipositive n-vector p and number β such that

$$\beta \text{ is a minimum} \tag{1}*$$

subject to

$$Bp \leqq \beta Ap \tag{2}*$$

The minimum value of β is called the *economic expansion rate* of the model and is denoted by β_0. The corresponding price vector p_0 is then called an *optimal price vector*. We remark that from Assumption I, for any price vector p, $b_i p > 0$ for some index i and therefore

---

[1] A standard "compactness" argument is needed here to show that there actually exists a semipositive x_0 such that $x_0(B - \alpha_0 A) \geqq 0$.

$\beta_0 > 0$. An argument analogous to that of Theorem 9.8 shows that β_0 always exists.

There are various possible economic interpretations of the dual problem. If $a_i p > 0$ then the ratio $b_i p / a_i p$ is return divided by cost, which is the rate at which the value of goods is increasing in activity P_i, a sort of profit factor. Now if one makes the assumption of a free competitive economy, the forces of competition between activities will tend to make this profit factor a minimum. A second interpretation of β is as an *interest factor*. Suppose the activities are financed by borrowing and that at the end of each period of production, for each dollar borrowed, the activities must pay back β dollars (the usual interest rate would be $\beta - 1$). Then condition (2)* is the familiar condition that no activity shall make a profit.

We remark that, although the pair of dual problems treated here seem very similar to dual linear programming problems, there is a fundamental difference in that the constraints are not linear. In fact we shall see that a model all of whose matrix coefficients are integers may have expansion rates which are irrational.

We also make the trivial observation that both our problems are homogeneous, so that if x_0 or p_0 is optimal so also is any positive multiple of either.

We now proceed to derive the relationship between the dual problems. The situation is somewhat more complicated than the case of linear programming.

Lemma 9.4. For models satisfying Assumptions I *and* II, $\beta_0 \leqq \alpha_0$. (We shall see from examples that equality need not hold.)

Proof. Define the matrix C by $C = B - \alpha_0 A$. Now the inequality $xC > 0$ has no nonnegative solution, for if x' were such a solution then we would have $x'B > \alpha_0 x'A$, or $x'B \geqq (\alpha_0 + \epsilon)x'A$ for some $\epsilon > 0$ so that α_0 would not be maximal. Now apply Theorem 2.10 (page 49), which asserts that there exists $p \geq 0$ such that $Cp \leqq 0$; so $Bp \leqq \alpha_0 A p$. Therefore, from the definition it follows that $\alpha_0 \geqq \beta_0$, as was to be shown.

Although one cannot assert that $\alpha_0 = \beta_0$ without some further assumptions, there is an interesting analogue of the linear programming Equilibrium Theorem 1.2, which we now give.

Theorem 9.9 (von Neumann).   *If the model (A, B) satisfies I and II then there exists a semipositive m-vector $x_0 = (\xi_1, \ldots, \xi_m)$, a semipositive n-vector $p_0 = (\pi_1, \ldots, \pi_n)$, and a number γ such that*

$$x_0 B \geqq \gamma x_0 A \tag{i}$$
and $\text{if } x_0 b^j > \gamma x_0 a^j \quad \text{then } \pi_j = 0 \tag{ii}$

$$B p_0 \leqq \gamma A p_0 \tag{i}*$$
and $\text{if } b_i p_0 < \gamma a_i p_0 \quad \text{then } \xi_i = 0 \tag{ii}*$

Proof.   Let $\gamma = \alpha_0$, the technological expansion coefficient, and let x_0 and p_0 be optimal intensity and price vectors.   Then (i) holds by definition of α_0.   Also $B p_0 \leqq \beta_0 A p_0 \leqq \alpha_0 A p_0 = \gamma A p_0$, using Lemma 9.4; so (i)* is established.

Next, from (i) and (i)* we have $\gamma x_0 A p_0 \leqq x_0 B p_0 \leqq \gamma x_0 A p_0$; so $x_0 (B - \gamma A) p_0 = 0$, or $\Sigma \xi_i (b_i - \gamma a_i) p_0 = 0 = \Sigma x_0 (b^j - \gamma a^j) \pi_j$, and since the terms $(b_i - \gamma a_i) p_0$ and $x_0 (b^j - \gamma a^j)$ are all nonnegative we obtain (ii) and (ii)*.

Interpretation.   The constant γ is both expansion rate and interest factor.   Condition (i) states that the amounts of all goods increase at a rate at least equal to γ.   Condition (i)* is the requirement that no activity show a positive profit.   Condition (ii) states that if any good is expanding at a rate greater than γ then, being "oversupplied," its price drops to zero, and (ii)* is the obvious condition that activities which show a negative profit will not be used.

In order to obtain the full duality theorem we need a further concept which is a generalization of the notion of independent subset of the preceding chapter.

Definition.   Given a model (A, B) the set of indices $S \subset \{1, \ldots, n\}$ is called an *independent subset* if it is possible to produce each good G_i, $i \, \varepsilon \, S$, without consuming any good G_j, j not in S.   More formally, the set S is independent if there exists a set $T \subset \{1, \ldots, m\}$ such that $\alpha_{ij} = 0$ for $i \, \varepsilon \, T$ and $j \, \varepsilon \, S'$ and for all $j \, \varepsilon \, S$, $\beta_{ij} > 0$ for some $i \, \varepsilon \, T$.   The model is *irreducible* if there are no proper independent subsets.

If we reorder rows and columns of the matrix A so that the indices T correspond to the first t rows of A and the indices S to the first s columns then the matrix takes the form

$$t\left\{\left(\begin{array}{cc}\overbrace{A_1}^{s} & 0 \\ \hline & A' \end{array}\right)\right.$$

In economic terms, a set of goods S is independent if these goods can be produced from themselves, that is, without consuming any other goods.

Theorem 9.10 (duality theorem).   *If the model (A, B) is irreducible then $\alpha_0 = \beta_0$.*

Proof.   We have already shown that $\beta_0 \leqq \alpha_0$; so we need only show the reverse inequality.   If x_0 and p_0 are optimal then $x_0 B \geqq \alpha_0 x_0 A$ and $Bp_0 \leqq \beta_0 A p_0$ so $\alpha_0 x_0 A p_0 \leqq x_0 B p_0 \leqq \beta_0 x_0 A p_0$, and if we can show that $x_0 A p_0 > 0$ the desired inequality will follow.   Letting S be all indices j such that $x_0 b^j > 0$, we see that S is an independent subset, for taking T to be all indices i such that $\xi_i > 0$, we must have $\alpha_{ij} = 0$ for $i \varepsilon T$, $j \varepsilon S'$, for otherwise we would get $x_0 a^j > 0$, $x_0 b^j = 0$ and we could not have $x_0 b^j \geqq \alpha_0 x_0 a^j$.   From irreducibility, then, $x_0 b^j > 0$ for all j, or $x_0 B > 0$.   Since $p_0 \geqq 0$ it follows that $x_0 B p_0 > 0$ and therefore $\beta_0 x_0 A p_0 \geqq x_0 B p_0 > 0$, which shows that $x_0 A p_0$ is positive, completing the proof.

6. Some Examples

Consider the model whose input and output matrices are the following:

$$A = \begin{pmatrix} 0 & 1 & 0 & 0 \\ 1 & 0 & 0 & 1 \\ 0 & 0 & 1 & 0 \end{pmatrix} \quad B = \begin{pmatrix} 1 & 0 & 0 & 0 \\ 0 & 0 & 2 & 0 \\ 0 & 1 & 0 & 1 \end{pmatrix}$$

This model is irreducible, as one easily verifies.   We assert that the optimal intensity and price vectors are

$$x_0 = (2^{-1/3}, 2^{-2/3}, 1)$$
$$p_0 = (1, 2^{-1/3}, 2^{-2/3}, 0)$$

for then the input and output vectors are

$$x_0 A = (2^{-2/3}, 2^{-1/3}, 1, 2^{-2/3}) \qquad x_0 B = (2^{-1/3}, 1, 2^{1/3}, 1)$$

and the corresponding expansion rate α is given by

$$\alpha = \min [2^{1/3}, 2^{1/3}, 2^{1/3}, 2^{2/3}] = 2^{1/3}$$

Also

$$A p_0 = (2^{-1/3}, 1, 2^{-2/3}) \qquad B p_0 = (1, 2^{1/3}, 2^{-1/3})$$

and the expansion rate β is

$$\beta = \max [2^{1/3}, 2^{1/3}, 2^{1/3}] = 2^{1/3}$$

Since $\alpha = \beta$ it follows from the duality theorem that this common value is α_0 and β_0. Note that the good G_4 is overproduced since its expansion rate is $2^{2/3}$, and consequently its price is zero in accordance with the theory.

One can easily construct models for which $\beta_0 < \alpha_0$. If one simply "puts together" two models which have no activities or goods in common and which have different expansion rates then for the composite model α_0 will be the larger, β_0 the smaller of the expansion rates. A somewhat more complicated example of nonuniqueness is the following:

$$
\begin{array}{c}
\overbrace{\hspace{4em}}^{A} \\
\begin{pmatrix}
0 & 1 & 0 & 0 & 0 & 0 \\
1 & 0 & 1 & 0 & 0 & 0 \\
0 & 0 & 0 & 1 & 0 & 0 \\
0 & 0 & 1 & 0 & 0 & 1 \\
0 & 0 & 0 & 0 & 1 & 0
\end{pmatrix}
\end{array}
\quad
\begin{array}{c}
\overbrace{\hspace{4em}}^{B} \\
\begin{pmatrix}
1 & 0 & 0 & 1 & 0 & 0 \\
0 & 1 & 0 & 0 & 0 & 0 \\
0 & 0 & 1 & 0 & 0 & 0 \\
0 & 0 & 0 & 0 & 2 & 0 \\
0 & 0 & 0 & 1 & 0 & 1
\end{pmatrix}
\end{array}
$$

Note that the "submodel" consisting of the last three rows is exactly the model of the previous example and therefore has expansion coefficient $2^{1/3}$. On the other hand, the submodel consisting of the first three rows has expansion coefficient 1, as can be seen by setting $x = (1, 1, 1, 0, 0)$, $p = (1, 1, 0, 0, 0, 0)$. Therefore $\alpha_0 = 2^{1/3}$, $\beta_0 = 1$.

7. *The Expanding Simple Model*

The simple linear model is a special case of the general model (A, B) in which there are exactly n activities and B is the identity matrix I. For simple models the expansion problem takes the form: Given a nonnegative matrix A, find a semipositive vector x and number α such that

$$\alpha \text{ is a maximum} \tag{1}$$

subject to

$$x \geqq \alpha x A \tag{2}$$

The simple model has the following important special property.

Theorem 9.11. *If x_0 and α_0 solve* (1) *and* (2) *above, then*

$$x_0 = \alpha_0 x_0 A$$

The theorem says that for a simple model expanding at a maximum rate there is no overproduction, all goods expanding at the maximum rate α_0.

Remark. We may rewrite the above equation in the form $x_0 A = (1/\alpha_0)x_0$. This shows that $1/\alpha_0$ is a positive *eigen-value* of A and x_0 is a corresponding nonnegative *eigen-vector*. Thus we are proving the classical result that a nonnegative matrix always has a nonnegative eigen-value and eigen-vector.

Proof. Suppose there were an optimal vector x_0 such that $x_0 \geqq \alpha_0 x_0 A$. We cannot have $x_0 > \alpha_0 x_0 A$, for then α_0 could be replaced by a larger number. Now choose an optimal vector $x = (\xi_1, \ldots, \xi_n)$ such that the strict inequality

$$\xi_j > \alpha_0 x a^j = \alpha_0 \sum_{i=1}^{n} \xi_i \alpha_{ij} \tag{3}$$

holds for as many indices as possible, say all indices in the set S, while for the remaining indices S' we have

$$\xi_j = \alpha_0 x a^j = \alpha_0 \sum_{i=1}^{n} \xi_i \alpha_{ij} \qquad \text{for } j \, \varepsilon \, S' \tag{4}$$

We now assert

$$\xi_i \alpha_{ij} = 0 \qquad \text{for } i \,\varepsilon\, S, j \,\varepsilon\, S' \qquad (5)$$

for if this were not the case then, say, $\xi_{i_0}\alpha_{i_0 j_0} > 0$, $i_0 \,\varepsilon\, S$, $j_0 \,\varepsilon\, S'$. Then we could replace ξ_{i_0} by $\xi_{i_0} - \epsilon$, where ϵ is positive but sufficiently small so that inequalities (3) remain valid. But from (4)

$$\xi_{j_0} = \alpha_0 \sum_{i=1}^{n} \xi_i \alpha_{ij_0} > \alpha_0 [\xi_1 \alpha_{1j_0} + \cdots + (\xi_{i_0} - \epsilon)\alpha_{i_0 j_0} + \cdots + \xi_n \alpha_{nj_0}]$$

so we would have a vector which increases the number of strict inequalities (3) contrary to the choice of x, and this proves (5).

Now let $x' = (\xi_1', \ldots, \xi_n')$, where $\xi_i' = \xi_i$ for $i \,\varepsilon\, S$, $\xi_i' = 0$ for $i \,\varepsilon\, S'$. Replacing x by x' in (3) we see that the inequalities are if anything strengthened, and in (4) we get $0 = 0$ because of (5). But this means that we could again increase α_0 contrary to its definition. Accordingly there are no strict inequalities (3) and the theorem is proved.

Using the above result one can now give a complete analysis of the possible optimal intensity and price vectors for the simple model. We state the results here. The proofs are precisely like those of Theorems 8.2 and 8.3 and are left as exercises.

Theorem 9.12. *If the matrix A is irreducible then $\alpha_0 = \beta_0$ and the optimal intensity vector is positive and unique up to multiplication by a positive number.*

If A is reducible with irreducible subsets $S_1, \ldots, S_k$, let A_i be the submatrix corresponding to S_i and let α_i and β_i be the technological and economic expansion coefficients, respectively, of A_i.

Theorem 9.13. *If A is as above then $\alpha_0 = \max [\alpha_i]$ and $\beta_0 = \min [\beta_i]$.*

Bibliographical Notes

The theorems on the simple linear production model are classical results in the theory of positive matrices. As presented here our proofs are similar to some of those given by Arrow [1]. The substitution theorem was first discovered by Samuelson [1], and a general proof was given by Arrow [1]. The one presented here based on duality was communicated to the author verbally by Dantzig. The relationship between efficient production and profit maximization is extensively developed by Koopmans in his fundamental paper [1]. The linear expanding model was introduced by von Neumann in a paper [3] which has been translated to English [4]. The particular formulation and results on the expanding model presented here were given by the author [3]. A somewhat different analysis has been given by Kemeny, Morgenstern, and Thompson [1].

Exercises

1. Show that the production matrix

$$A = \begin{pmatrix} \alpha_{11} & \alpha_{12} \\ \alpha_{21} & \alpha_{22} \end{pmatrix}$$

is productive if and only if the *determinant*

$$|I - A| = (1 - \alpha_{11})(1 - \alpha_{22}) - \alpha_{12}\alpha_{21}$$

is positive.

2. Prove: If the matrix A is productive then the sum of the entries in at least one column is less than one.

3. Is the following matrix productive?

$$A = \begin{pmatrix} 0 & 0.4 & 1 \\ 1.2 & 0 & 0.3 \\ 0.2 & 0.2 & 0 \end{pmatrix}$$

4. Consider a 3×3 model with activity vectors

$$P_1 = (4, -3, -1)$$
$$P_2 = (-1, 3, -1)$$
$$P_3 = (-2, 2, 3)$$

Show that this model can produce some but not all positive output vectors. Why does this not contradict Theorem 9.1?

5. A matrix M is called *positive definite* if $xMx > 0$ for all $x \neq 0$ (see Chap. 2, Exercise 25). Show that if the production matrix $I - A$ of a simple model is positive definite then A is productive.

6. Show that if the consumption matrix A of a simple model satisfies

$$\lim_{n \to \infty} A^n = 0$$

then A is productive. [Hint: Show that $(I - A)^{-1}$ is nonnegative.]

7. Let the consumption matrix of a simple model be

$$A = \begin{pmatrix} 0.2 & 0.5 \\ 0.7 & 0.1 \end{pmatrix}$$

Find the input vector needed to produce one unit of each good. Compute x_n of Theorem 9.4 for $n = 3, 4, 5$ and compare with your answer above.

8. Show by an example that the substitution Theorem 9.6 is not valid for models in which there is joint production.

9. In a general Leontief model let the consumption matrix be the following:

	G_0	G_1	G_2
P_1	0.4	0.1	0.6
P_2	0.3	0.2	1.0
P_3	0.6	0.4	0
P_4	0.5	0.3	0.2

where P_1 and P_2 produce one unit of G_1

P_3 and P_4 produce one unit of G_2

G_0 is labor

Find a pair of these activities having the same output space as the original model.

What is the minimum amount of labor needed to produce one unit of each good?

10. Show that the substitution theorem does not hold in the example given in Remark 3 of Sec. 3.

11. Give an example of a linear production model involving 2 goods in which the point $(1, 1)$ is efficient but there are infinitely many price vectors p for which $(1, 1)$ maximizes income.

12. Give an example of a linear production model involving 2 goods in which there are many output vectors which maximize income at prices $p = (1, 1)$.

13. Let y be a vector in the output space Y of a linear model which maximizes income at prices p. Show that either y or p is *not* unique; that is, either there exists a vector $y' \neq y$ in Y which also maximizes income at prices p, or there is a price vector $p' \neq p$ such that y also maximizes income at prices p'. (Hint: Consider the finite cone generated by $Y - y$ and examine the dual cone.)

14. Consider the linear model whose input and output matrices are

the following:

A			
0	1	0	0
1	0	0	0
0	0	1	0
0	0	0	1
0	1	0	0

B			
2	0	0	0
0	0	2	0
0	2	0	0
0	0	1	0
0	0	0	1

Is this model reducible? Find the expansion rates α_0 and β_0.

15. Show from the above example that if S_1 and S_2 are independent subsets (see definition in Sec. 5) then $S_1 \cap S_2$ need not be independent. What about $S_1 \cup S_2$?

16. Prove Theorems 9.12 and 9.13.

17. Show that for the simple expanding model if A is irreducible then the optimal price vector is positive and unique up to multiplication by a positive number.

18. Show that the expansion rate of an irreducible simple model is greater than 1 if and only if A is productive.

19. Find expansion rates and optimal intensity and price vectors for the simple model whose consumption matrix is

$$A = \begin{pmatrix} 0.3 & 0.5 \\ 0.6 & 0.4 \end{pmatrix}$$

20. Show that Theorem 9.3 is not true if either Assumption I or II does not hold.

21. In an expanding linear model involving n goods show that it is always possible to find an optimal intensity vector which depends on at most n activities. (Hint: Let $\xi_i > 0$ for $i \varepsilon S$. Then show that the vectors $b_i - \alpha a_i$, $i \varepsilon S$, belong to a subspace of dimension at most $n - 1$. Now use the theorem on basic solutions of equations.)

Bibliography

Arrow, K. J. [1]: Alternative Proof of the Substitution Theorem for Leontief Models in the General Case, in Koopmans [2], pp. 155–164.

Bohnenblust, H. F., S. Karlin, and L. S. Shapley [1]: Solutions of Discrete Two-person Games, in Kuhn and Tucker [2], pp. 51–72.

Bray, H. E. [1]: Rates of Exchange, *Am. Math. Monthly*, vol. XXIX, no. 10, pp. 365–371, 1922.

Brown, G. W. [1]: Iterative Solutions of Games by Fictitious Play, in Koopmans [2], pp. 374–376.

Charnes, A. [1]: Optimality and Degeneracy in Linear Programming, *Econometrica*, vol. 20, pp. 160–170, 1952.

Dantzig, G. B. [1]: Programming in a Linear Structure, *Econometrica*, vol. 17, pp. 73–74, 1949.

[2] Maximization of Linear Functions of Variables Subject to Linear Inequalities, in Koopmans [2], pp. 339–347.

[3] A Proof of the Equivalence of the Programming Problem and the Game Problem, in Koopmans [2], pp. 330–335.

Dantzig, G. B., A. Orden, and P. Wolfe [1]: Generalized Simplex Method for Minimizing a Linear Form under Linear Inequality Restraints, *Pacific J. Math.*, vol. 5, pp. 183–195, 1955.

Eisenberg, E., and D. Gale [1]: Consensus of Subjective Probabilities: the Pari-mutuel Method, *Ann. Math. Statist.*, vol. 30, no. 1, 1959.

Ford, L. R., Jr. [1]: "Network Flow Theory," RAND paper P-923, Santa Monica, Calif., 1956.

Ford, L. R., Jr., and D. R. Fulkerson [1]: Maximal Flow through a Network, *Can. J. Math.*, vol. 8, pp. 399–404, 1956.

[2] A Simple Algorithm for Finding Maximal Network Flows and an

Application to the Hitchcock Problem, *Can. J. Math.*, vol. 9, pp. 210–218, 1957.

Fourier, J.-B. [1]: Solution d'une question particulière du calcul des inégalités, *Nouveau bulletin des sciences par la société philomathique de Paris*, 1826, p. 99.

Frisch, R. [1]: Circulation Planning: Proposal for a National Organization of a Commodity and Service Exchange, *Econometrica*, vol. 2, pp. 258–336, 1934.

Fulkerson, D. R.: See Ford and Fulkerson.

Gaddum, J. [1]: A Theorem on Convex Cones with Applications to Linear Inequalities, *Proc. Am. Math. Soc.*, vol. 3, pp. 37–49, 1950.

Gale, D. [1]: The Basic Theorems of Real Linear Equations, Inequalities, Linear Programming and Game Theory, *Naval Research Logist. Quart.*, vol. 3, pp. 193–200, 1956.

[2] A Theorem on Flows in Networks, *Pacific J. Math.*, vol. 7, pp. 1073–1082, 1957.

[3] The Closed Linear Model of Production, in Kuhn and Tucker [1], pp. 285–330.

Gale, D., H. W. Kuhn, and A. W. Tucker [1]: On Symmetric Games, in Kuhn and Tucker [2].

[2] Linear Programming and the Theory of Games, in Koopmans [2], pp. 317–329.

Gale, D., and S. Sherman [1]: Solutions of Finite Two-person Games, in Kuhn and Tucker [2].

Goldman, A. J., and A. W. Tucker [1]: first three chapters of Kuhn and Tucker [1], pp. 3–52.

[2] Theory of Linear Programming, in Kuhn and Tucker [1], pp. 53–98.

Hall, P. [1]: On Representatives of Subsets, *J. London Math. Soc.*, vol. 10, pp. 26–30, 1935.

Halmos, P. R., and H. E. Vaughan [1]: The Marriage Problem, *Am. J. Math.*, vol. 72, pp. 214–215, 1950.

Hitchcock, F. L. [1]: Distribution of a Product from Several Sources to Numerous Localities, *J. Math. Phys.*, vol. 20, pp. 224–230, 1941.

Jacobs, W. W. [1]: The Caterer Problem, *Naval Research Logist. Quart.*, vol. 1, pp. 154–165, 1954.

Kakutani, S. [1]: A Generalization of Brouwer's Fixed-point Theorem, *Duke Math. J.*, vol. 8, pp. 451–459, 1941.

Karlin, S.: See Bohnenblust, Karlin, and Shapley.

Kemeny, J. G., O. Morgenstern, and G. L. Thompson [1]: A generalization of the von Neumann Model of an Expanding Economy, *Econometrica*, vol. 24, pp. 115–135, 1956.

Koopmans, T. C. [1]: Analysis of Production as an Efficient Combination of Activities, in Koopmans [2], pp. 33–97.

[2] editor, "Activity Analysis of Production and Allocation," John Wiley & Sons, Inc., New York, 1951.

Kuhn, H. W. [1]: Extensive Games and the Problem of Information, in Kuhn and Tucker [3].

[2] Solvability and Consistency for Systems of Linear Equations and Inequalities, Am. Math. Monthly, vol. 63, pp. 217–232, 1956.

[3] The Hungarian Method for Solving the Assignment Problem, Naval Research Logist. Quart., vol. 2, pp. 83–97, 1955.

Kuhn, H. W., and A. W. Tucker [1]: editors, "Linear Inequalities and Related Systems," Ann. Math. Studies, no. 38, Princeton, 1956.

[2] editors, "Contributions to the Theory of Games," vol. I, Ann. Math. Studies, no. 24, Princeton, 1950.

[3] editors, "Contributions to the Theory of Games," vol. II, Ann. Math. Studies, no. 28, Princeton, 1953.

See also Gale, Kuhn, and Tucker.

Leontief, W. W. [1]: "The Structure of the American Economy 1919–1929," Harvard University Press, Cambridge, Mass., 1941.

McKinsey, J. C. C. [1]: "Introduction to the Theory of Games," The RAND series, McGraw-Hill Book Company, Inc., New York, 1952.

Morgenstern, O.: See Kemeny, Morgenstern, and Thompson, and von Neumann and Morgenstern.

Neumann, J. von [1]: Zur Theorie der Gesellschaftsspiele, Math. Ann., vol. 100, pp. 295–320, 1928.

[2] Privately circulated notes.

[3] Über ein ökonomisches Gleichungssystem und eine Verallgemeinerung des Brouwerschen Fixpunktsatzes, Ergeb. Math. Kolloquiums, no. 8, 1937.

[4] Translation of [3] in Rev. Econ. Studies, 1945–1946.

Neumann, J. von, and O. Morgenstern [1]: "Theory of Games and Economic Behavior," Princeton University Press, Princeton, N.J., 1944.

Orden, A.: See Dantzig, Orden, and Wolfe.

Prager, W. [1]: On the Caterer Problem, Management Sci., vol. 3, pp. 15–23, 1956.

Remak, R. [1]: Kann die Volkswirtschaftlehre eine exakte Wissenschaft werden? Jahrb. für Nationalökonomie und Stat., Band III, Folge Band 76, pp. 703–735, 1929.

Robinson, J. [1]: An Iterative Method of Solving a Game, Ann. Math., vol. 54, pp. 296–301, 1951.

Samuelson, P. A. [1]: Abstract of a Theorem Concerning Substitutability in Open Leontief Models, in Koopmans [2], pp. 142–146.

Shapley, L. S., and R. N. Snow [1]: Basic Solutions of Discrete Games, in Kuhn and Tucker [2].

See also Bohnenblust, Karlin, and Shapley.

Sherman, S.: See Gale and Sherman.

Snow, R. N.: See Shapley and Snow.

Solow, R. [1]: On the Structure of Linear Models, *Econometrica*, vol. 20, pp. 22–46, 1952.

Stiegler, G. J. [1]: The Cost of Subsistence, *J. Farm. Econ.*, vol. 27, pp. 303–314, 1945.

Thompson, G. L.: See Kemeny, Morgenstern, and Thompson.

Thrall, R. M., and L. Tornheim [1]: "Vector Spaces and Matrices," John Wiley & Sons, Inc., New York, 1957.

Tornheim, L.: See Thrall and Tornheim.

Tucker, A. W.: See Gale, Kuhn, and Tucker; Kuhn and Tucker; and Goldman and Tucker.

Vajda, S. [1]: "Theory of Games and Linear Programming," John Wiley & Sons, Inc., New York, 1956.

Vaughan, H. E.: See Halmos and Vaughan.

Ville, J. [1]: Sur la théorie générale des jeux, in E. Borel, "Traité du calcul des probabilités," vol. 4, part 2, pp. 105–113, Paris, 1938.

Wolfe, P.: See Dantzig, Orden, and Wolfe.

Index